Evolution: Possible or Impossible?

Evolution: Possible or Impossible?

MOLECULAR BIOLOGY AND THE LAWS OF CHANCE
IN NONTECHNICAL LANGUAGE

A new approach to the subject, based on exciting recent discoveries involving proteins and DNA, the "golden molecule" of heredity

by

JAMES F. COPPEDGE, Ph.D.

Director of
Probability Research in Biology
Northridge, California

ZONDERVAN
PUBLISHING HOUSE
OF THE ZONDERVAN CORPORATION
GRAND RAPIDS, MICHIGAN 49506

EVOLUTION: POSSIBLE OR IMPOSSIBLE?

Grand Rapids, Michigan
Library of Congress Catalog Card Number 72-95524

Third printing 1976

Grateful acknowledgment is made to the following:
SCIENTIFIC AMERICAN, INC., for permission to reprint the diagrams and illustrations used in this book.

ACADEMIC PRESS, New York, for permission to quote from A. I. Oparin, *Genesis and Evolutionary Development of Life,* Copyright © 1968.

OXFORD UNIVERSITY PRESS for occasional quotations of texts from *The New English Bible*. Copyright © 1961 by The Delegates to the Oxford University Press and The Syndics of the Cambridge University Press.

Printed in the United States of America

Dedicated to my mother
Annie Ogilvie Coppedge
whose confidence has always been an inspiration

Contents

List of Figures

Preface

Among the sciences, biology holds a unique place in the thinking of many people. It is the study of living organisms and we are all included in its realm. This field is intriguing not only because living things are fascinating to study, but also because it encompasses the amazing structures and processes of our own bodies and brains. In addition, it may possibly provide clues as to the meaning of our existence. All this may serve to enrich one's present life and give some indication concerning how it ties in with the rest of the universe.

This short volume presents certain of the most interesting discoveries from the recent rapid advances in molecular biology which have excited scientist and layman alike. Such information is available of course in many books and journals. These facts, however, will herein be examined in the context of that philosophy of science which has been predominant throughout the recent past, namely the philosophy of evolution. Certain key facts of current biological knowledge are studied in the light of that overview by applying the rules of probability reasoning, to find if such an overview can logically be sustained.

This book may serve as a vehicle by which alert adults and older young people may obtain a quick grasp of the central facts of current molecular biology and of their significance. No prior background in the field is required, since the book is written in nontechnical language, yet information concerning our present understanding of life on the molecular level is presented in some detail. The student of biology may find it a source for such facts and for ideas on how those facts may reasonably be interpreted.

Perhaps all who write in this fast-developing field suffer the concern expressed by one author in his book when he wrote, "It will surely be out-of-date before there is time to get it printed." Since this particular volume does not deal with data alone, there is hope of escaping that early obsolescence, because timeless principles are involved when it comes to examining and evaluating the facts in the light of probability rules. Once a person has an understanding of these principles, he can apply them to new research discoveries as they appear on the horizon. In the process of doing so, it will be found that it is possible to interpret the significance of the discoveries more accurately, and that life is more interesting and rewarding as a result of a clearer comprehension of the overall picture.

June 1973 JAMES F. COPPEDGE

Acknowledgments

Grateful appreciation is hereby expressed for the invaluable assistance received from the following eminent professors and/or research scientists. Their taking time to share information from their wealth of professional knowledge is not to be construed as any endorsement of this book. There was no occasion for some of them to know the author's views, and it is probable that some would differ strongly with certain of the conclusions reached herein. These scientists represent a variety of viewpoints, yet all courteously shared information on particular subjects via mail or telephone. In alphabetical order, the following are among those who were most helpful:

Harry Block, University of Liverpool
James Bonner, California Institute of Technology
Larry Butler, Purdue University
Melvin A. Cook, IRECO Chemicals
Margaret O. Dayhoff, National Biomedical Research Foundation
Robert DeLange, University of California at Los Angeles
Arthur Elliott, King's College, London
Sidney W. Fox, University of Miami
Jesse L. Greenstein, California Institute of Technology
Philip C. Hanawalt, Stanford University
Joseph L. Henson, Bob Jones University
Thomas R. Howell, University of California at Los Angeles
Norman Hughes, Pepperdine University
John C. Kendrew, Cambridge University
Elias Klein, Gulf South Research Institute
Harold J. Morowitz, Yale University

Marshal W. Nirenberg, National Institutes of Health
John H. Ostrom, Yale University
Linus Pauling, Stanford University
George Preston, California Institute of Technology
John G. Read, Hughes Aircraft Company
Fred D. Williams, Michigan Technological University

We are grateful to Dr. Arthur Kornberg of Stanford University for his courtesy in providing an electron micrograph of DNA and permitting its use.

Biologists George F. Howe and Bolton Davidheiser kindly read the manuscript before revisions and offered vital encouragement. In addition, Dr. Howe played a key role in generously going out of his way to advocate publication and offer assistance to that end. Earlier a class taught by Dr. Davidheiser had much to do with inspiring the author to go into this field.

Dr. Kenneth L. Perrin, mathematician, helped to ascertain the "substitution formula," used in calculations involving multiple substitutions.

Mrs. Louise Carroll exhibited her characteristic careful excellence in typing and correcting the manuscript from very rough drafts. Mrs. Lavonne Cart cheerfully typed prodigious quantities of research notes.

The California Graduate School of Theology, recognizing the importance of the subject, allowed the author to do extensive research in biology and probability theory for his doctoral dissertation in this essential field of science and religion. This contributed greatly to the scope and early appearance of this book.

Evolution: Possible or Impossible?

Introduction

. . . the most golden of all molecules.[1]

—James D. Watson

In this brief volume the two most vital and interesting molecules present in every living thing on earth, namely nucleic acids and proteins, will be examined in some detail in plain language. The reader will also have a chance to become familiar with a few simple key rules of probability reasoning. These will then be combined to determine if it is possible that such molecules might possibly have had their origin in natural processes of evolution. These main subjects will lead to many related ones in biology.

The Golden Molecule

The exciting discovery of the structure of "DNA" was made in 1953 at Cambridge University in England by James Watson and Francis Crick. From then till now knowledge has increased rapidly about this cryptic substance. "DNA" is shorthand for "deoxyribose nucleic acid," the molecule which carries the hereditary information from parent to offspring in all living things which have been examined thus far, except certain viruses which use RNA—a nucleic acid almost identical to DNA, as we will see.

DNA is the main component of genes and chromosomes. One writer in a scientific journal called it "the genetic scripture," because this amazing chemical is in the form of a code or message.[2] With careful precision, this message directs the cell's activities via protein synthesis. Figure 1 gives a preliminary idea of the shape of DNA. We will study its fascinating structure and function in chapters 8 and 9.

[1] James D. Watson, *The Double Helix* (New York: Atheneum Press, 1968), p. 18.

[2] Philip Morrison, *Scientific American* (in Book Reviews), Vol. 225 (October 1971), p. 118.

FIGURE 1

Forms of the DNA Molecule

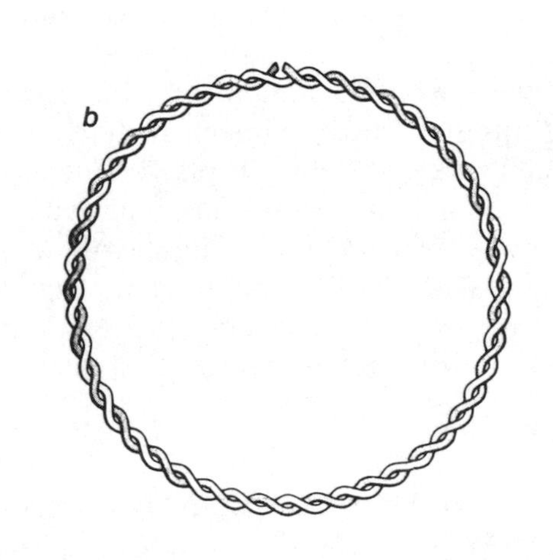

DNA MOLECULES are found in three forms. In each the DNA consists of two twisted strands that form a double helix, or spiral; the strands are connected, as by the rungs of a ladder, by paired subunits (nucleotides) whose particular sequence constitutes the genetic code. The basic form is linear. This is shown in (a). If the ends are joined through one strand, the structure is a nicked duplex loop (b). If both strands are joined, the structure is an intact loop, usually found in the supercoiled form (c).

Adapted from Royston C. Clowes, "The Molecule of Infectious Drug Resistance."

Such revelations have made the whole field of biology more popular with the layman. Some of the suspense and thrill of discovery have been transmitted to the public by several of the group of scientists who participated in the exploration leading to the original breakthrough. One of them, John C. Kendrew, wrote the following in the preface of his excellent book, *The Thread of Life:*

> We all find it natural to be interested in biology because we ourselves, being living organisms, are part of its subject matter; and, finally; molecular biology is advancing with such tremendous rapidity that it should be possible to communicate some of the excitement which scientists feel.[3]

Watson, in his popular book, *The Double Helix,* recorded how, working alone, he hit upon a key part of the plan of the DNA structure. He felt with deep emotion that the arrangement of the atoms was "too pretty not to be true."[4]

DNA consists of microscopic threads on which ride, in the case of human beings, a billion words of coded instructions.[5] A copy of this entire encyclopedia of instructions for the whole body is provided for every individual cell of the many trillions of cells that make up your body.

Applying Probability Theory

During the early decades of this century, scientists in the field of physics began to learn about "quantum mechanics." They found that electrons and other elementary particles behave in ways that seem unpredictable in some respects. It was found that the statistical laws of probability could be used to average out these individual random motions. This brought order out of the confusion and made the behavior predictable *on the average.*

This has given rise to a large new literature on the "science of probability."[6] The resulting rules of chance are now in wide use in industry, government, and especially science. French scientist Pierre Lecomte du Noüy said, "The laws of chance have rendered, and will continue to render, immense services to science. It is inconceivable that we could do without them."[7]

We will be applying the primary rules of probability to the

---

[3] John C. Kendrew, *The Thread of Life* (Cambridge, Mass.: Harvard University Press, 1966), Preface.

[4] Watson, *The Double Helix,* pp. 194-210.

[5] Throughout the book, whenever we use the words *billion* and *trillion,* it will be with the value given to it in Canada and the U.S.A., where a billion is a thousand million (10^9) and a trillion is a million million (10^{12}). In Great Britain and Australia, a "billion" is a million million, and a "trillion" is a million times larger than the American trillion.

[6] Darrell Huff, *How to Take a Chance* (New York: W. W. Norton and Co., 1959), p. 63.

[7] Pierre Lecomte du Noüy, *Human Destiny* (New York: Longmans, Green & Co., 1947), p. 37.

formation of DNA and protein molecules: What is the chance that they might have become arranged and organized, unaided by intelligence? The odds, we will discover, are astonishing.

Do not be discouraged if you are not familiar with these two subjects, namely probability theory, and the major living molecules—DNA and proteins. There will be sufficient introduction to them in the chapters that follow.

Science and Philosophy of Science

Although many do not realize it, the pursuit of science is well-nigh impossible in the absence of a "philosophy of science," or an overview of what science is all about. Distinguished physicist David Bohm wrote, "Metaphysics is fundamental to every branch of science." By metaphysics he refers to one's basic assumptions which attempt to explain the real nature of things. He continued:

> It seems clear that everybody has got some kind of metaphysics, even if he thinks he hasn't got any. Indeed, the practical 'hard-headed' individual who 'only goes by what he sees' generally has a very dangerous kind of metaphysics, i.e. the kind of which he is unaware . . . dangerous because, in it, assumptions and inferences are being mistaken for directly observed facts, with the result that they are effectively riveted in an almost unchangeable way into the structure of thought.[8]

Dr. Bohm then offered this interesting suggestion on how one might escape the wrong conclusions which result from confusing philosophy with scientific evidence:

> One of the best ways of a person becoming aware of his tacit metaphysical assumptions is to be confronted by several other kinds. The first reaction is one of violent disturbance. . . . Nevertheless if he will "stay with it," rather than escape into anger or unjustified rejection of contrary ideas, . . . he becomes aware of the assumptive character of a great many previously unquestioned features of his own thinking.[9]

It is not that we need rid ourselves of metaphysics or assumptions, according to Professor Bohm, because it is a necessity that we have such a philosophical viewpoint. "All of us," he says, "will think more clearly when we frankly and openly admit that a lot of . . . 'factual science' is actually a kind of poetry,

---

[8] David Bohm, "Further Remarks on Order," in *Towards a Theoretical Biology*, ed. C. H. Waddington (Chicago: Aldine Publishing Co., 1968), p. 41.

[9] Ibid., p. 42.

which is indispensable to our general mental functioning."[10]

There are two major philosophies of science current today. The one heard most often is the essentially materialistic belief that all phenomena can be explained by physics and chemistry without resorting to anything "supernatural." The other major philosophy of science was expressed well by Wernher von Braun, the U.S. missile scientist who pioneered our moon rockets, a physicist by education, when he said in a 1969 interview:

> Through a closer look at creation, we ought to gain a better knowledge of the Creator, and a greater sense of man's responsibility to God will come into focus.[11]

In that statement, von Braun went outside what is ordinarily considered the domain of science. If we wonder if he was being unscientific to speak thus, we need but reflect a moment. Let's leave out the idea of anything "supernatural" while we consider the following hypothetical situation: Suppose it is discovered that some unexpected influence (like, say, a mysterious radiation) pervades our material universe. The evidence, let us assume, shows that this effect flows from a cause which can never itself be precisely measured or directly observed. Nevertheless, this cause has a real and concrete influence upon events and laws of our physical-chemical universe, an effect that is considerable.

It is clear that to ignore such a fact would keep one from being able fully to understand physics or any related science, since the cause that is involved is intimately related to the way things are in the material world. Even though that cause were beyond full scientific investigation, it would have to be taken into consideration in order for us to have a correct comprehension of anything. It would be artificial and restrictive to deprive any scientist from contemplating *anything* that is "outside his field" if it affects the subject of his study. To place such limitations would itself be unscientific as just seen from the postulated situation. (It is clear today that we likewise cannot draw absolute boundaries between scientific disciplines, e.g., between physics and chemistry, without limiting knowledge.)

A correct "world view" or general outlook is essential for accurate scientific comprehension in many cases. Consider how

---

[10] Ibid.

[11] Wernher von Braun, in Associated Press Dispatch, *The Cleveland Plain Dealer* (Cleveland, Ohio, July 19, 1969), p. 5.

a scientist who believes the earth is flat will be limited by his outlook. When he interprets experiments or makes "scientific observations," the results will be colored by that erroneous notion. Much of his work will be invalidated, because his overview is not in line with reality. It may be even more of a hindrance in science if one fails to consider whether there is design in the universe. It is therefore logical in the introduction of our subject to take up this matter of a philosophy of life which will be adequate for scientist and layman alike because it is in tune with the real universe. In so doing, we should openmindedly consider anything which may be deeply involved in the realities of our material universe and its laws.

In that view, "religion" is not necessarily involved at all in leading one to consider creation as a scientific theory to account most fully for what one sees in the universe about him. (If a person *does* arrive at such a conclusion, however, the only logical sequel is to honor the Creator who could engineer such a cosmos, and to seek to know more about the plan involved.)

There apparently exists in the minds of some individual scientists who do not share Dr. von Braun's outlook a reluctance to consider evidence beyond the substances and forces which can be examined in our laboratories or by scientific observation in a materialistic sense, and this results in nervousness about anything which might be called "religious" in any sense. Similarly, there is a corresponding uncomfortableness on the part of some who cannot accept the materialistic overview with regard to naturalistic evolution.

Reasonable individuals of either viewpoint have no cause for alarm if their honest desire is to follow where truth leads. One's philosophy of science (and philosophy of life) must be based solidly on what is true, insofar as that can be determined, or he is in for recurrent uneasiness and unhappiness, not to mention more serious consequences which may follow building on a false foundation. (Consider, for example, the consequences if von Braun and others had used incorrect formulas in calculating moon orbits as a result of some departure from truth because of wrong metaphysical assumptions.)

In view of what has been said, it can be seen that the research and writings and conclusions of any scientist are likely from time to time to mirror the overview he accepts. Although not always stated explicitly, the philosophy of a biologist, for example, usually can be discovered from his writings. (It will not be difficult in this book, in that respect, to discern the author's esteem for science in general, his high regard for the scientific method, and an enthusiasm for widening the scope of present scientific knowledge. The overview will also be easily evident, since it is a philosophy of science which has proved most exhilarating and productive of a spirit of scientific inquiry.)

Before going ahead into the study of DNA, proteins, and probability, it may be worthwhile to look briefly at how an individual might go about building an adequate philosophy of science, which is part of one's philosophy of life or general outlook. For one thing, any viewpoint which leaves one in perplexity is undesirable.

The Value to You of Certainty

To succeed in the business of living, a person needs a feeling of confidence. It is important that one's philosophy of life provide a strong basis for assurance without lingering doubts on the main issues. If life is to be rich with meaning, it is vital to understand what life is all about. Only then is a person best equipped, logically, to undertake and understand scientific investigation. Otherwise it would be easy to spend time in fruitless directions.

Every modern person of normal intelligence sooner or later asks himself: Who or what made us and the universe? Is man just "an ape who made good"? Is the entire cosmos "a mere mechanical dance of atoms," as C. S. Lewis described the materialist view?[12] Is there no author, no reason for what exists? Or is there a Power beyond nature which created all things for some purpose or other?

It makes considerable difference what we believe on this subject. If our existence came about by chance, then we don't have to answer to anyone. In practical life, no rules would limit us except those we choose and those forced on us by other people and natural laws.[13]

If on the other hand we are the product of an intelligent

[12] C. S. Lewis, *Mere Christianity* (New York: The Macmillan Co., 1958), p. 21.

[13] A study of human nature might lead us to expect this to issue in certain unhappy social consequences on the part of at least a percentage of the population. There is a story of a French agnostic of a past century who was discussing his philosophy with guests of like mind. "Don't let the servants overhear us," he cautioned, "or they will steal the silverware."

source, we need to be aware of it. There may be consequences for failure to cooperate, if the universe has an Owner.

Where can one begin his search for the truth on this key question? The most obvious source of information is the universe around us, or "Nature." Study of the physical universe, therefore, may help us in beginning a strong philosophy of life and of science. Since the discovery of the DNA structure, no doubt many a scientist has asked himself, at least secretly: Can this remarkable code of life and its complex translation machinery be accounted for without postulating a Designer possessing awesome intelligence?

If one does consider the possibility of an intelligent Power back of that universe, a logical question would then be whether he has revealed himself or his truth to his intelligent creatures in any more direct way than through nature, since it seems reasonable that such a result would follow.

There do exist many "sacred writings" which claim to have such a supernatural origin. Of these, only the Bible is satisfactorily vindicated from many standpoints. It claims, moreover, to be specially "inspired" by God, but then so do some other sacred writings, past and present. In the case of the Bible, however, Hal Lindsey, in the best seller, *The Late Great Planet Earth,* has made graphically clear how the Bible's many accurate, detailed prophecies which were written centuries or millennia before their exact fulfillment give strong objective reason to believe that the Bible is in fact what it claims to be.[14]

We have been discussing *objective* sources of evidence, in the quest for truth on which to build a philosophy of life and a sound metaphysics for a scientific overview. If we cross over into the *subjective* or inner realm, the situation can get hazy. Of course, a supernatural Being could easily reveal truth directly to a man's inner consciousness. Dramatic subjective experiences, however, may also proceed from quite natural or earthly causes, such as drugs or mental disturbances. It is important, therefore, that we have objective truth by which to check the validity of any inner experiences. A subjective experience originating from a supernatural source might be completely real and correct, but without some objective evidence by which to verify it, we would be in danger of error in attributing it to "God."

---

[14] Hal Lindsey, *The Late Great Planet Earth* (Grand Rapids, Mich.: Zondervan Publishing House, 1970).

As a tentative conclusion before going on in our study of science, we may say that the two main objective sources from which we may draw information are nature and the Bible. Ideas from other people and from our own reasoning may be helpful also, if derived logically from these *primary* sources.

Both nature and the Bible offer help if we seek answers on the question of the origin of life. It might be noted in passing that the origin of life is a subject which is beyond the reach of observational and experimental science except for speculation based on present conditions. The subject has, nonetheless, occupied a great amount of the time and attention of many biologists and other scientists because of its interesting nature, and because some of them perhaps would prefer a naturalistic explanation.

With regard to the Bible, we live at a time when a great many people have not arrived at a settled faith regarding its accuracy and supernatural inspiration. This makes it impossible for them to begin their search with complete confidence in its authority as to truth on which to base their philosophy. It is interesting that the Bible itself recognizes that such individuals need a more tangible basis on which to *start* their structure of belief.

No one is likely to consider a Supreme Being in his philosophy of life, or in his philosophy of science, who does not believe there actually is a God, of course. "Anyone who comes to God must believe that he exists," says the Bible itself, in the book of Hebrews.[15]

By sensibly observing nature, one can find assurance that there is, indeed, a God. Notice again the statement by Wernher von Braun, perhaps the world's most outstanding missile scientist, quoted above on page 23. It accords perfectly with the following from the Bible:

> For all that may be known of God lies plain before their eyes; indeed God himself has disclosed it to them. His invisible attributes, that is to say his everlasting power and deity, have been visible, ever since the world began, to the eye of reason, in the things he has made (Romans 1:19, 20 NEB).

Observation of nature, then, is the logical point of beginning

---

[15] Hebrews 11:6 (from the translation known as *The New English Bible*, hereafter abbreviated NEB. If no translation is indicated, the reference is from the King James Version.)

for those who feel they cannot take anything for granted without concrete evidence. One should keep in mind that it is just the beginning, however. Nature can't take us all the way that we need to go. It may, nevertheless, lead to some knowledge of God and to an elementary faith. Sincere, open-minded individuals are then likely to consider the Bible as a source of more information about him, since it claims to be divine revelation and has reliable credentials. It seems logical that nature's God would give us a more complete revelation such as the Bible provides. The Bible and nature seem to go well together, and both may be essential to a satisfying and full-orbed philosophy of life. (Interestingly, one occasionally finds quotations or references to it even in scientific treatises, at the most unexpected places.)

It may be objected that it is being taken for granted that one will eventually believe in God if he is a reasonable individual. While this objection may in part be valid, perhaps the reader, if he happens to find difficulty in such a belief, may tolerate the assumption for the moment, and we will soon be into the more concrete subjects mentioned at the start.

As we pursue our quest for a meaningful and true philosophy of life by looking first at nature, there is a major barrier to any acceptance of belief in a Supreme Being. It is the widely held doctrine of evolution. The word "evolution" is used in many ways, so we will need to define it as used in this book.

As employed herein, evolution may be defined as *the belief that all living things, including man, resulted by natural changes from lifeless matter, with no supernatural intervention involved.*[16] This is the common current understanding of the term in its general use by most biologists, though of course there are many exceptions. Like many other words, this one has numerous meanings. It will be helpful to remember this definition for this book.

Are Evolution and Science Synonymous?

Textbooks, literature, and the tacit acceptance expressed by seemingly almost everyone would give the impression that evolution and science are one.

Perhaps you, like most people, do not find it possible or con-

---

[16] This definition substantially follows one given in the textbook, *Biology, A Search for Order in Complexity*, Ed.: John N. Moore and Harold Schultz Slusher (Grand Rapids: Zondervan Publishing House, 1970), p. 93.

venient to study extensively in all the fields of science to find out firsthand what is true. If you are constantly told in effect that science accepts evolution as a fact, you may naturally ask yourself, "Who am I to question science?"

Many who would like to believe in God or the Bible find themselves in the position of Dr. James Orr, a noted theologian of the late 1800's. He seemed to have been convinced "that the scientists had proved evolution to be true and that he had to do the best he could with it."[17]

A number of authors, writing as believers in God, seem to be in the same position—trying earnestly (some even desperately) to mold Bible teachings to fit the latest evolutionary assumptions. Many materialists scoff at this as an impossible task. More logically, it turns out to be a case of "either-or" rather than evolution "and" the Bible.

Still, many religious leaders have tackled the unenviable job of trying to work out a compromise, simply because there appeared to be no alternative. Unwilling to throw overboard all ties with religion, they find a temporary shelter in "theistic evolution" or some other type that lets God in on the process. While this may at first appear to have the advantage of making a person acceptable in both camps, it leaves him a citizen of neither, when the matter is examined.

Some otherwise great Christian thinkers have taken this adaptive position on evolution, believing that scientists have really proved evolution, and, of course, one can't argue with facts. Fortunately, we live in a time when more has just recently become known. Recent discoveries in biology make it clear that there was no reason to stretch the interpretation of Scriptures, after all.

At the moment, it can be noted that it would be difficult to keep confidence in any of the Bible if it is mistaken about origins. At the least, it would then seem to be merely a human book, containing some good perhaps, but not standing as the authoritative revelation of God, if it is wrong on that subject.

Later on, we will refer to an excellent study which examines theistic evolution. Meanwhile, let us first, however, proceed on the assumption of "either-or"—either the Bible account of creation is true, or evolution is true.

---

[17] Bolton Davidheiser, *Evolution and Christian Faith* (Nutley, N.J.: Presbyterian and Reformed Publishing Co., 1969), p. 38.

"Is it proper," someone may ask, "to compare the Bible account of creation with a scientific theory like evolution?" Not all scientists agree as to evolution's scientific credentials. For example, R. Clyde McCone, professor of anthropology at California State University in Long Beach, wrote in 1973:

> There are no data for evolution. Proponents use the idea of evolution to create or generate data by appropriating the synchronic data of science in an effort to use that very synchronic order to explain how it came into existence.

Dr. McCone went on to show logically the truth of his assertion, and concluded as follows:

> The scientific study of the existing order of creation must necessarily be kept distinct from any consideration of how that order came to be. In attempting to ignore this necessary distinction, evolutionists follow an irrational approach to data that are products of their own speculation resulting in a value structure rather than scientific theory.[18]

Could chance account for life on earth through natural processes, or is it evidently designed? If designed, does that mean the individual human being (whether scientist or layman) has some kind of responsibility to the Designer?

It Is Now Possible to Be Sure

There is now a quick way to an accurate answer to this question. A person need not wait for years of study to discover whether life could have begun from nonliving matter by natural processes. It is not even necessary to build on the *opinions* of others, in becoming certain on this matter.

One also does not need to become expert in various fields of science, in order for his conclusions to be on solid footing that will be soundly logical and valid. The worth of such personal certainty is easily apparent, and may seem almost too good to be attainable. It will soon become clear how it is possible.

We should pause to note that there is also possible, as the reader may happen to know, a valid spiritual type of assurance on such matters as the existence of God. What we are discussing here, however, is the assurance arrived at by considering objective evidence. This is especially important in this scientific age. It can serve to encourage or to reinforce any spiritual as-

---

[18] R. Clyde McCone, "Three Levels of Anthropological Objection to Evolution," *Creation Research Society Quarterly,* Vol. 9 (March 1973), p. 209.

surance one may already have, and it is in line with the Bible, as we have seen.

The reader is presumed to be a serious searcher for truth, either for his own assurance on the subject of this book, or in order to reassure others more effectively. If you are still in school getting formal education, you may find this prospective short-cut to certainty exciting and understandable. Because of what that certainty can mean to a person, it may also prove useful to those of all ages who are not satisfied with superficial answers. Many Christians, for example, feel a need to know whether they are on scientifically solid ground when they repose confidence in Christ and in the Bible—at least to know that true science is not contrary to this.

It will be evident to the reader as he progresses that the main approach suggested in this volume will stand on its own merits. Its logic is self-evident, not depending upon who says it. It will also be susceptible to any degree of further study or experimentation that one may choose. An open, inquiring mind, willingness to think and *persistence* are all one needs to arrive at certainty.

It is fortunate that during the past few years several highly intelligent scientists who are devout Christians have written on evolution. Men of extensive education and scientific background have dealt with many phases of the subject quite effectively. Some of these authors were naturalistic evolutionists themselves before conversion to their present faith in Christ as Savior. Their writings are in contrast to the approach mentioned earlier in which some have tried to mold Christianity to fit evolution, although the motives of many of the latter may have been admirable. We will be recommending some of the more excellent books later on.

Why This Particular Book?

The new and rewarding approach we have been mentioning is now possible because of two things. Some of the recent dramatic discoveries in biology can now be combined with the principles of probability to give a rewarding new advantage to the searcher after truth on this matter. In this study, we will merely introduce the reader to this combination. Together, we will apply it to a few interesting subjects. The idea can then be used on your own in countless ways when pondering the things about you as time goes by. Serving merely to bring together these two existing ingredients more explicitly, this book introduces a practical *shortcut to certainty about evolution.*

It is undeniable that a great many well-known scientific volumes, including textbooks, promote the philosophy of evolution with ardent intensity. It is not out of order, therefore, that books also be written frankly from the overview of design or creation, calling attention to some of the vast body of scientific evidence which accords with such a view, much of which evidence disputes evolution.

The author claims no special knowledge and shares with many persons of varied backgrounds who write in biology the excitement and wonder involved in the discovery of how living beings are constructed and how they function. Hopefully, the reader will find that the evidence presented herein is obviously reasonable and/or accurately referenced, and the calculations may be checked.

The realm of science is not restricted to those of special pedigree. For example, Gregor Mendel, recognized rather universally as the father of modern genetics, was a monk and did his famous experiments in the small monastery garden while he was a part-time teacher. Much of his scientific knowledge was self-taught. Although sometimes called an "amateur scientist,"[19] his ideas and conclusions have not been discounted for such reasons (nor have those of Charles Darwin, whose only degree was in theology!) The merits of any work on science should depend primarily on other criteria, such as the content of its evidence and its ideas.

Your Certainty Can Remain Up-to-Date

Regardless of what new discoveries in science may be announced tomorrow or years from now, *one's certainty need not become outdated.*[20] That is a bold statement, but it will become clear why it is true when we get into the main subject. It is readily apparent what an advantage that provides. It has be-

---

[19] Eldon J. Gardner, *Principles of Genetics,* 4th ed. (New York: John Wiley & Sons, Inc., 1972), p. 3. Gardner, like others, praises Mendel's accomplishments.

[20] The research data and understanding of processes reported herein share the same risk of aging which is common to all writings of science in these days of fast-paced unfolding of knowledge in biology, physics, and space exploration. As more perfect information is learned, the partial knowledge is outdated. On the other hand, the general principles we will learn in applying probability reasoning are ageless.

come available because these recent scientific discoveries are ideal for applying the laws of chance. The certainty which can result is *in addition* to any spiritual or intuitive assurance one may have on this matter.

Many students and others with some background in biology would be perfectly at home with professional terminology. However, since most have not made it their field, we will largely be using nontechnical language. To do otherwise would confuse those new to the field, or as one scientist phrased it, would only "obfuscate the uninitiated." So, we will usually be able to avoid complicated jargon such as: "The probability expectance of the fortuitous non-enzymatic polymerization of a viable amino acid chain of 400 monomers. . . ." since this thought can be stated more simply in this way: "The probability that a usable protein molecule of average length would link up spontaneously. . . ."

The subject is alluring. Let us begin with a look at the simplest underlying rules of probability theory. The reader may need to concentrate at times, and to reread and ponder occasionally (unless mathematically trained or mathematically minded). It will be worth it, however. In the process, a high degree of certitude on this subject can develop. Any sound conclusions gained in this study should increase the value and richness of life, and will also benefit those you influence. Any difficulty or weariness involved in study can be offset, "If we let ourselves feel the thrill of such a series of facts as now unfold themselves before us."[21]

The Plan of This Book

Purpose: To invite attention to evidence which will enable the reader to arrive at the certainty that materialistic evolution cannot be true. To promote positive appreciation of the Creator, leading one (as the Creator's conditions are met) to a new awareness and rich meaning in science and life—meaning which is tragically missing from the barren land of naturalistic evolution.

Main Approach: (1) To learn the two first principles of probability theory, and to examine the interesting structure of proteins and DNA molecules, and the translation system from DNA to proteins. (2) To discover that natural selection could

[21] Nathan R. Wood, *The Secret of the Universe* (Grand Rapids: William B. Eerdmans Publishing Co., 1955), p. 70.

offer no help toward the origin of these complex molecules, such that, if intelligent design is ruled out, only chance is left as the means for producing such order. (3) To use probability calculations which lead to discovery of the practical impossibility of the origin by chance of usable sequences for proteins or DNA. The first ten chapters are devoted to this main approach.

Removal of Obstacles: Two difficulties remaining in the path to certainty are these: (1) Why do so many scientists accept evolution? and (2) What about the convincing-sounding "proofs" of evolution that are widely heralded? These are dealt with briefly but definitely in chapters 11 and 12 and the reader is referred to more extensive works on these subjects.

Positive Given: To remove a negative and erroneous philosophy is a prerequisite if a positive philosophy of life is to be built in its place. To stop after finding that evolution could not be true would leave a vacuum. Chapter 13 points out a few of the exciting evidences in nature that add to the understanding of life and that encourage appreciation for the exalted privilege of being a conscious and rational part of such an amazing universe. Finally chapter 14 reviews briefly the probability calculations made by others from different directions and ties together the theme, to connect it with the overall purpose the Creator may have had for His human creatures as revealed in nature (and in the Bible).

Three Kinds of Use: (1) General reading by individuals, from a variety of backgrounds, who are consciously uncertain about evolution. (A large percentage of those who have had some exposure to religion, as well as many who question evolution from the standpoint of contrary scientific evidence, are unsettled in varying degrees on this subject.) Serious students who would be unsatisfied with a superficial treatment or the undocumented views of any mere author may find this approach especially rewarding. Readers may become convinced by verifying for themselves much of the reasoning and calculations without the necessity for specialized advanced study.

(2) Use by individuals or groups who disbelieve evolution already, but who wish to increase their confidence and information in order to help others more effectively.

(3) Possible textbook or collateral source material for courses such as: (a) "Evolution in the Light of Probability Theory" or (b) "Proteins, DNA, and Probability Theory."

About Quotations and References: When any author or researcher is quoted favorably in this book, this of course does not necessarily mean that we are encouraging the reader to agree with everything else he says or believes.[22] Excellent writers on some subjects may possibly be quite mistaken on others. Chapter 11 explains in detail how it has come about that many otherwise fine and sincere people have been caught up in the evolutionary trend for unscientific and fallacious reasons. (Most of the references are merely to document the source of the data used, as is customary in writing on scientific subjects.)

It should be quite clear, too, that we claim no special knowledge or insights, but are merely pointing out evidence that is available and testable by anyone. The reader should accept only what is provably or logically sound.

The road to certainty is longer for some than others, depending on background and starting point. A short pamphlet might suffice for many. For others, however, to deal briefly with all the facets involved in achieving real assurance calls for more extensive treatment. This book offers a shortcut in the sense that in one comparatively short volume there is included the essence of a path by which open-minded individuals may likely be able to find that certainty which they desire. There is so much more helpful material that might have been included that the author's most difficult task was condensing even to this length.

In order to limit the amount of technical data in the main text, we have made much use of footnotes. For the noncasual reader, some of these footnotes will contain research information that may prove valuable as well as references where further details may be obtained. Others may prefer to bypass the footnotes except those which explain items in which they are interested. The dual purpose of the book is to assist in making access to certainty available to both the nontechnical reader and for the student or searching inquirer who wishes to study the subject more deeply.

---

[22] Nor does it necessarily mean that he would agree with us in all that we say.

1

How the "Laws of Chance" Affect You

No theory of chance can explain the creation of the world. Before chance can send atoms whirling through infinite void, the atoms have to exist! What has to be explained is the being of the world and matter. It makes no sense to say that chance can account for the creation of being.[1]

—Claude Tresmontant, University of Paris

MATERIALISTS USUALLY DO not stop to consider that naturalistic philosophy cannot satisfactorily explain the very existence of being—of atoms or anything else. This is a serious flaw.

For the purpose of this study, however, we will start with the earth and the universe already existing. Logic may lead us to the conclusion that evolution is not a tenable way to explain how things got "from there to here," from nonliving to living complexity.

The Path We Will Take

The approach to be followed to this valuable certainty is this: First, it is important to understand clearly two of the main ideas of probability theory, the "laws of chance." This can be done in a comparatively short time with the help of information in this chapter and the next. Then we will see how these "laws" serve to limit what can be expected to happen by chance, regardless of what other natural laws are invoked.

Could molecules link up and organize themselves to form

[1] Claude Tresmontant, "It Is Easier to Prove the Existence of God Than It Used to Be," *Réalités* (Paris, April, 1967), p. 46.

living things without planning? Could matter in motion bring about the array now existing without an Intelligence directing its formation? It will be exciting to apply these laws of chance to the formation of protein molecules, for example, and eventually to genes of the amazing DNA molecule itself!

If we ask: Does any intelligent person actually suppose that chance does account for what we now find existing on earth? Strange to say, the answer is yes. It is a very widespread belief. To say that chance plus "natural selection" has done it is the same as to say chance has performed it. Natural selection involves no outside intelligence, but is merely the natural process which weeds out those organisms which are not sufficiently equipped to survive and reproduce. When we look into this process in chapter 5, we will find it has been greatly overrated. Natural selection as presently understood by most evolutionists in the United States can use only what is furnished to it by chance or random occurrences.

Chance is still the original hero of the story on which all else must wait.[2] Most evolutionists are reluctant to say this directly, however. (It should be remembered that the word evolution, as we are using it, indicates the idea that life arose from nonliving matter and has reached its present state without the direction of any outside intelligence.)

It is currently quite common for scientists to attempt "to explain all biology in terms of physics and chemistry." At least one scientist has endeavored to explain it by physics alone.[3] Later on, it will become clear how there can be intelligent scientists who nevertheless believe, contrary to reason, that all things can be explained "without recourse to a 'deus ex machina,'"[4] without God or any intelligence involved. In the absence of intelligence, chance is all there is as the ultimate source of what happens (outside of unbranched causal chains). We are therefore dealing with the crux of the matter, the heart of evolution, when we study the laws of chance, or probability theory.

---

[2] To save time, we will often speak of chance and other natural processes in this anthropomorphic (as-if-human) sense. Although it is not scientific wording, it is easy to understand, like the nonscientific term "sunrise."

[3] Dean E. Wooldridge, *Mechanical Man* (New York: McGraw-Hill, 1968).

[4] Murray Eden, "Inadequacies of Neo-Darwinian Evolution as a Scientific Theory," *Mathematical Challenges to the Neo-Darwinian Interpretation of the Theory of Evolution,* ed. Paul S. Moorhead and Martin M. Kaplan (Philadelphia: Wistar Institute Press, 1967), p. 5. Dr. Eden does not indicate whether he agrees with this materialistic idea.

Probability is a practical concept. The uncertainties of chance affect our everyday lives. How likely is it to rain on the particular day on which you've planned to have an outdoor activity? What are the odds your airline flight will be hijacked? Is there a good chance your car will operate without major repairs if you delay trade-in for six months? What amount of cash will probably be sufficient to take along on a planned overseas trip? What is the likelihood that you will pass a certain exam in a school course without more study?

Besides personal planning in which we must consider uncertainties, "probability and statistics are used in insurance, physics, genetics, biology, business, as well as in games of chance," and as the basis of analysis of the stock market, intelligence tests, and much of modern mathematics, as the authors of *Pathways to Probability* remind us.[5] Modern factory production relies on a "quality control department engaged in applying statistical method, which is in the main a use of probability theory."[6] An airliner in which you travel may change course, depending on the *probability* of clear air turbulence as indicated by satellite reports.

By the way, it perhaps is already clear to the reader that the "laws" of chance are not laws in the deterministic sense. The laws of probability do not say that things must necessarily happen in a certain way, but that on the average that is the way things occur. John P. Hoyt explained this well. In some experiments such as observing the time of sunrise, he said, the outcome can be predicted accurately. He adds:

> There are many other experiments in many diverse fields whose outcomes cannot be predicted accurately in advance. Even if the same experiment is repeated again and again under what seem to be the same conditions, the outcomes vary in such a way that they cannot be predicted precisely before the conclusion of the experiment. However, if the same experiment is repeated many times, we often see a certain regularity in the relative frequency with which different possible outcomes actually occur. It is this type of experiment that led to the development of probability theory and to which this theory can be applied.[7]

---

[5] Amy C. King and Cecil B. Read, *Pathways to Probability* (New York: Holt, Rinehart & Winston, 1963), pp. 30, 130.

[6] Darrell Huff and Irving Geis, *How To Take a Chance* (New York: W. W. Norton & Co., 1959), p. 113.

[7] John P. Hoyt, *A Brief Introduction to Probability Theory* (Scranton, Pa.: International Textbook Co., 1967), p. 1.

Who Figured Out the Laws of Chance?

Rather than leave important matters to mere guesswork and complete uncertainty, many brilliant thinkers have investigated this subject from the time of the Renaissance on. One of the first to delve deeply into probability was Blaise Pascal, the famous French mathematician, scientist, and theologian of the seventeenth century. It was not considered unusual for a man to be proficient in both science and theology in those days. Many of the early scientific discoveries were by clerics and many were by devout nonclerical believers.

There is something of a resurgence of that today, in the case of men like Claude Tresmontant. In his early forties at present, Dr. Tresmontant lectures at the Sorbonne in Paris on the philosophy of science. He also has written highly regarded works on theology, such as his *Christian Metaphysics* (1965).[8] Dr. James Whitcomb, Jr., was at the same time a professor of Old Testament at Grace Theological Seminary and coauthor of an exhaustive geological investigation. The resulting book, *The Genesis Flood,*[9] is the epitome of scholarly and scientific thoroughness. There are scores of similar instances.

It is questionable if modern science could have attained nearly as great a degree of knowledge and accomplishment if it had not been for devout Christian scholars of earlier centuries, men who marveled at the Creator's wisdom as they peered scientifically through early microscopes and telescopes, just as some scientists with far more complex and sophisticated instruments marvel today.

After Pascal, Jakob Bernoulli, a Swiss mathematician, further developed the study of chance. He can be regarded as the founder of probability theory as a branch of mathematics.[10] He saw it as "The Art of Conjecture."[11] The resulting principles were put to practical use. Life insurance rates, for one example, have been based on probability theory from early times.

Probability Theory in Modern Physics

The science of physics has been responsible for much more study of probability in this century. Danish physicist Niels Bohr

---

[8] Claude Tresmontant, *Christian Metaphysics* (New York: Sheed and Ward, 1965).

[9] John C. Whitcomb Jr., and Henry M. Morris, *The Genesis Flood* (Philadelphia: Presbyterian and Reformed Publishing Co., 1960).

[10] *Encyclopaedia Britannica* (1967), s.v. "probability."

[11] Huff, *How to Take a Chance,* p. 57.

in 1913 brought forth some of his epic conclusions regarding the nature of the atom. He built on work done some years before by Max Planck in Germany. Planck had written of the "quanta"—or amounts—of energy given off and absorbed by atoms.[12]

These and other discoveries were culminated in 1926 by the appearance of the full-fledged theory of "quantum mechanics." This refers to the rules which govern phenomena that are so small-scale that they cannot be explained by ordinary mechanical laws.

In this exceedingly complex field, probability theory found its greatest development. In many situations where the behavior of atomic particles seemed purely arbitrary and random, the statistical laws of probability furnished the only "order." By the middle of the twentieth century, "the concept of probability had become one of the fundamental notions of a modern science and philosophy of nature."[13]

The need for carefully investigated principles of probability has yielded many books on the subject. Your public or school library doubtless has a number of them. Averages and formulas have been worked out in great detail and are extremely trustworthy. Skyscrapers are built and moon expeditions are launched as a result of engineering that depends on these laws. Stores decide how many goods to stock, plane schedules are made up, traffic signals are timed, and city planning is accomplished—all with the help of probability theory.

Books on Probability

Books in this field can be very confusing to those who have not been carefully educated in higher mathematics. There are actually hundreds of volumes. Pick a book at random on the subject, and, chances are, it will take a lot of long, ardent cogitation, study and restudy, before one can make heads or tails of it, unless he is a mathematician or already trained in probability theory. Many writers on probability seem to take for granted that the reader knows a lot about it from the start.

There are several books which are not quite as difficult as the many ultratechnical volumes. One of the best is *Probability*

---

[12] David Bohm, *Causality and Chance in Modern Physics* (Princeton, N. J.: D. Van Nostrand Co., Inc., 1957), p. 72.

[13] *Encyclopaedia Britannica,* op. cit., p. 571.

and Statistics.[14] It was the textbook for a television course called "Continental Classroom." Another is Warren Weaver's *Lady Luck: Theory of Probability.*[15] A third is *Probability and Statistics for Everyman,* by Irving Adler.[16]

In books on probability, code words that mean little to anyone who has not taken math recently are used—including expressions such as "N-tuples," "sample space," and "the empty set." We need not become involved in technical terms here. It can occupy a tremendous amount of time to become proficient in the use of the mysterious terminology of advanced mathematics.

The main principles needed for our purpose in this study are rather simple, in contrast to the complexity of books on the subject. Enough will be given in this chapter and in subsequent pages for one to grasp the basic ideas. To go into advanced probability theory is completely unnecessary unless one needs it for other reasons. The first few chapters of books like those mentioned offer additional understanding for those who wish to pursue the subject further. Beyond those early chapters, the strange symbols and complex formulas of this form of higher mathematics tend to develop suicidal tendencies in the non-professional.

Are the Laws of Chance Intuitive?

"Chance is a characteristic feature of the universe," said Adler.[17] We are better equipped for life's decisions if we understand this subject to some degree.

The principles of probability are in many respects just what one would expect in any given situation. He flips a coin, and feels that logically he has a fifty-fifty chance of getting heads. Quoting again from *Pathways to Probability:*

> We are inclined to agree with P. S. Laplace who said: "We see . . . that the theory of probabilities is at bottom only common sense reduced to calculation; it makes us appreciate with exactitude what reasonable minds feel by a sort of instinct, often without being able to account for it."[18]

---

[14] Frederick Mostellar, Robert E. K. Rourke, and George B. Thomas, *Probability and Statistics* (Reading, Pa.: Addison-Wesley Publishing Co., 1961).

[15] Warren Weaver, *Lady Luck: Theory of Probability* (New York: Doubleday, Garden City, 1963).

[16] Irving Adler, *Probability and Statistics for Everyman* (New York: John Day Co., 1963).

[17] Ibid., p. 11.

[18] King and Read, *Pathways to Probability,* p. 130.

We will mention briefly that much study into the *meaning* of the principles of probability has been done. This study has had an impact on science and philosophy and the general understanding of the nature of things. C. S. Lewis once wrote an interesting chapter on probability in which he said, "According to Hume, probability rests on what may be called the majority vote of our past experiences." In a penetrating study of the deeper meaning of the subject, Lewis, one of the most profound thinkers of this century, went on to say,

> The whole idea of Probability (as Hume understands it) depends on the principle of the Uniformity of Nature.... And how do we know the Uniformity of Nature? A moment's thought shows that we do not know it by experience.... Experience therefore cannot prove uniformity, because uniformity has to be assumed before experience proves anything.[19]

For our study here, however, there is no need to dig any deeper into this facet of probability. We will be dealing with the world of nature as evolutionists see it. The laws of chance will be applied to that assumed world to see if things could logically have turned out as they now are on the basis of that theory. In doing this, we will proceed on their own assumption that the uniformity of nature is true, keeping in mind that it is an assumption.

When Probability Does Not Apply

There are areas in which chance has little to do. We have seen that it is not involved when specific outcomes can be precisely predicted. Also, situations in which there is advance purpose are generally not a field for applying probability theory. Neither are cases where there are known chains of cause-and-effect. When you flip a light switch, the bulb lights up. This does not ordinarily involve probability.

It is a different story if we consider the case in which a light goes out because a tree accidentally falls across the power line somewhere. Although cause and effect are involved, we cannot trace the exact sequence, and we don't consider that anyone

---

[19] C. S. Lewis, *Miracles, A Preliminary Study* (New York: Macmillan, 1947), pp. 104, 105.

If you are interested in the philosophic meaning, we highly recommend Lewis' study "On Probability" in this perceptive little book. Lewis was an Oxford University professor and a prolific author.

purposed or caused the tree's fall at that particular instant. There is no way to figure out in advance when and where such a thing will happen. From our human point of observation, we say it happened "by chance" to occur at that time and place.

Another example is the number of cars passing a particular point on the street in a ten-minute interval. Traffic engineers must plan streets and signals, and are concerned with such facts. Although each car has its own chain of cause-and-effect as to why the driver happened by at that moment, it is obviously not possible to predict with certainty the exact number of cars that will pass that point. There are too many factors involved that cannot be ascertained. It is not a situation in which the traffic engineer can see a clearly discernible chain which reads: this-cause-produces-this-effect. He therefore must use probability reasoning that is ultimately based on past experience and uniformity.

It Is Proper to Apply Probability Theory to Evolution

Probability theory is primarily involved when (1) there is believed to be no intelligent planning and (2) a cause-and-effect chain is not decipherable because the "causes are too complex to permit prediction."[20]

Harold J. Morowitz, Professor of Biophysics at Yale University, wrote:

> Often a process is so complicated or we are so ignorant of the boundary conditions, or of the laws governing the process, that we are unable to predict the result of the process in any but a statistical fashion. . . . Randomness is in a certain sense a consequence of the ignorance of the observer, yet randomness itself displays certain properties which have been turned into powerful tools in the study of the behavior of systems of atoms.[21]

Evolution is an ideal subject in which to apply the laws of chance. As defined earlier, evolutionary doctrine denies advance planning, and has random matter-in-motion as its basic causal source. "Chance mutations" furnish the variability upon which

---

[20] Émile Borel, *Probabilities and Life* (New York: Dover Publications, Inc., 1962), p. 1. On the same page, Borel says, "The principles on which the calculus of probabilities is based are extremely simple and as intuitive as the reasonings which lead an accountant through his operations."

[21] Harold J. Morowitz, *Entropy for Biologists* (New York: Academic Press, 1970), pp. 64, 65.

presently accepted evolutionary thinking in America is generally founded.

A central question we will be investigating is this: Do the laws of chance allow one to consider evolution as being within the realm of conceivable probability?

Probability—Not Always What One Would Expect

In tossing a coin, our intuition was right. There is one chance in two that heads will result. There are other situations where probability does *not* turn out as we might suppose. That is why it is important to study the principles of chance. Then we will be more likely to guess correctly in casual thought. Here is a case where most people guess wrong:

Suppose we have ten similar coins and number them one through ten. We put them in a container and shake them thoroughly. If we draw out one without looking, we naturally expect that we have a one-out-of-ten chance of getting the number one coin first. In that, our intuition is correct. Each coin is "equally likely" to be chosen at random. The probability is therefore 1/10. In this experiment, each time we will return the coin after drawing it, so there will always be a complete set. This is called drawing "with replacement."

Now, suppose we start over from the beginning and ask what the chances are of getting the number one coin on the first try followed by the number two coin on the next try. To many people, it seems it should be one in twenty. The truth is, however, that there is only one chance in one hundred of getting those two in order. If this is hard to accept, don't be surprised; you are not alone in such an impression. This is an important step in progress toward certainty on our main subject; so it will be worthwhile to examine thoroughly the rule involved here. Before discussing this further, it may be noted that one can find out by actual trial that this is correct.

Prove It to Yourself So You May Be Sure

It was mentioned earlier that this approach is susceptible to your own verification. You can perform easy experiments privately or with others, drawing coins or other numbered objects, to find out if chance really follows these rules. The time involved in brief experiments may be worth a lot toward arriving at solid conclusions that satisfy your own desire to be sure. One may follow through to whatever extent desired, to gain firsthand proof that it really does turn out that way, *on the average.* The next chapter will include important ideas on how to make experiments scientific and how to make them yield the most information in a short time by using fewer than ten from which to draw.

2

The Heart of Modern Probability Theory

> *It is truth very certain that, when it is not in our power to determine what is true, we ought to follow what is most probable.*
>
> —René Descartes[1]

SCIENTISTS CANNOT SAY how the world came to be or how life began. There was no human observer on the scene to record with technical data whether God created or things just evolved. Until one arrives at faith in the Bible record, the only logical course is to use inductive reasoning and follow what is most probable. Let us begin now to learn the main rules of probability. We will need only two central principles. Here is the first, sometimes called the "law of averages."

The Law of Large Numbers

Probability theory applies mainly to "long runs." If you toss a coin just a few times, the results may vary a lot from the average. As you continue the experiment, however, it levels out to almost absolute predictability. This is called the "law of large numbers." Here is how physicist George Gamow stated it:

> Thus whereas for 2 or 3, or even 4 tosses, the chances to have heads each time or tails each time are still quite appreciable, in 10 tosses even 90 per cent of heads or tails is very improbable. For a still larger number of tosses, say 100 or 1000, the probability curve becomes as sharp as a needle,

---

[1] In Darrel Huff and Irving Geis, *How To Take a Chance* (New York: W. W. Norton & Co., 1959), p. 7.

> and the chances of getting even a small deviation from fifty-fifty distribution becomes practically nil.[2]

The long run serves to average out the fluctuations that you may get in a short series. These variations are "swamped" by the long-haul average. When a large number of tries is involved, the law of averages can be depended upon quite closely. This rule, once called the "law of great numbers," is of central importance in this field of probability. By the way, in the popular sense, probability theory, the laws of chance, and the science of probability can be considered to be simply different expressions for the same general subject.

Make Your Experiments Scientific

To be exact, the theory of probability deals not with material objects, but with *ideal theoretical models* or mental pictures. If we use objects that are reasonably identical, however, the results of our experiments will be close to the same as with the abstract mathematical models on which the laws are based.

When we do experiments such as coin tosses or drawings of numbered objects, it is important to insure that there is equal likelihood of the different outcomes or "events" as they are called. If one of the objects to be drawn is heavier than the others, it may tend to settle to the bottom of the group, thus giving results that are inaccurate. Different rules might be involved if the various possible results are not made equally probable.

In selecting coins or letters at random, they must, of course, be thoroughly mixed before each drawing. If they are not shaken sufficiently, the same one that was just drawn might remain near the top to be more easily drawn again. Objects also should be drawn without looking, to avoid the possibility that the choice is influenced by sight of the various objects. The purpose is to find out what chance can do, and chance is blind.

If other articles are used instead of coins, they should as nearly as possible be the same size and shape and weight. This makes the experiment more scientific and assures more accurate results. Experimenting may mean more to you if first you read on a few pages farther.

The Multiplication Rule (Learn It Well!)

We now come to the most important rule of all for the

[2] George Gamow, *One, Two, Three—Infinity* (New York: Viking Press, 1961), p. 209.

purposes of our study. It is the second of the two principles. Let's go back to the ten numbered coins. Why is there only one chance in one hundred that we will get the number one coin on the first draw followed by the number two coin on the next draw?

Here is the principle involved, as described clearly by Adler: "Break the experiment down into a sequence of small steps. Count the number of possible outcomes of each step. Then multiply these numbers."[3] This important "multiplication rule" is most often used where the various outcomes of a particular step are all *equally probable* and the steps are independent.

In the experiment with ten similar coins numbered one through ten, we want to know the probability of getting the number one coin on the first try followed by the number two coin on the second try. Divide this into steps as Adler suggested. Our first step will be to draw one coin. There are ten different outcomes we could get on that first draw. There are also ten different possible results when we get to the second step. Multiplying, as Adler said, we have 10 x 10 = 100. So, the chance is 1 in 100 of getting the two desired coins in order. The probability is 1/100, on the average.

Before the first draw, we know intuitively that there is a 1-out-of-10 chance of success in getting the number one coin.[4] Therefore, whatever chance the *second* step will have must be multiplied by 1/10, because there is only that 1/10 chance of success on the *first* step. But the second step also has 1/10 probability of success. As we have just seen, that will have to be multiplied by the 1/10 probability from step one. This will give the answer for *both* steps together, which is 1/100. If such an experiment is continued long enough, about once in every hundred draws the number one coin will be followed by the number two. Remember, however, the law of large numbers. There will be deviations unless you do several hundred and average them.

The principle is: *If you seek first "this outcome" and then "that outcome," the probability of getting both is the product of their separate probabilities,* in cases where one outcome does not affect the other. George Gamow said it in these words:

---

[3] Irving Adler, *Probability and Statistics for Everyman* (New York: John Day Co., 1963), pp. 58, 59.

[4] This probability arises partly because of equivalence or symmetry, and we sense its logic.

> Here we have the rule of "multiplication of probabilities," which states that if you want several different things, you may determine the mathematical probability of getting them by multiplying the mathematical probabilities of getting the several individual ones.[5]

Perhaps this may seem to be much ado about a minor point. Some who are mathematically minded or knew the principle beforehand may have gotten it easily. For most people, however, it is hard to believe that the chances are that slim—just one in one hundred. This is the average outcome one can expect.

It will be worthwhile to stay with this matter until thoroughly convinced that it is true. One's mind may be slow to accept the idea. Darrell Huff wrote that "even intelligent adults confuse addition with multiplication of probabilities." That is why actual experimenting may be such a help. Much depends on becoming certain in one's own thinking that this is correct. A little later, we will suggest quicker methods for experimenting that will lead to the certainty of the truth of this rule.

This one point is *absolutely vital* to the whole process of this approach to certainty. It may be mastered by rereading and by experimenting as described a little farther on, and by pondering the matter until one's mind will accept its truth. All probability theory used in science and industry builds from this multiplication rule.

Can Chance Count to Ten?

What is the probability of drawing *all ten* coins in order? Remember the multiplication rule. For each of these steps, there are ten possible outcomes. For all ten steps, we must multiply ten by itself until the figure is used ten times: 10 x 10 x 10 x 10 x 10 x 10 x 10 x 10 x 10 x 10 = 10,000,000,000. So, the chances are quite small of getting all ten in a row. Once in ten billion selections we will get the number one followed in order by all the rest. Chance will succeed on the average only once in ten billion attempts.

To absorb the meaning of that fully is to be well on the way to the assurance that we seek. *Chance requires ten billion tries on the average in order to count to ten!*

Shorten Your Experiment Time

The reader has doubtless already realized that the experiment

[5] Gamow, *One, Two, Three—Infinity,* p. 208.

with ten coins is too long for any reasonable chance of success if done properly. If a person could draw and record one coin every five seconds day and night, it would take over 1,500 years to complete the time in which *one* success could be expected! In all that time, the outlook is for chance, on the average, to succeed just once in counting to ten.

Perhaps we get the gist of the idea that chance is not very capable when we need an ordered result. Consider the difference intelligence makes—even a limited intelligence. Give an eight-year-old the coins, and ask the child to arrange and pick up each one in order and return it. Chance is blind, and has no intelligence. The child is not thus limited. The child can do it in a few moments. Chance takes 1,500 years—just to count to ten once.

The same principle can be learned with shorter experiments, using fewer coins. If you try it with three or four or five numbered coins long enough to average out any short-run fluctuations, you will see that the rules hold true. With five coins, the probability of getting the number one and the number two in order on the first two draws is naturally 1 in 5 x 5 = 1 in 25.

In tossing a coin, the probability of four heads in a row is 1/2 x 1/2 x 1/2 x 1/2 = 1/16. What would be the probability of ten heads in a row?

To Spell "Evolution" by Chance

Suppose, instead of numbers, we use the letters of the alphabet. As a substitute for coins, any small, similarly shaped objects may be used if they are practically *identical* in size, weight, and shape. (The party game called "Scrabble" has small letters on wooden squares quite suitable for this.)

With one set of the twenty-six letters of the alphabet, you have 1/26 probability of getting the "A" on the first draw. To get "A" followed by "B" (replacing the letter after each draw, as before) your probability by the multiplication rule is: 1/26 x 1/ 26 = 1/676. To get ABC in order, the chance is 1 in 17,576, by the same rule.[6]

To spell the word "evolution," obtaining the nine letters in order, each having a 1/26 probability, you have a probability

[6] We tried such an experiment at the Center for Probability Research in Biology. In 30,000 alphabet letters drawn, only once did we get ABC in order! (Of course, there were other reasons for the experiment. The main purpose is explained in chapter 6 where it provides an analogy for usable and nonsense chains of amino acids.)

of 1 in 5,429,503,678,976. This, as you will realize, comes from multiplying 26 by itself, using the figure 9 times. If every five seconds day and night a person drew out one letter, he could expect to succeed in spelling the word "evolution" about once in 800,000 years!

Further Tests for Chance

Suppose we put chance to a test which is less simple, yet something that would be quite easy for any school child. Let it spell this phrase: "the theory of evolution." Drawing from a set of twenty-six small letters and one blank for the space between letters, what is the probability expectance?

All that is needed is simply to get those twenty-three letters and spaces in proper order, selecting them at random from the set of twenty-seven objects (twenty-six letters and one space). By the multiplication rule we learned, it will be 27 x 27 x 27 . . . x 27 using the figure twenty-three times.

The probability when computed is 1 in approximately 834,390,000,000,000,000,000,000,000,000,000; that is, one success in over 8 hundred million trillion trillion draws.

To get an idea of the size of that number, let us imagine that chance is employing an imaginary machine which will draw, record, and replace the letters at the speed of light, a BILLION draws PER SECOND! Working at that unbelievable rate, chance could spell "the theory of evolution" once in something over 26,000,000,000,000,000 years on the average!

Again, a child could do it in a few minutes. Chance would take more than five million times as long as the earth has existed (if we use the five-billion-year rounded figure which some evolutionists now estimate as the age of the earth).

If we are drawing from a set which contains both small letters and capital letters and one blank for the space between words to spell "The Theory of Evolution," the probability is 1 in 4,553,500,000,000,000,000,000,000,000,000,000,000,000. Our machine drawing at the speed of light, a billion draws per second, would require 140,000,000,000,000,000,000,000 years. That is 28,000,000,000,000 times the assumed age of the earth!

Chance Is Moronic

So chance requires twenty-eight trillion times the age of the earth to write merely the phrase: "The Theory of Evolution," drawing from a set of small letters and capitals as described, *drawing at the speed of light, a billion draws per second!*[7] Only once in that time could the letters be expected in proper order.

Again, a child can do this, using sight and intelligence, in a few minutes at most. Mind makes the difference in the two methods. Chance really "doesn't have a chance" when compared with the intelligent purpose of even a child.

"In the beginning, God . . ." begins to appear more scientific, as we see how limited are the abilities of mindless chance.

Perhaps the alphabet experiments just described may help to emphasize how important it is fully to understand the multiplication rule we studied earlier. It's hard to believe at first. Try drawing alphabet letters for a few hours to become really convinced! Remember in doing so that chance has no intelligence, no purpose. It cannot purposefully choose one correct letter and discard unwanted ones until it finds the next one needed.

In the next two chapters, we will make some actual use of what we have learned. We are to apply probability theory to the strange phenomenon of the "left-handed" molecules which are used in proteins. We will use that as a practice field in applying the laws of chance. It is ideal for this, because only two possible outcomes are involved for each step. It is similar, therefore, to the experiment of tossing a coin.

Special Note to the Reader

Most of this book is in plain, easy-to-understand language. In a few places, however, we must go far enough into certain areas of biology to apply the laws of chance in logical manner. This will require the use of a small amount of mathematics, but not much—mostly just arithmetic. It is a necessary part of the process in gaining certainty by the approach which we are following.

For the reader who happens to have an absorbing interest in biology, it is unlikely to involve any strain or confusion as a rule.

Perhaps, on the other hand, you have only a casual interest in the details of science. Does that rule out the value to you of this method of seeking assurance on evolution? Not at all. A great number of people may not have any engrossing interest in biology, and yet may attain that valuable certainty.

---

[7] The imaginary machine is considered as moving slightly less than a foot per draw, round trip. The letter is recorded during the return trip so that no time is taken up except the actual travel, round trip, of .98 foot at the speed of light, to allow 1,000,000,000 draws per second.

If you plow on through any places that seem somewhat technical, you will at least get the general idea and you will soon be back into easier reading. In the process, you will realize that the actual facts and figures are there in print for anyone who wishes to dig into the subject more thoroughly. The conclusions, moreover, are always in easily grasped speech. Without the actual reasoning and figures, and without the references, the reader would have little to depend on except an author's words, and that is a poor basis for certainty. Don't worry, then, if you strike sections that you do not quickly comprehend completely. Just read on through. You can return later to those sections that you may wish to reread.

Before going on, we will confess that (to the horror of mathematicians) we have oversimplified a bit, to make the ideas accessible to people not trained in mathematics. The recurrent phrase, "on the average," needs more explaining when it is used with experiments which are repeated. The footnote below goes into this, for the noncasual reader.[8] Now, let's look at left-handed molecules.

---

[8] Our figuring thus far has been the kind where "success" was getting a certain result *once, on the average* in a series of trials. Now, consider the different concept of *at least once:* the desired event may happen once or more than once, but the main thing is that it happens at all.

If we draw from ten coins (with replacement), what is the probability that the No. 1 coin will show up *at least once* if we make two draws? Here is what can happen: (1) We may obtain the No. 1 coin *just once* from the two draws; (2) we may get it *both times;* or (3) *not at all.* Either the first or the second of these results would be a "success," because in each the event occurs: "No. 1 coin at least once."

We see that success can happen in more than one way, but failure can happen just one way. We therefore first figure the chance of failure. It is 9/10 on any one draw, and we can use the multiplication rule for two draws, because we need failure both times—"this *and* that." 9/10 x 9/10 = 81/100. Now to find the chance of success:

Always, if one adds the probability of success and the probability of failure, the total is exactly one. We can obtain the probability of success by subtracting 81/100 from 100/100 (which is the same as one). The answer is 19/100, the chance of getting the No. 1 coin *at least once.* A mathematician might write the formula thus: where n is the number of draws, and p is the probability of success in one draw: $p_n = 1-(1-p)^n$.

With the large figures we will encounter, it would make virtually no difference if we used this more exact method, so we will save confusion by figuring the much simpler probability *on the average.* Chapter 10 will give more details on this. (The difference between the two methods is less than just adding one to an exponent of ten. The exact method would be even harder on evolution.)

3

The Mystery of the Left-Handed Molecules in Proteins

There are here mysteries which prepare immense labors for the future, and from this time invite the most serious meditations of science.

—Louis Pasteur[1]

OVER A HUNDRED years have passed since Pasteur wrote those words in 1860. He was referring to one of the strangest puzzles in biology, that proteins are made exclusively of "left-handed" molecules.[2] Although immense labors *have* been done as he suggested, the mystery remains without adequate solution to this day.

We now have the interesting task of applying the laws of chance learned in the previous chapter to this intriguing subject. Naturally, we will first need to know what is meant by "left-handed molecules."

It should be pointed out that although this is a *shortcut* to certainty, it will require a bit of effort. The philosophy of evolution is so deeply entrenched in our culture that one will find it hard to counteract its error without solid evidence and accurate logic. The gold of the certainty we seek will require some digging. The effort, however, can produce the riches desired.

To avoid being superficial, we will need to get into some areas of the field of biology in detail. This may prove interesting,

---

1 In Alton Meister, *The Biochemistry of the Amino Acids* (New York: Academic Press, 1965), vol. 1, p. 113.

2 Pasteur was actually writing of the broader mystery that living molecules in general are "one-handed." We will concern ourselves only with proteins at the present.

for it is the study of *life*. Those with more than a passing interest will see the value of thoroughness on the key issues for our mutual purpose.

Darrell Huff said that there are two important steps in probability reasoning: (1) bring your information on the particular subject to a maximum; then (2) bring an understanding of the laws of probability to bear.[3] In this chapter, we will attempt to bring our information on the left-handed molecules in proteins to the maximum needed. Then, in the following chapter, the laws of chance will be applied: What are the odds against a protein having only left-handed components?

The plan will be to keep to the main facts which will enable the reader to get a clear picture. In so doing, we will have to bypass many interesting sidelights not involved directly in the subject, since this is not a textbook on general biology or biochemistry. Necessary technical information will usually be placed in footnotes or in an appendix, so that it will not interrupt or delay a quick grasp of the main ideas. It will thus be available to those who want to dig into the subject. It will also be possible, for those who wish, to research the sources or authority for items mentioned where space may limit us from going into details. For this purpose, the references may be consulted. Some are easily found, others are less accessible, but at least the source is indicated, as is conventional in scientific literature.

Usually, in scientific writings, references are at the end of the chapter. For the convenience of nontechnical readers, however, in this book they are on the same page, as footnotes, so they will be quickly accessible. Since many of the references contain important additional data, this may prove useful to students as well. (When an author is quoted more than once in the same chapter, a short reference form will be used after the first time, giving the author's last name, key words of the title, and page number.)

Also, since math doesn't come easy to a lot of us, we will keep the form of the calculations quite simple so that a person with practically no mathematical training may be able to get the ideas.

---

[3] Darrell Huff, *How to Take a Chance* (New York: W. W. Norton & Co., 1959), pp. 60, 61.

Understanding Proteins—Complex, Yet Built on a Simple Plan

To preface the left-handed mystery, it may be of value to those in other fields if we first review what proteins are like. They are, of course, a major class of the complex molecules of which all living things are made. Since all molecules consist of atoms bonded together, we can get an idea of the size of a molecule by the number of atoms it contains. Water, for example, has three atoms. Nitric acid has five. Now, by comparison, the smallest of proteins contains around a thousand atoms, and the largest has close to a million! Proteins, then, are enormous compared to most molecules.

In primary structure, proteins are long, slender filaments or threads. Even giant molecules, like proteins, are unbelievably small from our viewpoint. In fact, Max Perutz of Cambridge University notes that a protein fiber is 500 times thinner than the thinnest object a good optical microscope could reveal.[4] This miniature long filament is often precisely folded into a somewhat globular shape which differs for each type of protein.

Proteins Are Chains of Amino Acid Molecules

It seems to be a universal rule in biology that complex things are built from simple components. This is a source of amazement to scientists. It also makes it much easier for us to understand things like proteins and DNA.

Proteins are simply long chains of smaller molecules called *amino acids.* There are twenty varieties of these that are commonly used in proteins. These will be listed in chapter 6. There are indications that all of the twenty kinds occur in proteins of all organisms.[5]

The number of these building blocks in a single protein ranges roughly from 100 to 50,000, since there is great variety in the size of different proteins. The hormone insulin is usually called a protein although it is smaller than this range, having only 51 amino acids. It is not, however, a completely typical protein. The average number of amino acids in proteins of the smallest known living thing is 400, at the very least.[6]

---

[4] Max Perutz, "A House for Living Molecules," *1970 Yearbook of Science and the Future* (Britannica), p. 365.

[5] John F. Thompson, Clayton J. Morris, and Ivan K. Smith, "New Naturally Occurring Amino Acids," *Annual Review of Biochemistry,* Vol. 38 (1969), p. 137. Also:

Margaret O. Dayhoff, *Atlas of Protein Sequence and Structure 1972* (National Biomedical Research Foundation, Washington, D. C., 1972).

[6] Harold J. Morowitz, personal communication, November, 1970.

There are many thousands of kinds of proteins, and they perform numerous different jobs in living things. Many are digestive enzymes, others are structural molecules, and some perform their specialized tasks as hormones or as hemoglobin in blood cells. All of this complexity comes from those twenty amino acids and the particular order in which they are arranged in the chain. A different sequence may make an entirely different type of protein.

Commenting on this, one scientist noted: "Thus, from about twenty different amino acids, the colossal array of different proteins required by different forms of life is constructed."[7]

Amino Acids Also Are Built on a Simple Plan

It is fortunate for our understanding that even the amino acids possess a degree of uniformity. All are made of four kinds of atoms: carbon, hydrogen, nitrogen, and oxygen. Two of the amino acids also have a sulfur atom each.

Besides this, all of the amino acids are exactly alike in the main section or "backbone" which consists of three atoms, two of which are carbon and the other nitrogen. The center one of those three, which is a carbon atom, is called the *alpha carbon.* ("Alpha," being the first letter of the Greek alphabet, is usually written in Greek in scientific writings, thus: α. To avoid complexity, we will spell out in English any such Greek letters.)

Having noted some of the similarities, we now come to the difference between the amino acids. To the central carbon atom, the alpha carbon, there is attached a *side group,* often called the *R group. The sole difference between the various types of amino acids is that each has a different side group.*[8]

In the various amino acids, the distinguishing side group contains from one to eighteen atoms. The considerable diversity in these side groups makes possible many of the things proteins do. They have different electrical and chemical properties which affect other molecules. Other amino acids at various distances in the same protein chain may be attracted in this way, with the following result:

When the units of the protein chain are in any particular

---

[7] *Encyclopedia Britannica,* (1967), s.v. "chemistry."

[8] In the amino acid, proline, the side group bends around and also fastens to the adjacent nitrogen atom. This technically makes proline an "imino" acid, since it replaces a hydrogen atom usually located on that nitrogen atom.

sequence, the resulting chain will coil or spiral and fold in a specific way.[9] This final shape makes the protein able to do its unique job in the cell.

When two amino acids are united, a "peptide bond" is formed between them, and a molecule of water is released.[10] It takes energy to get the amino acids to bond together. It is difficult to bring this about outside of living things. In the laboratory it can be done by special techniques.[11]

In living organisms, on the other hand, protein chains are linked up or *polymerized* rapidly. This system for making proteins is very complex and efficient, employing special enzymes and several other unique molecules. It is an extremely interesting process that takes place under direction from the DNA code, the hereditary "language of life." It will be described in chapter 9.

How Can a Molecule Be Left-Handed?

Amino acids can exist in both right-handed and left-handed forms. A person's two hands show how this can be. They have the same components—fingers and thumbs—yet they are different. The thumb of one is on the left and the thumb of the other on

---

[9] Conformation is also affected by temperature, solvents, "pH" reading (acidity), etc.

[10] This water molecule is composed of atoms that were formerly part of the amino acids. For this reason, amino acids in a protein chain are often called amino acid *residues*, since they are no longer complete.

[11] If the following is confusing, don't be concerned. The purpose of these technical details at this point is merely to indicate some of the difficulties in joining amino acids outside of living things:

Amino acids, in order to join, must be activated or energized by chemically combining with another substance. One such chemical is $COCl_2$ (carbonyl chloride, also known as phosgene), which may be prepared by passing carbon monoxide and chlorine gases over heated charcoal. $COCl_2$ is decomposed by water, so a nonaqueous solvent must be used as the scene where this reaction with an amino acid takes place. The product of the reaction is a high energy derivative of the amino acid called its N-carbonic anhydride (NCA). To cause NCA's to join, an "initiator" chemical is next added to a solution of NCA's. Initiators used include various bases, salts, weak acids, and certain ions.

A typical example is the joining of the amino acid derivatives gamma-ethyl-L-glutamate NCA's. The reaction can be brought about in an organic solvent known as N,N-dimethylformamide, at 25° C, using the base di-isopropylamine as an iniator. (C. H. Bamford and H. Block, "The Polymerization of Alpha-Amino Acid N-Carbonic Anhydrides," *Polyamino Acids, Polypeptides, and Proteins,* ed. Mark A. Stahmann, [Madison: University of Wisconsin Press, 1962], p. 66.) Many other factors must be attended to, such as the concentrations of constituents, and the blocking of reactive groups which are not supposed to get into the action.

Polymerization by heat can be accomplished at 180° C if certain precise artificial ratios of amino acids are used, with large amounts of aspartic acid and glutamic acids. (Sidney W. Fox and Klaus Dose, *Molecular Evolution and the Origin of Life* [San Francisco: W. H. Freeman and Co., 1972], p. 345.)

the right. They are "mirror images" of each other. Some molecules are like that.

Let's imagine that we are able to look at an amino acid molecule. Remember that each is built on the same simple plan. The three atoms of the backbone are in the direct line of the protein chain when the amino acid is united with others. In the center is the alpha carbon atom. On one end of it there is a nitrogen atom, and on the other end another carbon.[12] If we look at it from the carbon end, it will be possible to tell whether it is left- or right-handed (see Figure 2).

FIGURE 2

Left-handed *Right-handed*

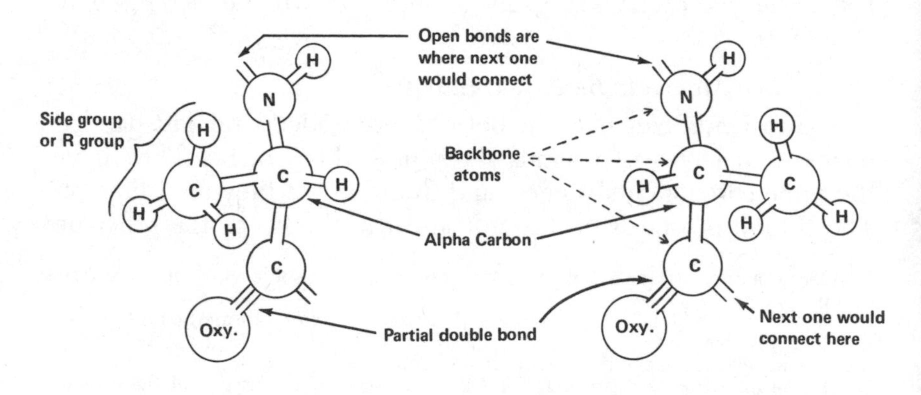

L-*Alanine* D-*Alanine*

Left- and right-handed amino acid residues. The molecules shown are L-alanine and D-alanine (L=levo, or left-handed; D = dextro, or right-handed). Alanine is the simplest of the amino acids which are isomeric or handed.

The bonds in the figure are not drawn to scale, but are lengthened so that the left- and right-handedness is more easily seen. In real molecules, the bonds are shorter so that the "surfaces" overlap, making the molecules more compact. The initials on the atoms indicate carbon, nitrogen, oxygen, and hydrogen. Note that the only difference between the two is the position of the side group, on either the left or right side.

---

12 The carbon end is called the *carboxyl* end, if that end of the amino acid is free and complete, or the *carbonyl* end if it is joined to another.

Notice the center carbon atom of the backbone. It appears to be elevated a bit compared to the other two atoms of the main part. That alpha carbon is *asymmetric,* that is, different on every side. This difference is not in the atom itself, but it results from the fact that the four items bonded to it all are different.

As we view it from our vantage point at the carbon "end" of the amino acid[13] (considering the lower carbon atom in Figure 2 as the carbon end), we note that the central or alpha carbon has two side projections that angle outward to the right and to the left. On one side, this extension is simply a hydrogen atom. Opposite it is the side group mentioned earlier, the group which differs for each of the twenty amino acid types.

If that identifying side group is on the left, the molecule is "left-handed." If instead it protrudes to the right, the amino acid is said to be "right-handed."

These two forms of the same chemical contain the exact same components and are called *isomers* or *stereoisomers* of that chemical. Their side groups are just positioned oppositely in space. Each form is the *antipode* of the other. They are *enantiomorphs* or *enantiomers* of each other.

We may note in passing that this difference was discovered in an accidental way. A French physicist named D. F. Arago in 1811 shined a beam of plane-polarized light through a quartz crystal. He discovered to his surprise that the plane of the light was twisted or rotated as it passed through the crystal. Later it was found that some chemicals dissolved in water would also cause this twisting of the beam of light. Whether the light was rotated to the right or to the left depended on the substance used. Solutions which rotate polarized light in this manner are said to be *optically active,* since they deflect the path of light.

Pasteur, while investigating this strange phenomenon in 1848, found that the optically active substance he was studying was made of one-handed molecules.[14] To his surprise, he found that optically active materials from living things were different from

[13] J. M. Barry and E. M. Barry, *An Introduction to the Study of Biological Molecules* (Englewood Cliffs, N.J.: Prentice-Hall, Inc., 1969), p. 99.

[14] Solutions made of the opposite enantiomorph of such a chemical will rotate the light plane the opposite way. Both forms mixed together equally will not usually rotate the light plane at all. One might suppose that left-handed molecules would rotate light to the left, but this is not necessarily so. There is no simple universal relationship between left-handed configuration, for example, and the direction of optical rotation, because complex factors are involved.

optically active crystals of inorganic substances like quartz. *Crystals* of the latter come in both left- and right-handed configuration, whereas the *individual molecules* are neither left- nor right-handed.

Only Left-Handed Amino Acids in Proteins

Francis Crick, codiscoverer of the DNA structure, describes this strange characteristic of the molecules of living organisms:

> It has been well known for many years that for any particular molecule only one hand occurs in nature. For example the amino acids one finds in proteins are always what are called the "L" or "levo" amino acids, and never the "D" or "dextro" amino acids. Only one of the two mirror possibilities occurs in proteins.[15]

That is the mystery. English biologist John Maddox called it "an intellectual thunderbolt that natural proteins should contain only the left-handed forms of the amino acids."[16]

This is a special difficulty for those who believe that life originated from nonliving matter by natural processes. A. I. Oparin, Russian biochemist, has perhaps had more to do with current evolutionary thought than any man since Darwin because of his pioneering attempts to explain the origin of life through natural chemical processes. He brought up this mystery in a recent book thus: "It is necessary to touch briefly on a problem which has been discussed in the literature for a long time."[17]

In an earlier book he went more into detail. The atoms involved in the different positions (right and left) are subject to the same forces. When amino acids are formed, that varying side group could just as easily be on the right as on the left. Says Oparin:

> The probability of the formation of one antipode or the other is therefore the same. As the law of averages applies to chemical reactions the appearance of an excess of one antipode is very improbable, and, in fact, we never encounter it under the conditions of non-living nature and in laboratory syntheses. . . .
>
> In living organisms, on the contrary, the amino acids of

[15] Francis H. C. Crick, *Molecules and Men* (Seattle: University of Washington Press, 1966), p. 60.

[16] John Maddox, *Revolution in Biology* (New York: Macmillan Company, 1964), p. 59.

[17] A. I. Oparin, *Genesis and Evolutionary Development of Life* (New York: Academic Press, 1968), p. 80.

> which naturally occurring proteins are made always have the left-handed configuration.... This ability of protoplasm selectively to synthesize and accumulate one antipode alone is called the asymmetry of living material. It is a characteristic feature of all organisms without exception but is absent from inanimate nature.
>
> Pasteur pointed out this fact as follows: "This great character is, perhaps, the only sharp dividing line which we can draw at present between the chemistry of dead and living nature."[18]

In modern times, many others have expressed the same surprise as Pasteur. For example, Linus Pauling, Nobel laureate in chemistry:

> This is a very puzzling fact.... All the proteins that have been investigated, obtained from animals and from plants, from higher organisms and from very simple organisms—bacteria, molds, even viruses—are found to have been made of L-amino acids.[19]

He concludes, "Nobody knows why it is that we are built of L-amino acid molecules, rather than of D-amino acid molecules."[20]

Dr. Larry Butler, who teaches biochemistry at Purdue University, has said, "In all respects chemically and physically (except for physical properties associated with asymmetry...) D- and L-amino acids are not only equivalent but indistinguishable."[21]

Professor Dennis Englin calls attention to an amusing experiment. Scientists now can hook up proteinlike chains which contain both the L- and D-amino acids, and put such chains into a living organism, e.g., a bacterium. The organism immediately takes them apart, and in some cases rebuilds the amino acids in the left-handed form![22]

---

[18] A. I. Oparin, *Life, Its Nature, Origin and Development* (New York: Academic Press, 1961), pp. 59, 60.

[19] Linus Pauling, *General Chemistry* (Third Edition) (San Francisco: W. H. Freeman & Co., 1970), p. 774.

[20] Ibid.

[21] Larry Butler, Purdue University, personal communication, April 1971.

Some isomers can be distinguished from their opposites by taste, says Butler. They also can sometimes be detected by odor. ("Left- and Right-Handed Odors," *Scientific American*, Vol. 225 [August 1971], pp. 46, 47.) This may be due to physical difference in shape, if these sense receptors have "specifically shaped sites into which molecules of different forms fit."

[22] Dennis Englin, Los Angeles Baptist College, personal communication, June 1971.

For those interested in biology, it is intriguing to find that D-amino acids do have an occasional role in nature but never in proteins from evidence to date. Ordinarily no more than one or two right-handed isomers occur in such

Professor William Stokes of the University of Utah sums up the situation on this baffling question of the two forms as far as normal proteins are concerned:

> They are as identical in all other respects as a pair of gloves. When amino acids are prepared artificially, both L- and D-varieties occur in statistically equal amounts. But living things can use and construct only the left-handed type, probably for hereditary reasons going back to the first ancestor of all life on earth.[23]

Looking at it from the naturalistic standpoint for the moment, we may ask: *How could living things have gotten started which use only left-handed amino acids in proteins?*

The first problem is to discover how *any* amino acids could originate by natural means. For this, the current explanation is to postulate a primitive atmosphere that was totally different from ours today. Then it is claimed that amino acids might have been formed from that prescribed atmosphere by the action of ultraviolet rays, lightning, and perhaps heat.[24]

---

cases. These always occupy a precise position, usually in a small molecule or short peptide chain.

Bacteria have as part of the cell wall, outside the cell membrane, a molecular mesh known as *murein* which completely surrounds the cell. Murein consists of a polysaccharide containing two amino sugars crosslinked by means of tetrapeptides (which contain four amino acids, in final form.) Two of the four amino acids are the D- type, first formed as L-*amino* acids inside the cell and then changed to the D- variety.

The bacterium, *Bacillus anthracis,* has D-glutamic acid as the repeating subunit which forms its "slime capsule" outside the cell wall. Perhaps such use of D-amino acid units in cell walls and capsules may confer some protection from enzymes which predominantly are coded to react with L-isomers.

The antibiotic known as *polymyxin B* consists of a cyclic polypeptide ten amino acids in length. Occupying a specific site in the ring is D-phenylalanine. *Penicillin,* another antibiotic, and *luciferin,* a chemical involved in producing light in fireflies and other organisms, are other examples where one or two D-amino acids occur in small molecules.

None of these rare examples are proteins and all could give the impression that they are purposefully positioned rather than in random or interchangeable sites.

[23] William Lee Stokes, *Essentials of Earth History* (Englewood Cliffs, N.J.: Prentice-Hall, Inc., 1966), p. 176.

[24] The hypothetical primitive atmosphere conveniently happens to contain methane, ammonia, hydrogen, and water vapor, from which it is theoretically simple to derive amino acids. In a famous experiment, Stanley L. Miller duplicated that supposed atmosphere and subjected the mixture to an electric spark for a week. He succeeded in getting the two simplest amino acids and three others of doubtful identity. (George Wald, "The Origin of Life," *Scientific American* [August, 1954], p. 48.) *The results, however, included both left- and right-handed isomers.* (Oparin, *Life, Its Nature, Origin and Development,* p. 59.) Such a mixture containing both forms, is called a *racemic modification.* Later, Sidney W. Fox and K. Harada in complex experiments obtained twelve protein-type amino acids. They used considerable heat (around 1,000° C), ammonium hydroxide, and other laboratory controlled conditions. (Sidney W. Fox and Klaus

In experiments with this presumed primeval atmosphere, whenever any amino acids have been obtained in elaborate laboratory tests, they have consisted of both L- and D- varieties.

So we still have the problem. *Even if* the amino acids had occurred in that atmosphere naturally, these experiments indicate that the supply would have been "racemic" or mixed, instead of all L- or all D-.[25]

Efforts to Account for the Left-Handed Phenomenon

Scientists have let their imaginations range far and wide in quest of a solution. Without exception, each avenue has proved considerably less than satisfying. Materialists, for lack of anything better, have had to sound confident and to depend on one or another of the ideas put forward. One gets the impression that many just have a vague hope that maybe some one of these explanations may be valid, without specifying which specific one.

A summary of these attempts is given in Appendix 1, page 243, following the final chapter. The reader is encouraged to turn to it if he desires the details on this subject.

For a century, these efforts to find the answers have continued. Long and imaginative labors using many laboratory approaches have managed only to get "unequal amounts of enantiomers to form," by using reagents, catalysts, crystals, solvents, etc.[26] This is sometimes hailed as if it indicated success, and is credited to the "entirely expected effect of the atomic neighborhood, biasing, say, the ease of approach of the various reacting molecules to one of the possible sites of action." One such "success," we may note, yielded "an excess of 6 percent," the amount of one hand as compared to the other.[27]

All well and good, but getting "unequal amounts" is a far cry from explaining nature's success in producing 100 percent (all L-) products. Even if a way is found, the question will per-

---

Dose, *Molecular Evolution and the Origin of Life* [San Francisco: W. H. Freeman and Co., 1972], p. 81.)

[25] Six protein-type amino acids have been identified in the Murchison meteorite which fell in Australia in 1969. Both left- and right-handed isomers of each of these proteins were present "in roughly equal proportions," and thought to be of inorganic origin. (James G. Lawless, Clair E. Folsome, and Keith A. Kvenvolden, "Organic Matter in Meteorites," *Scientific American*, Vol. 226, [June, 1972], p. 42.) This strengthens the conclusion that there is no natural way known which could produce all-left-handed amino acids, outside of living cells.

[26] Philip Morrison, in Book Reviews, *Scientific American*, Vol. 225, (July, 1971), p. 120.

[27] Ibid.

sist: *Why is it so difficult for our most intelligent scientists to solve in modern laboratories what nature has done without apparent effort?*

No Satisfactory Answer Has Been Found

After considering all the attempts, it is clear that unless chance could do it, there is at present no adequate answer from a naturalistic standpoint to explain how this left-handed condition began. As a result, there is little evidence of any agreement or consensus among scientists regarding its source. Oparin must presume that this stereoselectivity started without prior design. Any other belief would be inconsistent with his communist philosophy. (Interestingly, that viewpoint—dialectical materialism—is not atheistic after all. Professor Claude Tresmontant of the University of Paris has pointed out with unanswerable logic that communists are actually pantheists, worshiping matter-in-motion.)[28]

Dr. Oparin never does make clear which of all the various ideas he prefers, to account for the origin of the exclusive use of left-handed amino acids in proteins, but he assumes it happened naturally, nevertheless. He is admirably straightforward in realizing the difficulty:

> Even when we know how the asymmetry arose, though, we still cannot answer the question of why one antipode, rather than the other, should occupy such a monopolistic position in the life of all the organisms inhabiting the Earth. This question is important for an understanding of the essential nature of life but it remains for future investigators to supply the answer.[29]

On that subject, Pauling made this imaginative comment:

> The earth might just as well be populated with living organisms made of D-amino acids as with those made of L-amino acids. A man who was suddenly converted into an exact mirror image of himself would not at first know that anything had changed about him. . . . He could drink water, inhale air and use the oxygen in it for combustion, exhale carbon dioxide, and carry on other bodily functions just as well as ever—so long as he did not eat any ordinary food. If he were to eat ordinary plant or animal food, he would find that he could not digest it.[30]

---

[28] Claude Tresmontant, Interview in *Réalités* (April, 1967), p. 47.
[29] Oparin, *Life, Its Nature, Origin and Development*, p. 61.
[30] Pauling, *General Chemistry*, p. 775.
Whether or not one agrees with his political actions, in the laboratory Linus

He then noted a strange coincidence. As long ago as 1872, Lewis Carroll's *Through the Looking Glass* was published. In it, Alice (in a land of mirror images) said, "Perhaps looking-glass milk isn't good to drink."[31] It is possible that Lewis Carroll was aware of Pasteur's work in this field.

In attempting to account for the one-handed phenomenon, Oparin and others have depended upon natural selection. As we will see in chapter 5, there is no way that natural selection could have operated at all until there was a way to duplicate all the essential parts accurately. There is no method known whereby this could take place except the intricate DNA-RNA-enzymes-ribosome process which we will examine in later chapters. Therefore, natural selection is of no help whatever in the effort to find the way that left-handed amino acids obtained their complete monopoly in naturally occurring proteins.

No Natural Solution Unless Chance Could Produce This Effect

Since natural selection was unable to operate before accurate duplication, and since no way has been found to account for the exclusive use of left-handed components in proteins, chance is all that is left, from the materialistic standpoint. Some evolutionists have recognized this explicitly. For example, S. E. Bresler, a top biochemist in the U.S.S.R. Academy of Science, wrote,

> How and why the complete separation of stereoisomers in living tissue was started remains an enigma. . . . We can only speculate that this remarkable phenomenon originally occurred as the result of very rare large-scale fluctuations associated with the origin of life.[32]

By this he plainly means chance fluctuations. Before applying the rules of probability, there are two questions we need to resolve: (1) Can each of the amino acids be linked with any other, regardless of hand? (2) Will they link with equal ease whether of the same or the opposite hand?[33]

Pauling's scientific discoveries have been outstanding, and his books in the realm of science are classics, yet written with humility.

[31] We have seen earlier that certain organisms can convert *some* of the D-amino acids into the L- form. Similar conversion to the natural form does not seem to be possible, however, in the case of the energy food, glucose sugar (*Encyclopaedia Britannica*, 1967, s.v. "stereochemistry"), and other vital foods, such as Vitamin C, which is L-ascorbic acid (Linus Pauling, *Vitamin C and the Common Cold* [San Francisco: W. H. Freeman & Co., 1970], p. 89.

[32] S. E. Bresler, *Introduction to Molecular Biology* (New York: Academic Press, 1971), pp. 6, 7. First published in Russia in 1966.

[33] To ascertain the current status of information on these questions, the author, in 1971, talked by telephone with several prominent scientists in the United States

Left- and Right-Handed Amino Acids Can Be Linked

Are the two forms of the amino acids shaped so that any of them can unite, whether they are L- or D- in type? The answer is yes. Whether left- or right-handed, any amino acid can be linked with any other of either hand. There seem to be no exceptions.[34]

Pauling wrote (1964): "We have no strong reason to believe that molecules resembling proteins could not be built up of equal numbers of right-handed and left-handed amino acid molecules."[35] Since that was written, this has actually been done on numerous occasions in many laboratories, resulting in a voluminous literature in the scientific journals.

While it is true that opposites can be linked in the laboratory, what about that question if we consider the conditions that evolution assumes to have been existing before life began? Dr. Sidney W. Fox, of the University of Miami has done experiments which involve this. Some years back, Dr. Fox heated all the common amino acids at 200° C temperature under certain conditions and obtained chains containing all the amino acids.[36] When asked if both left- and right-handed amino acids were included in the same chain, he replied that he was almost 100 percent certain that they were, but that there was no way to tell absolutely at the time.[37] Temperatures of 170° C and above were typically used in such experiments.

---

and England who are knowledgeable in this field. Much of the material in this chapter and the next was first published as a separate paper (James F. Coppedge, "Probability and Left-Handed Molecules," *Creation Research Society Quarterly*, Vol. 8 [December, 1971], pp. 163-174.) See also Appendixes 1 and 2.

[34] Telephone conversations April, 1971, with James Bonner, California Institute of Technology; Sidney W. Fox, University of Miami; Arthur Elliott, King's College, London; Harry Block, University of Liverpool.

[35] Linus Pauling, *College Chemistry*, 3rd ed. (San Francisco: W. H. Freeman & Co., 1964), p. 731. Repeated in his 1970 edition of *General Chemistry*.

Dr. Pauling, in commenting on this question by telephone (April 1971), mentioned the possibility of "steric hindrance" (interference because of shape), but referred me to his book quoted above.

We will discuss the matter of preference for the same hand shortly, but there seems to be no doubt that any amino acid can be linked to any other, as indicated by many scientists who have experimented extensively on this particular matter.

[36] Sidney W. Fox, ed., *The Origins of Prebiological Systems and of Their Molecular Matrices* (New York: Academic Press, 1965), pp. 361-382.

Encyclopedia Americana (1971), s.v. "amino acids."

[37] Fox, personal communication, 1971.

A difficulty in using heat to join amino acids is "the easy thermal decomposition" of amino acids. (Sidney W. Fox, Kaoru Harada, & Duane L. Rohlfing, "The Thermal Copolymerization of Alpha-Amino Acids," in *Polyamino Acids, Polypeptides, and Proteins*, ed. Mark A. Stahmann [Madison: University of Wisconsin Press, 1962], p. 47.)

Will Opposites Join With Equal Ease?

Although there is a degree of uncertainty on this subject at the present stage of scientific knowledge, it appears that the answer lies in one or the other of the following extremes, or somewhere between: (1) There may be equal ease of linking opposite hands, on the average. This seems most likely, when considering all the factors. The individual amino acids are different in ease of fit. Some work better with the same hand, and some with the opposite. The shape of the chain, when it begins to form a spiral, also may be involved.

(2) The other possibility is indicated in a few reports of preference for the same hand in some particular instances.[38] In some other instances there is preference for the opposite hand.[39] The extreme limit seems to be a possible preference of 6/7 for the same hand. It is quite unlikely that this is the case on any general basis, but we will use it as one limit to consider.

Since this subject gets quite technical, we will include the details in Appendix 2, page 249, leading to the conclusions which have just been stated briefly. The reader can experiment with models of the amino acids in order to satisfy himself on the comparative equal ease of fit, whether of the same or opposite hand. Numerous opposite hand linkups are routinely made in various laboratories with no notice of any more hindrance than with the same hand,[40] except in the occasional instances mentioned.

In the next chapter, probability reasoning will be applied to these two outside limits—equal ease of linkup, or 6/7 preference for the same hand.

---

[38] R. D. Lundberg and Paul Doty, "A Study of the Kinetics of the Primary Amine-initiated Polymerization of N-Carboxy-anhydrides with Special Reference to Configurational and Stereochemical Effects," *American Chemical Society Journal,* Vol. 79 (1957), pp. 3961-3972.

E. R. Blout and M. Idelson, in *American Chemical Society Journal,* Vol. 78 (1956), pp. 3857, 3858. These authors also mention a *reverse* preference as one explanation for some of their results.

Fred D. Williams, M. Eshaque, and Ronald D. Brown, "Stereoselective Polymerization of Gamma Benzyl Glutamate NCA," *Biopolymers,* Vol. 10 (April, 1971), pp. 753-756.

[39] Fred D. Williams, Michigan Technological University, telephone conversation, June, 1971.

Eberhard Shröder and Klaus Lübke, *The Peptides* (New York: Academic Press, 1965), pp. 274, 275, 319-326.

[40] E. Klein et al., "Permeability of Synthetic Polypeptide Membranes," *Biopolymers,* Vol. 10 (April, 1971), pp. 647-655; E. Klein, Gulf South Research Institute, New Orleans, telephone conversation, June, 1971.

4

The Odds Against Proteins With Only Left-Handed Components

All possible knowledge, then, depends on the validity of reasoning.[1]

—C. S. Lewis

FROM EVIDENCE DISCUSSED in the preceding chapter, it is clear that nothing other than chance has been discovered that can adequately account for the all-left-handed phenomenon. It is logical, therefore, to apply the laws of probability, to see if proteins could have by chance used only left-handed amino acids.

To be completely fair, we will figure the chances for the two outer limits of what may be the true situation. As noted earlier, those limits are as follows: (1) either there is equal probability, on the average, of opposite hands linking, under the presumed conditions on earth prior to life, or (2) a preference of 6/7, at the most, in favor of amino acids of the same hand joining. Because it is simpler, the odds will first be figured for equal probability.

The Simplest Possible Living Thing

Dr. Harold J. Morowitz of Yale University has done extensive research for the National Aviation and Space Agency to discover the theoretical limits for the simplest free-living thing which could duplicate itself, or, technically, the minimal biological en-

[1] C. S. Lewis, *Miracles, A Preliminary Study* (New York: Macmillan Co., 1947), p. 19.

tity capable of autonomous self-replication. He took into consideration the minimum operating equipment needed and the space it would require. Also, attention was given to electrical properties and to the hazards of thermal motion. From these important studies, the conclusion is that the smallest such theoretical entity would require 239 or more individual protein molecules.[2]

This is not very much simpler than the smallest actually known autonomous living organism, which is the minuscule, bacteria-like *Mycoplasma hominis H39*. It has around 600 different kinds of proteins.[3] From present scientific knowledge, there is no reason to believe that anything smaller ever existed. We will, however, use the lesser total of 239 protein molecules from Morowitz' theoretical minimal cell, which comprise 124 different kinds.[4]

It was noted earlier that there obviously can be no natural selection if there is no way to duplicate all of the necessary parts. In order to account for the left-handed phenomenon, chance alone, unaided by natural selection, would have to arrange at least one complete set of 239 proteins with all-left-handed amino acids of the universal 20 kinds. There is reason to believe that all 20 of these were in use from the time of life's origin.

Using figures that were furnished by Morowitz,[5] it can be calculated that the average protein molecule in the theoretical minimal living thing would contain around 445 amino acid units of the usual 20 kinds. One of the 20 types of amino acids, glycine, cannot be left- or right-handed, because its "side chain"

---

[2] This data via personal communications from Morowitz, October and November, 1971.

This reflects Morowitz' most recent estimate from continuing research with co-workers at Yale. Earlier estimates were that the smallest possible living thing would be much less complex. (Harold J. Morowitz and Mark E. Tourtellotte, "The Smallest Living Cells," *The Living Cell*, ed. Donald Kennedy [San Francisco: W. H. Freeman and Co., 1965], pp. 31-39. Also: Harold J. Morowitz, "Biological Self-Replicating Systems," *Progress in Theoretical Biology*, ed. Fred M. Snell, Vol. 1 [1967], pp. 52-57.)

[3] Hans R. Bode and Harold J. Morowitz, "Size and Structure of the *Mycoplasma hominis H39* Chromosome," *Journal of Molecular Biology*, Vol. 23 (1967), p. 198. For number of proteins, Morowitz, personal communication, November, 1970.

[4] Although recognizing that there are hypotheses of origin from simpler forms than this, Dr. Morowitz agreed that *in actual experimental evidence*, there is no assurance that anything simpler could meet the test of autonomous replication and viability (personal communication, 1971).

[5] Harold J. Morowitz, *Energy Flow in Biology* (New York: Academic Press, 1968), p. 84. Also data by personal communication, 1971.

The total molecular weight of 239 protein molecules is 11.6×10^6. The average molecular weight per amino acid residue is around 109 in some bacteria.

is not really a chain, but merely a hydrogen atom like the one opposite it. It can be presumed that this minimal theoretical cell would in many ways resemble bacteria in its make-up. In some bacteria, glycine accounts for just over 8 percent of the total amino acid molecules,[6] so we will estimate that in the average protein of the minimal cell, there will be 35 glycine units in the chain. That will leave 410 of the total 445 which could be either left- or right-handed.

If amino acids had been formed naturally in the "primitive" atmosphere, they would have occurred in statistically equal amounts of the left- and right-handed isomers. This became clear from experiments described in the preceding chapter.[7] That means, then, that if a protein chain is to form by random linkups,[8] all 410 of the nonglycine sites could be occupied with equal ease by either L- or D-type amino acids.

The first one has a 1 out of 2 chance of being left-handed. The same is true for each of the other 409. Since we are now figuring this at equal probability for either hand, the probability at any one site is not affected by the amino acid before that one in the chain.

To calculate the probability in such a case, the formula to use is the multiplication rule, the heart of probability theory. Mathematician Darrell Huff said it thus: "To find the probability of getting all of several different things, multiply together the chances of getting each one."[9]

To get the probability of all 410 of the isomeric or handed amino acids of just one protein chain, we must multiply the 1/2 probability which is the case for each position in the chain. It is like flipping a coin 410 times, hoping to get all heads. For each step, there is 1 chance in 2, so we must multiply the 2 by itself (2 x 2 x 2 x . . . x 2). using the figure 410 times. That is 1 chance in 2^{410}. (The exponent means: Multiply together 410 two's.)

It will be easier to work with this figure if we translate it

---

[6] Harold J. Morowitz, *Life and the Physical Sciences* (New York: Holt, Rinehart and Winston, Inc., 1963), p. 35.

[7] Also in Appendix 1, p. 243.

[8] We're assuming linkup automatically without enzymes, etc., since we are here interested only in the L- and D- probability matter. (This is an exceedingly generous assumption, making it easier for chance to succeed.)

[9] Darrell Huff, *How to Take a Chance* (New York: W. W. Norton and Co., Inc., 1959), p. 22.

to powers of 10 instead of powers of 2. As you know, multiplying 10 by itself is just adding another zero.[10] The equivalent of 2^{410} is roughly 10^{123}.

The probability that an average-size protein molecule of the smallest theoretically possible living thing would happen to contain only left-handed amino acids is, therefore, 1 in 10^{123}, on the average.

That is a rather discouraging chance. To get the feel of that number, let's look at it with all the 123 zeros: There is, on the average, 1 chance in 1,000,000,000,000,000,000,000,000,000,000,000,000,000,000,000,000,000,000,000,000,000,000,000,000,000,000,000,000,000,000,000,000,000,000,000,000,000,000,000,000,000,000 that all of the amino acids of a particular protein molecule would be left-handed!

Using All the Proteins That Ever Existed on Earth

Professor Murray Eden at Massachusetts Institute of Technology estimated that the total number of protein molecules that ever existed on earth might be 10^{52} as an extremely liberal approximation.[11] If we assume for the moment that all these were the same size as the average protein in the smallest possible autonomous living thing, we can then figure the probability, on the average, that any one protein that ever existed on earth would have only left-handed amino acids just by chance:

The answer is 1 in 10^{71} (which is 10^{123} divided by 10^{52}).[12] Written out, that is only 1 chance in 100,000,000,000,000,000,000,000,000,000,000,000,000,000,000,000,000,000,000,000,000,000,000,000 that even a single one of all these protein molecules that ever existed on earth would on the average happen by chance alone to have only L-amino acids. Saying it another way, *the*

---

[10] For the nonmathematician (as most of us are), there is a simple way to change from 2 to 10 as a base. If we multiply 2 by itself until the total is about equal to a power of 10, we find that 2^{10} is about the same as 10^3. The convenient formula, then, is to take the exponent of 2 and multiply it by .3 in order to obtain the power of 10 which is approximately equal to it. Applying this to our figure of 2^{410}, we multiply the exponent by .3, and the result, the figure 123, is the proper power of 10. 2^{410} is therefore roughly 10^{123}. If tables of common logarithms are available, one need merely look in the first column opposite 2.

[11] Murray Eden, in *Mathematical Challenges to the Neo-Darwinian Interpretation of the Theory of Evolution,* ed. Paul S. Moorhead and Martin M. Kaplan (Philadelphia: Wistar Institute Press, 1967), p. 17.

[12] As you may remember from mathematics in school, to multiply large numbers which are written with exponents or powers, you merely add the exponents. To multiply 10^3 x 10^4 would be $10^{3+4} = 10^7$. To divide, all that is necessary is to subtract one exponent from the other. 10^{123} divided by 10^{52} is 10^{71}.

odds[13] *are a hundred billion trillion trillion trillion trillion trillion to one against that happening!*

That isn't all. Even if one *did* occur, 238 more all-left-handed ones would be needed to work with it, or all would be lost. Since all 239 would have to be together in space and time, the probability of each of the remaining 238 would be $1/10^{123}$. Those huge numbers would then have to be *multiplied* together and with the $1/10^{71}$ probability of the first one, according to the multiplication rule. This would give the probability of the needed group of 239 protein molecules being all left-handed.

The number is beyond all comprehension, namely 1 in 10^{29345}. Even if we allow for overlapping groups, it cuts the exponents only a few "orders of magnitude" (powers of 10). And, if we had all of them, they still could not duplicate themselves, so it would be the end of the line, unless chance could also produce the DNA code and the entire translating system. The code, moreover, would have to specify that amino acids would be manufactured in the left-handed form, and the coding for all the enzymes would have to match.

For comparison, the number of inches across the known universe from one side to the other is only about 10^{28}. The odds against even one average-size protein having all left-handed amino acids is a figure 10 million trillion trillion trillion times that big, namely, 1 in 10^{71}. Remember, that is out of all the protein molecules that ever existed on earth. The foregoing calculations were on the assumption of equal likelihood that either hand would link up.

Probability Figured If 6/7 Preference for the Same Hand

Now, the probability is to be computed if this extreme is assumed, namely, a preference factor of six chances in seven that the same isomer will link up next.

If a handed amino acid happens to be first in the chain, no preference would be exerted upon it, since there would be none preceding it. We will assume the same to be true whenever another amino acid follows a glycine residue in the chain, since glycine is neither left- nor right-handed. For all the rest, we

---

[13] The common expression, "the odds," may be defined as the ratio of failures to successes. If there is one chance in ten of success, then there are nine chances in ten of failure. The odds against success in that case are nine to one. When the probability of success is one in a very large number, then it is approximately correct to use that same large number also when speaking of the odds against that event. Otherwise, one would have to write out the entire figure in nines, to get the exact number, which is one less than the probability figure.

are to consider that the probability is 6/7 that the same hand will link up next as the one just preceding.[14]

Let it be supposed that there are 32 sites in the chain of 445 where an isomeric amino acid either follows a glycine or comes first in the entire chain. Each of these 32 will therefore have a probability of 1/2 of being left-handed, as there is no handed amino acid preceding it to exert any preference. Each of the other 378 sites will have a probability of 6/7 that the position involved will be occupied by the same hand as the one just before it. When we remember the 35 glycines, this accounts for all 445.

Computing this for the 32 sites at 1/2 probability and for the 378 sites at 6/7 probability, we arrive at a probability of 1 in 8.7×10^{34} that a particular protein would have only L-amino acids.[15] Since a minimum of 239 such proteins is required before there are enough for the theoretical minimal living entity, and each would have the same probability, by the multiplication rule, we conclude that on the average the probability would be around 1 in 10^{8350} that any given set of 239 would be all left-handed.

Going back to the 10^{52} protein molecules that ever existed according to Dr. Eden, we may divide these into contiguous sets of 239 for such a minimal cell. There are 10^{49} such sets, rounded. By dividing this figure into 10^{8350}, and further dividing by a million to allow for overlapping sets, we arrive at the astounding conclusion that there is, on the average, one chance in 10^{8395} that of all the proteins that ever existed on earth there would be a set of 239 together which were all left-handed, the minimum number required for the smallest theoretical cell. Another concession was given to make it easier for chance, in that we did not consider the time factor for the 10^{52} proteins that ever existed, and calculated as if they all existed at the same time.

Out of all the protein molecules that ever existed on earth, the odds against there being even one set with only left-handed components sufficient for the smallest theoretical living entity are 10^{8395} to 1. This is the conclusion when it is assumed that

---

[14] In this, a concession is being given to chance, in that we are figuring the preference at 6/7 even before there are several of the same hand in consecutive order. This would perhaps more than balance any steric selectivity that might conceivably be exerted by any helical section prior to a glycine residue in the chain.

[15] $1/2^{32} \times 6^{378}/7^{378} = 1$ in 8.7×10^{34}.

there is a 6/7 selectivity factor for the same enantiomorphic form. Compare that with the number of seconds since the universe began, which is 10^{18} for about the longest such estimate—about 15 billion years.

Even if the L-amino acids were 100 times as likely to link with L- as with D-, the odds would be 184 billion to 1 against an average size protein molecule having only L-amino acids. To get the required set of 239 would make the probability slimmer than 1 in 10^{2642} out of all the proteins that ever existed on earth. And, even if we also allowed 100 to 1 preference in the case of the 32 amino acids which follow glycine—supposing that the preceding portion of the chain could exert such selectivity—the probability would still be astronomical beyond the ability of the human mind to conceive, namely, 1 chance in 5×10^{373}, using all the proteins that ever existed on earth.

To be more realistic, however, let's go back to the figure for one minimum set if the preference is assumed to be 6/7. That was a probability averaging 1 in 10^{8295}. Just to print the number would require more than four full pages. It would take six minutes to say the number in billions, speaking rapidly all the while. These numbers are too fantastic to understand. Chapter 7 on large numbers will offer comparisons that will help.

What if we suppose, contrary to any actual evidence, that at the start there were only forty proteins required, of only forty units in length,[16] with 6/7 preference for the same hand? Considering three of these to be glycine, the odds would be sixty billion trillion trillion trillion trillion trillion to one that no single set of protein molecules out of all that ever existed would have only left-handed amino acids. (That is 60×10^{69} to 1.)

Conclusion: No Conceivable Probability

No natural explanation which can adequately explain this left-handed mystery is in sight. We have just seen that the odds against its happening by chance are so tremendous as to be completely incomprehensible.

If, on the other hand, there was a Creator of living things, He could have decided for reasons of His own to use just L-amino acids in proteins. He would have placed the proper L-enzymes and coding in the cells which would form only left-handed amino acids for use in proteins.

---

[16] As will be seen later (page 113) there may be a lower limit of fifty units, under which proteins are not stable in solution.

These created enzymes would thereafter be replaced as needed at the orders of the DNA code. The same Creator would be the Author of that amazing code which carries complete instructions that are incredibly comprehensive and detailed in the genes of every living thing on earth.

For those whose philosophy is evolution, this left-handed matter is an embarrassing problem. The many efforts at solutions that have been made are noteworthy for the questions they bring up rather than for answers. It is not likely that this mystery will ever be adequately explained, as long as the evidence of intelligent planning is ignored.

But what if some day we happen to find a really adequate natural solution to this question? It has frequently happened that in discovering "natural" explanations for mysteries, we uncover other complex new systems which only deepen the underlying mystery of this intricate universe. Here is just one such example:

It has been a puzzle that eggs of some birds all hatch so close to the same time. Now scientists actually have tape recordings of quail eggs "talking" to each other by clicks and vocal sounds to synchronize hatching.[17] Thus, a greater mystery appears.[18]

The amino acids in proteins are not the only one-handed molecules. The stereo-selective phenomenon is found throughout living nature. We have noted that vitamin C, which is L-ascorbic acid, is always left-handed in its natural form in foods. This compound can be made in the laboratory in both D- and L-isomers, but only L-ascorbic acid has vitamin C activity.[19] Glucose sugar molecules, conversely, are habitually D-, or right-handed.

Remembering the weakness of chance is an important and logical step in deciding what philosophy of origins one will believe, evolution or creation. Blind chance requires an average of ten billion tries to count to ten. Can this pathetic source account for the intricacies of the eye, a beehive, the song of a mockingbird, or the metamorphosis and 1000-mile migration of

---

17 "Biological Sciences," *1971 Britannica Book of the Year,* p. 166, regarding tape recording by biologist Margaret A. Vince of Cambridge University.

18 "As in other areas of science, attempts to answer questions have usually revealed only another, more sophisticated set of questions." Philip Handler, ed., *Biology and the Future of Man* (New York: Oxford University Press, 1970), p. 130.

19 Linus Pauling, *Vitamin C and the Common Cold* (San Francisco: W. H. Freeman & Co., 1970), p. 89.

the monarch butterfly? In the next chapter, we will discover that natural selection is completely inadequate as a solution.

The Wisdom Built In

We find that there is no lessening of confusion until one accepts the logic that "intelligent" systems could not arise without an intelligent Designer.

In Genesis, chapter one, we are given the idea that God decided how each living creature would be assembled. To construct proteins, he apparently used L-amino acids, formed by himself, for reasons unknown to us. We may some day discover those reasons. It is the privilege of scientists to experiment in our well-equipped cosmic laboratory, studying to find out how the Creator put things together, trying to understand the wisdom built in. "It is the glory of God to conceal a thing: but the honour of kings is to search out a matter."[20]

---

[20] Proverbs 25:2.

5

Where Natural Selection Fails

More times than not, scientists disagree in their interpretation of the evidence.[1]

—David I. Blumenstock

WITHOUT NATURAL SELECTION, evolution is dead. This process has become almost a deity to the more ardent followers of evolution, though of course they are entirely unaware of this. One often finds a bit of worship tucked in at the end of a scientific article. A writer, after waxing eloquent about some beautiful adaptation, will often end his dissertation in some such way as in this example: "We shall forever marvel at the astonishing truth that beings as intricate as ourselves can be produced by the long operation of natural selection."[2]

Before going on with the intriguing task of applying probability theory to the origin of protein molecules, it is important to realize the limitations of natural selection. Knowing these limits is a vital part of the desired certainty as to whether evolution could be true.

The Process of Natural Selection

Natural selection is the technique by which organisms that are best equipped to survive and reproduce become predominant. This seems perfectly logical, of course. There is such an operation in nature, *within certain limits.* Clearly, only those

[1] David I. Blumenstock, *The Ocean of Air* (New Brunswick, N.J.: Rutgers University Press, 1959), p. vii of preface.

[2] Francis H. C. Crick, "The Language of Life," *1969 Yearbook of Science and the Future* (Britannica), p. 139.

organisms that are able to exist and produce offspring will be represented in future generations.

This limits the continuance of animals which might weaken the line. It is a built-in mechanism that also prevents much unnecessary suffering by taking out those not sufficiently equipped for life's difficulties, so that they will not produce others to suffer through life. It is in perfect accord with the idea of creation.

However, natural selection has been given too big a job to accomplish. Evolutionists suppose it to be the means by which progress is made from lower to higher forms, all the way from one-celled animals to human beings.

A more accurate appraisal is the following, from an article by George F. Howe and P. William Davis: "Under close scrutiny, however, natural selection is seen predominantly as a 'weeding out' operation in which harmful mutations are slowly reduced in future populations."[3]

Natural Selection Cannot Select What Is Not There!

A man cannot select from the shelves of a store what the store does not carry. Before evolution can work, there must be varieties from which to select. The variations, moreover, must offer improvements which involve surviving or producing offspring. The improvements must also eventually lead to different kinds of animals or plants. Otherwise there is no evolution. But, alas, there is difficulty finding a source for new material with such a capability.

There are two prominent current ideas which attempt to provide for the desired variation. They are: (1) mutations, and (2) modern "Lamarckism." Lamarck, a French scientist whose famous hypothesis began to be accepted around 1802, believed that animals can pass on to their descendants the characteristics they have acquired in adapting themselves to their surroundings.

It was later proved to the satisfaction of nearly all scientists that such "acquired characteristics" are *not* inherited. Similarly, skills developed by deliberate practice—golf, typing, playing a trombone—are not passed on to one's children, at least not by heredity.

There is a modern form of Lamarckism, however. It holds that, as a result of an animal's practice or habits, its hormones are changed. This results in inheritance by the offspring of

[3] George F. Howe and P. William Davis, "Natural Selection Reexamined," *Creation Research Society Quarterly*, Vol. 8 (June, 1971), p. 43.

the variations thus called forth by the parents' adaptation to environment. Imagine a bird which must walk in shallow water and must continually attempt to stretch its legs. Its hormones, they say, will become modified by this practice. Its eggs are then supposed to be influenced by this hormonal change. The offspring will tend to have longer legs as a result, according to modern Lamarckism.

Many scientists, if not most, consider this a mere reversion to a hypothesis disproved earlier. They see no solid evidence that such a process exists. Evolutionists, however, must have some plan for producing change. As we will see, mutations are far from ideal as a solution. Lamarckism is taken by some as an alternative.

André de Cayeux, French paleontologist and geologist, wrote, "At the present time, most Anglo-Saxons believe in the idea of mutation. The French tend toward Lamarckism. The Russians, too, favor Lamarckism, which fits in well with the Marxist doctrine. But there are exceptions."[4]

Even if hormonal changes were possible, this could not begin to explain the first formation of complex protein molecules. The hormone system itself is complex, delicately regulated, and many hormones are proteins. They would first have to *exist*, before they could help evolution.

The Failure of Mutations to Explain Evolution

Mutations are the sole source depended on at present by most American evolutionists. Prominent evolution advocate George Gaylord Simpson writes with co-author William S. Beck:

> Mutations are, indeed, the ultimate sources of all *new* genetic materials, which then are endlessly shuffled in the processes of sexual reproduction. In the final analysis, all evolutionary change depends on mutations. . . .
>
> A capacity for mutation is one of the universal and definitive characteristics of life, and all organic evolution is contingent on it.[5]

Mutations are chance alterations in the DNA code message that are heritable. Such changes carry to the offspring deviations such as color-blindness or diabetes. Mutations are believed

---

[4] André de Cayeux, *Three Billion Years of Life* (New York: Stein and Day, 1969), p. 198. First published in France in 1964.

[5] George G. Simpson and William S. Beck, *Life: An Introduction to Biology*, Shorter Edition (New York: Harcourt, Brace & World, 1969), p. 143.

to be caused primarily by injuries and by copying errors in the DNA duplication process.

Just consider that last sentence. *The new material on which evolution is to proceed comes mainly by accidents and mistakes.* Does it not seem strange that the vast array of amazingly efficient and complex living things would have developed from random negative sources?

André de Cayeux uses this devastating metaphor against mutations: "The explanation for a sonata is not in a series of wrong notes." He elaborates as follows:

> We know that the great majority of mutations are bad. We can even see this exemplified in our own flesh, or at least the flesh of other men. Most congenital defects are of this origin. So to explain evolution and the progress of life throughout time by a process where defects and imperfections are dominant seems paradoxical. Resorting to selection attenuates the paradox, but does it erase it?[6]

John C. Kendrew, Cambridge University scientist who is a Nobel laureate for his discovery of the structure of the protein myoglobin, calls mutations "misprints." He wrote,

> Just as in a real book misprints are more likely to produce nonsense than better sense, so mutations will almost always be deleterious, almost always, in fact, they will kill the organism or the cell, often at so early a stage in its existence that we do not even realize it ever came into being at all.[7]

He calls development through mutations a "random process," and the only basis he gives for using it as a source for evolution is that it has operated for "more than five hundred million years." Some would quadruple that to two billion, or even three billion. In this connection, we might note that *chance would require forty-six trillion times that long*[8] to select just once the phrase: *The Theory of Evolution,* working at the speed of light, a billion tries per second.

The cell is an exceedingly delicately adjusted operating mechanism. Here is one of the usual descriptions such as scientists give, this one by Simpson and Beck:

> Organisms are the most intricate systems that exist, far more

---

[6] de Cayeux, *Three Billion Years,* p. 200.

[7] John C. Kendrew, *The Thread of Life* (Cambridge, Mass.: Harvard University Press, 1966), pp. 106, 107.

[8] More than forty-six trillion times three billion years. This is calculated from the figures obtained in chapter 2.

complicated and elaborate than even the most advanced electronic computers, detection and control systems, or automated factories so far constructed by man. Organisms produce replicas of themselves . . . exceedingly complex systems.[9]

Mutations may be caused by certain chemicals, heat, ultraviolet light, cosmic rays, or other radiation. A mutation in such a complicated system caused by ionizing radiation, for example, is comparable to the result of shooting a rifle bullet into the works of a computer, or into the instrument panel of a jet airliner. To expect improvement from any disarranging influence is a bit optimistic.

Occasionally, however, a rare mutation occurs which may seem to give an improvement. Perhaps, for example, a strain of wheat exists which has weak stalks which blow down in a strong wind. A mutation engineered by the scientist from one of the grains of this wheat then produces a type that has strong stalks. The "improvement" may represent a false impression. It may involve other weaknesses and be unable to survive in the wild. Some mutations, furthermore, have been found to be merely corrections of former harmful mutations. For example, Thomas H. Jukes told of a case where "a mutagenic chemical produced seven different changes in a coding triplet when added to a bacterial culture, each change favoring survival of the bacteria by restoring the function of a defective gene."[10]

In fact, evolutionists are in difficulty when asked to name any mutations *that have actually occurred in nature* which have involved any real improvement. Most have produced weaknesses and deformities—anemia, mental retardation, clubfootedness, in-

---

[9] Simpson and Beck, *Life*, p. 132.

[10] Thomas H. Jukes, *Molecules and Evolution* (New York: Columbia University Press, 1966), preface.

Such *reverse mutations* are common in laboratory work with bacteria. (Roger Y. Stanier, Michael Doudoroff, and Edward A. Adelberg, *The Microbial World*, 3rd ed. [Englewood Cliffs, N.J.: Prentice-Hall, Inc., 1970], pp. 471, 472). This doubtless arises in part from their rapid multiplication rate.

These authors also mention the probability that many "good" mutations which occur in experiments with bacteria might nevertheless make the possessors unfit for survival in the wild: "In adapting to existence in laboratory media, organisms may undergo genetic modifications that would lead to their speedy suppression in a competitive environment" (p. 478).

To understand this principle more clearly, imagine this extreme but comparable situation: a human being who is by mutation immune to athlete's foot (which is good) because he has no feet (which is bad for the entire organism except in the most artificial of situations.) An actually existing good/bad mutation makes the possessor immune to some forms of malaria but also predisposes him to sickle-cell anemia.

clinations to hernia, and other negative changes. Some others involve merely a *return* to a former better condition.

"Chance provides the raw material on which natural selection operates," said Adler.[11] We have already begun to discover, however, that chance is incapable and decrepit as to producing any ordered result, or *usable* raw material.

Mutations Produce No New Characters

Geneticist Bolton Davidheiser says, "When a gene mutates it produces an alternative form of the structure or condition it produced before. When a gene for wing form mutates it produces another wing form, and not an eye color."[12]

There is never any new type of organ that the particular species did not have before. Mutations do not result in adding a wing to a cow or a backbone to a worm or a new enzyme to a cell, though defective enzymes are sometimes *repaired* by reverse mutations. The most widely used example of a "good" mutation involves merely the color of a species of moth in England—changed from light to dark!

Any and all alterations, however, have absolutely nothing to do with changing one type of creature into a different type. Evolutionists cite a few plausible-sounding developments that might seem like a long continuous changeover in kind. When one carefully examines the evidence, the chain falls apart. An example of this is the presumed evolution of the horse, which will be discussed later.

The fruit fly, *Drosophila melanogaster,* has been subjected to radiation in laboratories for many years for the study of induced mutations. None of the results—changes in eye color, misshapen wings, or other grotesque deformities—indicate any progress toward evolving new types of insects. As Davidheiser points out in an excellent study on this subject, the reason mutations are retained as a source of evolutionary hope is that there is nothing better.

Much has been made of difference in the beaks of finches in the Galapagos Islands, made famous by Charles Darwin's study. (It has been pointed out, however, that Darwin evidently did not attach much significance to this at first, for it is not mentioned

---

[11] Irving Adler, *Probability and Statistics for Everyman* (New York: John Day Co., 1963), p. 239.

[12] Bolton Davidheiser, *Evolution and Christian Faith* (Nutley, N.J.: Presbyterian and Reformed Publishing Co., 1969), p. 212.

in his diary, and there is only a brief statement in his first edition of *The Voyage of the Beagle.*)[13] These, and other such modifications, are apparently only minor adaptations within types, as would be expected in any design of creation. Modern genetics indicates possible explanations of how these may occur. Eldon J. Gardner, of the University of Utah, writes "Basically, then, it is ranges of modifiability that are inherited. . . ."[14]

Too much trust is put in mutations, as in natural selection. A scientist who relies on mutation and natural selection for his philosophy of origins and development could be compared to a man who has trained a crow to say words. In his enthusiasm, he overestimates this feat and envisions using the crow as an office receptionist or telephone operator. Like evolutionists who depend upon natural selection, he is expecting what is beyond its capability.

Fred John Meldau in his excellent book, *Why We Believe in Creation, Not in Evolution,* repeatedly stressed the principle, "Mutations, but no transmutations."[15] All changes remain within kinds. This is in complete accord with the oft-repeated law in Genesis, chapter one: "after their kind."

---

[13] David Lack, "Darwin's Finches," *Scientific American,* Vol. 188 (April, 1953), p. 67.

[14] Eldon J. Gardner, *Principles of Genetics* (New York: John Wiley & Sons, Inc., 1972), p. 358.

Adaptation of animals of the same species to different environments is well known. Species which in warm climates have short hair may have longer hair when found in cold climates. Snowshoe rabbits (varying hares) change color from winter to summer. Any plan by a Creator would doubtless provide a method for such changes within species. This may perhaps be linked to environmental factors which trigger the proper genes into action to bring about the needed result by turning them on. Conceivably, we may speculate, this could also be done through changes in diet, or even possibly from large alterations in behavior. Such changes would merely make use of already existing genes that were dormant or turned off until thus induced into production. Mechanisms for such induction of idle genes are known at the cellular level.

While not necessarily meant to lead to such conclusions, the following statements of Professor Gardner would give a basis for the preceding hypothesis to account for adaptability:

"We know that environmental factors are interwoven with inheritance mechanisms at every point in the developmental process" (ibid., p. 357). "Quantitative traits, however, are influenced by the environment as well as by inheritance" (p. 367). "The inheritance of quantitative traits depends upon the cumulative or additive action of several or many genes, each of which produces a small proportion of the total effect. This is in marked contrast to the inheritance of qualitative traits which is an all-or-none phenomenon dependent on one gene or a few interacting genes. An important consideration in studies of inheritance of quantitative traits is that environmental factors also have an effect on end products such as height, weight, or color intensity" (p. 119). This might explain variations in the beaks of Darwin's finches.

[15] Fred John Meldau, *Why We Believe in Creation, Not in Evolution* (Denver: Christian Victory Publishing Co., 1959), p. 19.

In spite of the limitations, mutations are still accepted by many as the sole hope, as in this statement: "Mutations are the very source of genetic variability, and so they are ultimately responsible for the evolution of all present forms of life."[16]

Consider this remarkable pair of sentences from the *Encyclopaedia Britannica:* "Natural selection has used mutations for building up well-integrated organisms. New mutations are likely to upset this balance and are therefore mostly harmful or lethal."[17]

Natural Selection Cannot Explain "Fine-Tuning" Adaptations

Any mutation, in order to be adopted by natural selection, would have to present a certain kind of advantage, not just *any* improvement. It would have to be the kind of change that sooner or later makes the difference between life and death or the difference between leaving successful offspring and failure to do so. According to the logic of the idea, the changed organism could never take precedence over other forms unless the change affected actual survival or reproduction.[18]

Natural selection cannot account at all for the finely tuned adaptations and innovations we see all about us—things not necessary to life or to successful production of offspring. The beautiful hanging nests built by orioles are not necessary for survival. Many other birds build plainer nests. Some build none at all. The nest of a dove is a small flat bunch of sticks on the fork of a horizontal limb. In contrast, its neighbor, the oriole, weaves a complicated nest swinging below the end of a branch.

Natural selection cannot explain the beautiful designs and colors on bird eggs, each distinctive for its own species. One can identify many species of birds by their eggs alone. These differences have no connection with survival, or winning a mate,

---

[16] Björn Sigurbjörnsson, "Induced Mutations in Plants," *Scientific American* (January, 1971), p. 87.

One may suspect, however, that mutations have by mistake been given the credit for many changes which were not genetic at all. Authors of a study on Hawaiian lizard variation in 1973 included this suggestion in their report: "Perhaps environmental heterogeneity may be a very important source of variation in some morphological characters." (M. E. Soulé, et al., "Island Lizards: the Genetic-Phenetic Variation Correlation," *Nature*, Vol. 242 [March 16, 1973], pp. 191-193.) In line with the hypothesis explained in reference 14 a bit earlier, some of these outward variations may have resulted from the turning on of existing genes by environmental stimuli. Some mechanisms for such regulation will be described in chapter 9.

[17] *Encyclopaedia Britannica* (1967), s.v. "mutations."

[18] *Differential reproduction* is currently stressed as the key way natural selection operates. Organisms who survive to produce greater numbers of viable offspring will be selected.

or the successful leaving of progeny. A cat's instinctive technique for washing its face cannot have been selected for these reasons. This is also true of our own enjoyment of music, for example, which is not required for survival. The reader may think of dozens more such examples.

Micro-Mutations and Long Ages of Time

Lack of evidence of any large useful mutations has driven most evolutionists to take refuge in micro-evolution. It is postulated that changes occur in minute degree, to be followed sometime later by other small changes. Finally, the story goes, there is a complete new organ or function, perhaps a new animal or plant species. Of course, the changes eventually have to be spread throughout a population or *gene pool.* Another evolutionary precept involves geographical isolation from the unchanged group, so "intermarriage" will not dilute or cancel out the new characteristic.

Such a developmental process calls for a long period of time. This is a problem even if one accepts the geological time scale, without which evolutionists would be helpless.

While an organism would be waiting for a specific random mutation to help forward the presumed long process of evolving a new organ, there would be no way to hold all the other characteristics of the organism steady. All these other factors would be under attack by mutations most likely to be lethal or harmful. The laws of chance rule out any actual evolution upward.

The postulated small beginnings of new organs, in most cases, would be of no help to the organism and would be in the way; e.g., the wing membrane of a bat. Offering no help, it would be a hindrance until operationally complete. There is no real evidence, anyway, of any such changes ever starting. No organism evolves any new type of organ or function that did not exist already in that species.

Attempts to Find New Methods Other Than Mutations

Some evolutionary scientists, realizing the failure of natural selection by small mutations, have perseveringly looked for better methods. They seem to feel that it is absolutely necessary to find an explanation that does not require a Creator. Some will accept impersonal "Nature" as their god, but not a God who is an infinite Person as revealed in the Bible. That would involve responsibility.

Richard Goldschmidt showed quite clearly the poverty of evolutionary theory via micro-mutations. To supplant it, he postulated large changes of dramatic degree, occurring very rarely.[19] The fact that it was an idea without any solid evidence did not seem to trouble him. This, however, has made his hypothesis vulnerable to damaging attacks.

More recently, a Russian scientist, L. S. Davitashvili, writing in the periodical, *Evolution,* explained his own new Lamarckian plan. Different environments, and particularly changes in food, may bring about evolution in whole populations, he argues, producing quick changes.[20] Davitashvili's theory likewise suffers from lack of valid evidence, since all environmentally produced variation is within the same species and does not result in new species.

Natural Selection Helpless Before Duplication Developed

The most impossible jump required in evolution is the leap from nonliving matter to life. Many evolutionists have had the perception to realize it would be foolish to assume it happened by chance all at once. It has been necessary instead to find a process leading from the land of nonlife to fully functioning living cells. The communist biologist, A. I. Oparin, first, and other scientists by the hundreds following his lead, have spent much time in research on this problem. To get the job done, Oparin finds it necessary to call in the evolutionists' main work horse, natural selection, long before his "protobiont" or pre-cell is anywhere close to becoming a living system.[21]

The droplets of coagulated groups of molecules (which he assumes) are supposed to be "selected"—the better ones getting more of the "food" supply. Droplets with the "best" random molecules made of amino acids are supposed to grow. A plan was needed to insure that amino acids were formed nat-

---

[19] Richard Goldschmidt, *The Material Basis of Evolution* (Paterson, N.J.: Pageant Books, 1960), pp. 390, 391. First published 1940.

Goldschmidt made feeble attempts at citing examples. One was the short-legged dog, the dachshund, which is able to enter badgers' dens because of its short legs! However, the dachshund is bred by genetic engineering and would doubtless not survive in the wild.

[20] L. S. Davitashvili, in "Notes and Comments," *Evolution,* Vol. 23 (September, 1969), p. 514.

[21] A. I. Oparin, *Genesis and Evolutionary Development of Life* (New York: Academic Press, 1968), p. 130.

urally in great numbers. This required, as noted earlier, the assumption that the "primitive atmosphere" was very different.

Some droplets might contain mineral salts that might act as weak catalysts to help forward any natural reactions. This would, he says, give an advantage in the struggle for existence. It is not explained why the nonliving droplet would even struggle.

In process of time, the growing droplet or *coacervate* gets broken into two, by action of waves or other accident. That is supposed to give *two* "good" molecules and is a primitive duplication process, Oparin infers. But is it?

When the drop is split, the two parts will be different from each other, because the original could not make exact copies of everything in it. Suppose that there were such catalyst mineral salts in the original droplet, giving it an advantage. When the split occurred, there would be half as many of these salts in each, or perhaps none of some ingredients in one of the new "daughter" droplets.[22] There would be no way to duplicate these catalysts in the droplets.

Without any way to make exact copies of all components, that would be the end of the line. Sooner or later something would bring an end to that droplet with its better molecules. Since it could not replicate or duplicate all of its parts, there would have been no chance at all for natural selection to bring about continuing improvement.

Selection depends upon a continuing supply of the improved varieties. When there is only one copy of each, even if it is "selected," it has no future. It cannot make provisions for any "offspring" like itself. There is no logical place for considering natural selection here at all, *even if* such a process would work to produce evolution in truly living things.

Professor John Keosian indicated that many scientists recognize that natural selection could have no place at all before life existed, when he said:

> To the horror of some biologists the term natural selection is employed freely to indicate the process by which the prevalence of one type of molecule over another possible type

---

[22] If all droplets had those catalyst salts, they would be equal, and no selection could operate. If some, but not all, droplets had such an advantage as better catalysts, there could be no further progress without an accurate duplicating system. Each "better" molecule would be a blind alley. If we consider just the droplets lucky enough to get these catalyst salts and thereby to monopolize the "food" supply, this still provides for no *intrinsic* improvement, but depends wholly on external conditions.

> might have taken place or the process by which a nonliving macro-molecular system might grow increasingly complex.[23]

The ability to duplicate accurately would seem to be impossible, short of a complicated coding system like DNA. Evolutionists working earnestly to explain the origin of life spontaneously will sometimes make vague references to proteins serving as *templates* or patterns on which copies like themselves would form. No way has been found to make such an outcome occur. Theodosius Dobzhansky, well-known biologist with Rockefeller University in New York, stated this undeniable precept: "*For natural selection to operate, there must be reproduction, and reproduction is the key property of life*"[24] (italics added). Therefore, we may conclude, natural selection was impossible during the assumed natural origin of life.

Computers That Vetoed Natural Selection

In an ingenious experiment at Stanford University, Michael Conrad and H. H. Pattee tried to get computers to perform natural selection. The scientists programmed the computers to simulate "ecosystems"—imaginary environments with imaginary organisms of several types. The organisms were put through various lifelike stresses. They were given opportunities to "struggle for survival." Their food supply was slowly diminished so that some would not survive. They were jumped into new environments, to bring out possible adaptations leading to evolution. They were primed to seek *symbionts,* partner organisms which would help each other in the way that bees and flowers work together.

The carefully planned experiment turned out dismally discouraging for evolution. Reporting in the *Journal of Theoretical Biology,* the scientists wrote concerning the "organisms" that survived:

> The predominant types of organisms were definitely inefficient. Many organisms carried phenome sequences of no apparent selective value.... Organisms with efficiently placed parametric symbols exhibited no clear advantage over those with inefficiently placed symbols.[25]

---

[23] John Keosian, *The Origin of Life* (New York: Reinhold Publishing Corp., 1964), p. 89.

[24] Theodosius Dobzhansky, *The Biology of Ultimate Concern* (New York: New American Library, 1967), p. 48. (Dobzhansky is an evolutionist, but is quite definite in his protest against this careless use of the term "natural selection" to apply to the era before life existed.)

[25] Michael Conrad and H. H. Pattee, "Evolution Experiments with an Artificial

The professors told of the unforeseen failure of natural selection in this carefully arranged test which involved several "systems":

> The low efficiency of organisms and the decline in the matching ratio are somewhat surprising since improvement in these properties would often be regarded as a criterion for evolution. Yet System 1, which had a steadily increasing matching ratio did not exhibit behavior at all characteristic of evolution.[26]

Darwin Conceded an Error Which Weakens the Theory

Charles Darwin, in later editions of *The Origin of Species,* corrected a mistaken idea contained in the original version about the operation of natural selection. With his customary frankness, he confessed that until reading an article in the North British Review in 1867, "I did not appreciate how rarely single variations, whether slight or strongly marked, could be perpetuated." Because only a small percentage of the organisms of each generation survive, Darwin applied this fact also to an individual with a positive variation, stating, "The chances would be strongly against its survival." Suppose, however, that such an organism did happen to survive, and that half its young received the variation. Darwin showed that the probability of each particular offspring's survival would be quite small and "this chance would go on decreasing in the succeeding generations. The justice of these remarks cannot, I think, be disputed."

This, of course, was a serious blow to evolution. In an effort to get around it, Darwin then put his trust in the idea that the odds might be overcome if a particular variation occurred *in large numbers* of a population. Concerning perpetuation of such a variation, he theorized, "Judging by what we see taking place under domestication . . . this result would follow from the preservation during many generations of a large number of individuals"[27] with the variation involved. We may note, however, that domesticated animals have a completely different situation in this regard, and a *large* percentage of each generation may survive. This makes the comparison invalid.

Though valiant efforts by evolutionists since then may have

Ecosystem," *Journal of Theoretical Biology* (September, 1970), pp. 405, 406. These authors did not state their own philosophy regarding evolution in this article.

[26] Ibid., p. 406.

[27] Charles Darwin, *The Origin of Species,* Mentor Edition (New York: New American Library, 1958); all the foregoing quotations are on pp. 96, 97.

been partially successful in relieving this difficulty to which Darwin called attention, it remains a very real problem.

The key idea of evolution was envisioned in his book as a gradual, step-by-step process. Small variations would be preserved by natural selection, to be followed, after perhaps long intervals, by further variations in the same direction. Darwin admitted that this plan was "an assumption." "But whether it is true," he went on, "we can judge only by seeing how far the hypothesis accords with and explains the general phenomena of nature."[28] The evidence that has accumulated since then has tended to dispute that assumption rather than to verify it. In spite of this, many of Darwin's present-day followers have completely lost sight of the fact that it has always been merely an assumption.

The Crime of the Age

It is time the praise was taken back from natural selection and given to the God of Creation. Taking away the Designer's credit is the crime of the age. One wonders if there is any better application of this Scripture:

> Knowing God, they have refused to honor him as God, or to render him thanks. Hence all their thinking has ended in futility. . . . They boast of their wisdom, but they have made fools of themselves, exchanging the splendour of immortal God for an image shaped like mortal man . . . (Romans 1:21, 22 NEB).

Many scientists who are fine citizens otherwise may without intention have done just that. Such a course is tragic for them and for those they teach.

How much more logical for all who investigate and see the wonders built into all living things that instead we look up in adoration to Him of whom great throngs in heaven sing, "Great and marvelous are thy deeds, O Lord God, sovereign over all . . . Who shall not revere thee, Lord, and do homage to thy name?" (Revelation 15:3, 4, NEB).

---

[28] Ibid., p. 91.

6

Probability and the First Proteins

Even the simplest of these substances [proteins] represent extremely complex compounds, containing many thousands of atoms of carbon, hydrogen, oxygen, and nitrogen arranged in absolutely definite patterns, which are specific for each separate substance. To the student of protein structure the spontaneous formation of such an atomic arrangement in the protein molecule would seem as improbable as would the accidental origin of the text of Virgil's "Aeneid" from scattered letter type.[1]

—A. I. Oparin

THE QUESTION MAY have occurred to the reader: If evolution is so improbable, why do many scientists and other intelligent people accept it? This naturally is a central issue, and chapter 11 will be devoted to it.

It should be mentioned now, however, that even the most intelligent people may not get around to concentrating their intelligence on some specific issues. It is customary to accept without question many conclusions that are supposed to be "common knowledge" among scientists. No one has time to look into every subject. It is easy for even a scientist to take for granted that certain principles or axioms have actually been proved.

It is currently the conventional attitude among scientists never

[1] A. I. Oparin, *The Origin of Life* (New York: Dover Publications, 1953 edition), pp. 132, 133.

to question the notion that Darwin really proved the main idea of evolution.

An avowed communist like Oparin can freely admit, as in the quotation above, that it is futile to expect chance to put together anything so highly ordered. He resorts instead to his philosophy of dialectical materialism.

"Rationally," Oparin writes, "life can be materialistically comprehended only as a special form of the motion of matter, arising in a regular manner at a certain stage in the development of matter."[2]

For the noncommunist materialist, this makes a great difficulty. Many evolutionists have followed Oparin's careful step-by-step plan of evolving life from nonliving chemicals. They see no reason, however, to accept his communist philosophy. This leaves one in an intolerable position, as it turns out. The customary procedure seems to be to hope that nobody will notice the predicament, and to glide cheerfully over the problem.

The difficulty is that there is nothing left but chance to do the whole job of creating life from nonlife. Even to consider the thought of an intelligent Creator is completely out of the question, "an idea which of course has been long exploded."

As seen in the previous chapter, natural selection would have no way to come to the rescue at that stage, for lack of an accurate duplicating process.

Wrong Ideas About Probability

Probability theory does not deal with absolutes. It never says that a thing is "impossible" unless it is completely outside the realm of subjects which involve uncertainty. Charles-Eugène Guye, who was the eminent Professor of Physics at the University of Geneva, delineated this truth (using the word "evolution" in the general sense of any process of change, rather than as we are defining it):

---

[2] A. I. Oparin, *Genesis and Evolutionary Development of Life* (New York: Academic Press, 1968), p. 6.

This communist belief, as Tresmontant indicated (see page 66), is but a form of pantheism, the idea that "everything is God," a false faith which involves no responsibility to a higher Power. In the view of communists, matter by its very nature must develop. When life finally evolves as a matter of course, new biological laws come into play as just one stage in this development. This view actually is a religion, and "matter in motion" serves as its god. This, in effect, turns out to be a form of the "vitalism" which Dr. Oparin deplores in the writings of some other scientists (such as Erwin Schrödinger, the physicist who added much to our knowledge through his hypothesis on the wave nature of matter).

> The evolution of a phenomenon tends to take place according to the greatest probability, and it follows that physicochemical laws are viewed as statistical laws, very exact it is true on account of the law of large numbers, but no longer possessing that character of absolute determination which it has been customary to attribute to them.[3]

Knowing this, many scientists easily assume that since a thing is *theoretically* not impossible, then it can be expected sooner or later to occur.[4]

Scientists are human and are not immune to some common misconceptions. One such mistaken notion is that even extremely improbable events become certain to occur if you have a few hundred million years to wait. One Harvard Professor in 1954 wrote a widely quoted article proposing that life began by chance: "It becomes increasingly probable," he said, "as the trials are multiplied. Eventually the event becomes virtually inevitable."[5]

But does it? If you apply probability reasoning, you may well doubt if even that well-known scientist did much careful figuring before making such a statement. Hundreds of other biologists, reading his article, doubtless took for granted that someone had actually checked this. If anyone goes to the trouble to do so, however, it soon becomes evident that there is no basis for such a conclusion, although the writer may have been quite sincere.

Thus "myths" are propagated and become almost universal in acceptance. It is usually no one's fault in particular. It is in one sense like the train wreck immortalized by the ballad about Casey Jones, an Illinois Central railroad engineer. When several freight trains were unable to crowd onto one siding, some of the boxcars of the last train were left protruding out on the main line in the path of Casey's oncoming express. Each brakeman from the freight trains supposed someone else had gone back up the line to signal the passenger train to stop.

In the matter we're considering, many a scientist or other

---

[3] Charles-Eugène Guye, *Physico-Chemical Evolution* (New York: E. P. Dutton and Co., 1925), pp. 3, 4.

[4] Professor Guye, on the other hand, stated that the probability of an event may be so slight as to amount to *impossibility* in practical terms. "To assert," he said, "that a phenomenon is impossible or to declare that its chance of occurring is one in a hundred million is 'practically' to say the same thing" (ibid., p. 104). This is understood in the sense of an improbable event within a time limit such that its practical probability is nil.

[5] George Wald, "The Origin of Life," *Scientific American* (August, 1954), p. 47.

educated person supposes that surely someone has investigated these commonly believed scientific dogmas carefully.

With the information now at hand, you will find it possible to check firsthand for yourself the probability of certain popularly held conclusions.

Some Proteins Described

We now come to the exciting application of the laws of chance to this major question: What is the probability that a protein molecule might have been aligned by chance?

All known life on the earth consists largely of these giant molecules. "The chemical basis of all life," says the *Encyclopaedia Britannica,* "is protein in a watery medium."

To learn the secrets of the composition of such an entity as a protein molecule was no simple undertaking. Biologists spent years in painstaking, patient study. One of the first molecules to be mapped was insulin, which is the smallest molecule qualifying as a protein. It has fifty-one amino acid "links," in two chains—one with twenty-one and the other with thirty amino acids. The two chains are joined together by "sulfur bridges."

A method was discovered whereby an X-ray beam could be projected through a crystallized protein molecule. The individual atoms of the molecule scattered the beam as it passed through. From the pattern of this diffraction or deflection, it was possible to figure out the position of the various atoms.

John C. Kendrew completed mapping the myoglobin molecule in 1959. Then, by 1967, Max Perutz and others at Cambridge succeeded in solving the structure of the hemoglobin molecule, the most important protein in blood. Larger than myoglobin, it consists of four chains fastened together and folded in a complex pattern. In all, hemoglobin has 574 amino acid links. The molecule has 10,000 atoms![6]

Hemoglobin is just one of the multitudinous kinds of proteins.

[6] There are some 280,000,000 hemoglobin molecules per red blood cell (M. F. Perutz, "The Hemoglobin Molecule," in *The Molecular Basis of Life* [San Francisco: W. H. Freeman & Co., 1968], p. 39). A drop of blood may contain 35 million red blood cells. Imagine the task of mapping the 10,000 atoms of just one hemoglobin molecule when there are around 10,000,000,000,000,000 such molecules in a drop of blood! The average adult has around 27 trillion mature red cells (George G. Simpson and William S. Beck, *Life, An Introduction to Biology,* shorter edition [New York: Harcourt, Brace, and World, 1969], p. 211). This means that an adult has 75 hundred million trillion hemoglobin molecules!

The length of the average protein in the smallest known living thing is at least 400 amino acid links, containing more than 7,000 atoms.

Protein Links Must Be in Correct Order

Most proteins include all of the usual twenty kinds of amino acids. Each protein has a specific exact sequence of these units.[7] Of the hemoglobin molecule, John C. Kendrew wrote (using British spelling):

> Thus, practically everyone reading this book contains identically the same kind of haemoglobin molecules in his or her blood, identical down to the last amino acid and the last atom. Anyone having a different haemoglobin would be seriously ill or dead, because only the very slightest changes can be tolerated by the organism.[8]

Research has continued on whether variation can be tolerated. I checked, therefore, with Dr. Kendrew by telephone (November, 1971) for his understanding at that time on this matter. He indicated that the picture is about the same as in the above quotation, although it is now known that occasionally a variation can exist which does not seem to impair health. Most such changes, he noted, would never be discerned, but they probably do not occur very often.

Just how exact a sequence must be in order to work effectively as a protein is of course a crucial question. Even the simplest theoretical living system requires a high degree of precision and delicate regulation of timing and quantities of its protein molecules. Because of the teamwork that is essential, little variation is consistent with the degree of organization that must be present.

This involves a real problem for those who must explain the origin of life without planning, but valiant attempts continue to be made. Appendix 4 will give consideration to some of the interesting ideas which have recently been advanced to try to provide for molecular evolution.

It will be evident from calculations later in this chapter and in chapter 10 that *even if free substitution were allowable at most of the sites* in a chain of amino acids or DNA, the odds

---

[7] In chapter 12, we will list the actual sequences for insulin, toxin in bee sting, and cytochrome *c*, and present intriguing facts about comparing the sequences of different animals and plants.

[8] John C. Kendrew, *The Thread of Life* (Cambridge, Mass.: Harvard University Press, 1966), pp. 32, 33.

are astronomical against random production of a set of usable proteins for minimal life. There's no way without design.

We may assume from present experimental knowledge that many places in a protein chain might allow substitution. It appears probable, however, that only about one such substitution may be tolerated in an entire chain.[9] Moreover, any substitute may have to be similar to the one it replaces.[10] There can be absolutely no substitution in positions in the chain which comprise what is known as the "active site." *Any* substitution

---

[9] This is considered as an average, because some substituents work, but less efficiently. This conclusion (one allowable substitution per chain) is based in part on the actual observed variations in human hemoglobin, which involve with few exceptions just one amino acid replacement per individual with abnormal hemoglobin. "So delicately balanced are the equilibria involving the hemoglobin tetramer that single amino acid replacements can exert a very profound effect on the structure and reactivity of the whole protein," wrote Margaret Dayhoff (*Atlas of Protein Sequence and Structure 1972,* National Biomedical Research Foundation, Washington, D.C., p. 78).

Different species of organisms have different sequences of amino acids in their hemoglobin chains, but all species apparently have roughly half of the sites identical. In a 1971 conversation with Dr. Dayhoff, we seemed in agreement that the hemoglobin sequence of a particular kind of organism may work best for that organism because of the complex reactions involved between hemoglobin and other molecular entities in the blood of that species.

In the case of a simpler protein, insulin from some species will function when placed in other species, at least in its gross effectiveness. It likely will be found, however, that there are sophisticated or hidden advantages in a species' own characteristic insulin sequence. (A protein as simple as insulin would be more likely to have some characteristics of "universal fit" than more complex ones like hemoglobin. A pair of pliers fits many situations, whereas a complex wrench may fit one certain need. The difference in sequences of insulin in various species amounts in some cases to only one or two amino acids, anyway.)

In chapter 12, the assumed proof of evolution by sequence comparisons will be examined in the case of the protein, cytochrome *c*.

It will become clear later in this chapter that even if all the differences in protein sequences of different species came about by mutations through the ages, there would still be no practical possibility of getting a set of proteins by random action at the beginning under the rules of probability. (See pages 113, 165, 166.)

Of single substitutions and other mutations, Margaret Dayhoff wrote: "It is generally believed that many of the abnormal chains are deleterious to the individual, at least in a subtle way" (Ibid., p. 67).

In order for hemoglobin evolution, for example, to have occurred, there would have had to be a long series of such substitutions. Each would have had to be at least viable. This would doubtless require matching changes in other interrelated molecular entities in the organism, with synchronized timing of the mutations. At least in the end result, the entire mechanism would have to be advantageous enough to monopolize the gene pool, as is the observed situation in each species. Such precisely matched, intricately coordinated mutations are not a reasonable possibility, of course, under the laws of probability even when assisted by natural selection.

(Dr. Dayhoff would not necessarily concur in these general conclusions, since it seems clear from her writing that she is committed to the standard evolutionary interpretation as to the presumed *origin* of sequence differences. We did not discuss origins.)

[10] Dayhoff, *Protein Sequence,* p. 98, and Kendrew, personal communication, November, 1971.

anywhere is likely to be harmful if not lethal. All twenty of the amino acids are listed in Figure 3.

The present goal will be to find the probability that amino acids might happen to be in the right order by chance if natural forces were able to line them up. It will be considered a success if the resulting chain is *any usable protein molecule.* Also to be determined are the odds that the amino acids might be aligned correctly for a *group of 239 proteins* needed for the minimal living entity described by Morowitz.[11]

Every effort will be made to avoid getting overtechnical, so that the nonbiologist reader may follow the calculations and know for himself that the outcome is sound. That is important in the attainment of certainty. Even if one finds the figuring itself uninteresting or difficult, it is helpful to his progress toward certainty just to know the evidence is there if he ever

FIGURE 3

The Twenty Amino Acids Used in Proteins
With Their Abbreviations and Atoms
(in alphabetical order)

Alanine	Ala	$C_3H_7NO_2$	Leucine	Leu	$C_6H_{13}NO_2$
Arginine	Arg	$C_6H_{14}N_4O_2$	Lysine	Lys	$C_6H_{14}N_2O_2$
Asparagine	Asn	$C_4H_8N_2O_3$	Methionine	Met	$C_5H_{11}SNO_2$
Aspartic Acid	Asp	$C_4H_7NO_4$	Phenylalanine	Phe	$C_9H_{11}NO_2$
Cysteine	Cys	$C_3H_7SNO_2$	Proline	Pro	$C_5H_9NO_2$
Glutamic Acid	Glu	$C_5H_9NO_4$	Serine	Ser	$C_3H_7NO_3$
Glutamine	Gln	$C_5H_{10}N_2O_3$	Threonine	Thr	$C_4H_9NO_3$
Glycine	Gly	$C_2H_5NO_2$	Tryptophan	Trp	$C_{11}H_{12}N_2O_2$
Histidine	His	$C_6H_9N_3O_2$	Tyrosine	Tyr	$C_9H_{11}NO_3$
Isoleucine	Ile	$C_6H_{13}NO_2$	Valine	Val	$C_5H_{11}NO_2$

Alternate abbreviations for some amino acids are:

Asparagine	Asp-NH_2	Isoleucine	Ileu
Glutamine	Glu-NH_2	Trytophan	Try

The atoms, listed by atomic symbol are: carbon, hydrogen, sulfur, nitrogen, and oxygen. The subscript numbers indicate the number of atoms of that element. (The atomic symbol for these atoms is merely the initial letter.) Leucine and Isoleucine have the same numbers of atoms of each kind, but are different in spatial arrangement of the atoms.

[11] Harold J. Morowitz (Yale University Biophysics Dept.), personal communications, October and November, 1971.

needs to dig into it further. The next chapter will be easier to read.

The Odds Against a Single Insulin Molecule

Before figuring for average size proteins, just for practice we may calculate the odds for the random alignment of the amino acid units for insulin, since insulin is usually considered the smallest protein, with 51 amino acids. Even insulin, it turns out, is not as simple as it first appears.

The insulin molecule is composed of two strands that must be linked together in an exact manner by sulfur bridges. To bring this about, the cell first constructs a longer chain of more than 80 amino acids called *proinsulin.* It ranges in length from around 81 to 86 in various animals. We will consider an insulin molecule of length 84 amino acids (of which an example is the pig.) This extended sequence of 84 units causes the chain to fold and cross-bond correctly, and then a particular section of 33 units is cut out by special enzymes, leaving the final 51 amino acids in two chains properly oriented with cross links between them.

Chance will therefore need to align 84 amino acids in correct order to form proinsulin, as the *precursor* for insulin.

Since each of the 84 positions in the chain could be occupied by any one of the 20 kinds, the total possible arrangements is 20^{84}, which, after conversion to base 10, is roughly 10^{109}. The different arrangements are considered equally probable; so the probability of any one molecule being in the correct order for insulin is 1 in 10^{109}. Allowing for one substitution (to be tolerated) makes it a bit easier for chance, and brings the probability down to 1 in 10^{106} approximately.[12]

Going back to Dr. Eden's statement that the total number of protein molecules that ever existed on earth might be 10^{52} as a liberal estimate, we will give chance another big boost by assuming that the 10^{52} are all different and are all the proper length for insulin. We can now figure the probability that any one of those would by chance be in correct order for insulin.

Émile Borel, French mathematician, tells the rule for such cases: "If an event can occur in several different ways which are

---

[12] The formula for probability allowing one substitution is $\frac{(a-1)n+1}{a^n}$, where a is the number of kinds available and n is the number of units per chain. In this case, with 20 kinds and 84 in the chain, the result is roughly 1 chance in 10^{106}.

mutually exclusive, its probability equals the sum of the probabilities corresponding to the different alternatives."[13] Any one of those 10^{52} is a different way that *might* fulfill the event of a chain being in the order for insulin. Therefore, the sum of the different ways is 10^{52}. The probability that any one of all that ever existed on earth would be insulin is therefore $10^{52}/10^{106}$. Dividing in order to simplify the fraction, the probability is 1 in 10^{54}.

Therefore, *the odds are a million trillion trillion trillion trillion to one that not a single protein molecule of all that ever existed on earth would by chance be in the correct order for an insulin molecule!* (Adjusting for different kinds of insulin would have little effect on a figure this size.)

Usable Proteins and Nonsense Chains of Amino Acids

In this test, chance is supposed to come up with *any usable protein.* How many of the total number of possible arrangements could be considered usable proteins? There is obviously no way on earth that anyone could say for sure. One way to get a tentative idea is by comparison with other systems which have a number of parts that work only when in specific orders. The best analogy is our alphabet with its 26 letters. By putting them in various sequences, we can make multitudes of messages.

The letters are mere nonsense, however, unless they are in a *meaningful order.* What percentage of the possible orders of the alphabet letters are meaningful?

To answer that question, an experiment was conducted at the Center for Probability Research in Biology. Thirty thousand letters were drawn at random, and then all meaningful sequences were listed—words, phrases, or messages that would carry a meaning to the average American. The results are given below.

FIGURE 4

Meaningful Orders in 30,000 Random Letters

Meaningful sequences 7 letters in length	1
Meaningful sequences 6 letters in length	3
Meaningful sequences 5 letters in length	17
Meaningful sequences 4 letters in length	139
Meaningful sequences 3 letters in length	1,113
Meaningful sequences 2 letters in length	4,890

[13] Émile Borel, *Elements of the Theory of Probability* (Englewood Cliffs, N.J.: Prentice-Hall, Inc., 1965), p. 19. (First published in France in 1950.)

In 30,000 letters drawn at random, the longest meaningful sequence contained only 7 letters. The letters ABC appeared in order only once in the entire experiment. AB occurred 41 times.

It is quite clear that chance arrangements are predominantly nonsense arrangements. Even many of the sequences that could be said to be meaningful require a stretch of the imagination. For example, the six-letter sequences were: RUINPA, WEETED, and AGMCAP.

A working hypothesis derived from the experiment is that there is between 1/4 and 1/5 as good a chance of getting a meaningful sequence for each added letter of length, on the average. The probability of getting a 400-letter sequence that would be meaningful would then be between 1 in 4^{400} and 1 in 5^{400}. (If one considers different languages using the same alphabet, not many such languages would be possible without changing the value of the letters, so it would not affect the calculations more than a few orders of magnitude. Perhaps only one language should be considered, since the information value for the various letters is different in different languages, and amino acids only have to fit the one "protein language.")

For lack of any other way to estimate the proportion of meaningful amino acid sequences, let it be assumed that a similar probability exists as in the alphabet. We will, however, use the figure of 1 in 4^{400}, because the amino acids are fewer than the alphabet letters, there being only 20.

On that basis, for an amino acid chain 400 long, the probability of getting a usable protein would be 1 in 4^{400}, which is 1 in 10^{240}.

In using this formula based merely on the alphabet analogy, there is, of course, an uncertainty factor. There are many similarities, however, between the alphabet and the 20 amino acids. Some letters are much more "reactive" than others, like amino acids, and some are used sparingly.

This uncertainty affects only the first stage of our study, namely, the first protein molecule to be produced by chance. There must be at least 239 matching protein molecules for a set, in order to provide the minimum number for the smallest theoretically possible living entity. The second of these and all the ones following would not involve this alphabet formula, and hence the uncertainty factor would be eliminated.[14]

Allowing Concessions to Make Things Easier for Chance[15]

It has already become apparent that chance is very backward when it comes to producing an ordered result. There clearly will be no hope at all of arranging a protein by chance unless some extreme advantages are allowed.

Two approaches will be used. First, we will allow some exceedingly helpful concessions, for the present, to assist chance in arranging an average length protein, and to obtain one minimum set of such proteins for the theoretical smallest living thing. Afterward, we will check on the probability of much simpler protein chains resulting from such random alignment. In the latter case, the concessions will be reduced a bit, but chance will still be given numerous advantages that would not have actually existed at the time of the presumed evolution of the first living thing.

It can be seen at a glance that most of the following fourteen concessions could not have actually been true, but chance will have enough of a task even when offered all this help. If chance fails under such extreme conditions, it should indicate clearly that perhaps it is unreasonable to rely on it at all in the quest for the way life began. Here are the fourteen assumptions for this purpose. Some of these are extreme, and some are not.

1. Assume *that the primitive atmosphere was as evolutionists claim.*

2. Suppose *that all of the twenty amino acids did form naturally* and in the right proportions, by the action of ultraviolet rays, lightning, and heat.

3. Presume *that the amino acids were formed in only the left-handed configuration.*

4. In calculations that follow, consider *that the average protein molecule is 400 units in length,*[16] which is shorter than the

---

14 Perhaps it should be emphasized that the uncertainty factor in the first one does not carry over any uncertainty at all to the others in the set. These others would have to be not just any protein that might work *somewhere,* but an exact sequence to fit here.

15 Chance is constantly being used herein as if the word implied a conscious entity. Charles Darwin once excused a similar usage of words thus: "Every one knows what is meant and what is implied by such metaphorical expressions; and they are almost necessary for brevity." (*Origin of Species,* Mentor Edition, [New York: New American Library, 1958], p. 88.)

16 Avram Goldstein, Dora B. Goldstein, and Louise Lowney, "Protein Synthesis

445 average length computed earlier for the smallest theoretical cell from Morowitz' data.

5. Postulate *that all the atoms on earth have been used to form amino acids.* That is, all the carbon, nitrogen, oxygen, hydrogen, and sulfur atoms in air, water, and crust of the earth have been made up into amino acids for this all-out effort to get proteins by random alignment.

6. Consider *that all of these amino acids are grouped in sets.* Each set contains one of each kind available at each position of the forming chain. These groupings may be pictured as being in the form of coacervate droplets described by Oparin, or any other way so that they are together.

7. Let it be granted *that these groupings are permanently protected in some manner from the destructive effect of ultraviolet rays.* It is widely recognized that ultraviolet rays would be lethal to the life being formed unless protected in some way. These rays, particularly those in the wavelength range near 2600 Å, are "highly toxic (absorbed by protein and nucleic acids),"[17] with lethal chemical changes resulting.

---

at 0° Centigrade in *Escherichia coli," Journal of Molecular Biology,* Vol. 9 (1964), p. 234.

It should be noted that, although many proteins are shorter than that, a living organism requires a full set of many kinds of varied lengths, and the figure mentioned represents *average* length for a minimal cell as described earlier.

[17] Roger Y. Stanier, Michael Doudoroff, and Edward A. Adelberg, *The Microbial World,* 3rd. ed. (Englewood Cliffs, N.J.: Prentice-Hall, 1970), p. 217.

Consider this dilemma: For the natural origin of life, ultraviolet rays would have been needed to form amino acids, but ultraviolet rays would destroy the very life which is supposed to be formed! These rays would have reached the surface of the earth in great numbers through the primitive atmosphere which was assumed to contain no oxygen and therefore no *ozone shield.* The ozone shield in the upper atmosphere now screens out most of these dangerous rays. It was supposed to have been formed from oxygen mainly produced by photosynthesis in plants and algae over an immense span of time.

The peril from ultraviolet rays would have endangered protein and DNA molecules unless shielded by perhaps thirty feet of water or some other effective barrier. Davidheiser and others have pointed out, however, that even if beginning organisms had reached safety in deep water, the constant circulation of water even in fresh water lakes would have returned them to the danger area. (Bolton Davidheiser, *Evolution and Christian Faith* [Nutley, N.J.: Presbyterian and Reformed Publishing House, 1969], pp. 313, 314.)

Apparently the only bodies of water escaping such circulation are *meromictic* lakes, which are deep, narrow lakes in which the lower levels of water are permanently stratified. In such lakes, all of the oxygen-evolving organisms (algae) live in the top ten meters (around thirty feet.) Then, more than twenty meters (over sixty feet) below the surface, there is a thin layer of photosynthetic bacteria. (Stanier et al., cited above, pp. 575, 576.) These bacteria are incapable, however, of producing oxygen. Oxygen-evolving photosynthesis is a more advanced kind, which requires two reaction centers, and bacteria have only one. The dilemma remains, therefore, how to get an ozone shield made and how life could start and continue during long ages of its formation.

8. Concede also *that the amino acids would automatically unite,* even though this would require going against an "energy-gradient," and the complex system which unites them in all known living things would be absent.[18]

9. Suppose *that one substitution is allowable in each chain.* In this concession, it will not be required that the active site be exempt from substitution, and it will be considered permissible for *any* amino acid to substitute for any other at any point. (See discussion of substitution earlier in this chapter.) If future discoveries ever widen the viable limits of substitution, the extreme concessions we are allowing, such as in number ten below, would take up the slack. In some cases a protein with substitutions may be *partially* functional.

10. Assume *that the rate of chain formation is fantastically rapid,* such that an entire chain requires only one-third of a ten-million-billionth of a second! This is around 150 thousand trillion times the normal speed in living things which itself is quite fleet.[19]

---

[18] If the bonding is considered as having taken place in water, a further problem is that amino acids give up a molecule of water when joined. If they are already surrounded by water, that presents an obstacle. For this reason, Fox and his coworkers tried bonding them outside of water. This, however, would have left hypothetical early cells at the mercy of lethal rays.

[19] The much-researched bacterium, *Escherichia coli,* requires only five seconds per protein chain of 400 length at the congenial temperature of 37° C. (Goldstein, et al., "Protein Synthesis," p. 234.) Slower rates have been reported in vertebrates, e.g. one minute for a chain only 100 amino acids long. (Dayhoff, *Protein Sequence,* p. 54.)

The enormous speed we have chosen in concession 10 is some 1200 times the limit of speed for atomic processes, said to be close to $1/10^{16}$ second. (Harold J. Morowitz, *Energy Flow in Biology* [New York: Academic Press, 1968], p. 12.) From data by Pauling, it can be figured that a hydrogen electron orbits its nucleus around 10^{16} times per second, which is ten million billion times per second. (Linus Pauling, *The Chemical Bond* [Ithaca, N.Y.: Cornell University Press, 1967 edition], p. 11.) Concession 10 allows 400 units to be joined in 1/3 of $1/10^{16}$ second.

A normal rate in living things depends upon ideal temperature, the proper solvent, and the best concentration of hydrogen ions, as well as conveniently available all the working parts of the protein assembly line to be described in chapter 9, including all twenty of the amino acids in sufficient supply.

Actually, in the opinion of some prominent scientists, solar luminosity affecting the earth 4 billion years ago would have been 60% of present value, with the consequence that "the global temperatures on the earth were substantially below the freezing point of water at the time of the origin of life." (Philip Handler, ed., *Biology and the Future of Man,* [New York: Oxford University Press, 1970], p. 174.)

Consider that idea in relation to the following: "The total temperature span within which organisms can grow is a narrow one, extending from about –5 to +80° C." (Stanier et al, *The Microbial World,* p. 315.) They can *survive* at lower temperatures, but not *grow.* Lowering of temperature from an organism's ideal range has the effect of slowing down reactions. From the quotation just noted, at about 5° below zero C, the reactions would be so slow that there would be no growth. Yet the primitive temperature was supposed to have been "sub-

11. For each set of amino acids, let it be figured *that every unusable chain is immediately dismantled and another one made* at the same rate of around 30 million billion per second, which is a trillion trillion (10^{24}) per year in each set.

12. Assume that nothing will interfere, so that chance will have an ideal opportunity,[20] and that if a usable sequence is ever obtained, the action will stop so that it may be preserved. (In the matter of trying for a set of 239 proteins, regardless of the speed of trials, it would of course be necessary for 239 contiguous sets to obtain right sequences at the same time. However, even if there were a way to arrange for a long time of overlapping existence of each sequence that occurred, with staggered timing of different sets, it would not make enough difference to affect the outcome.)

13. Consider further *that if 239 proteins in contiguous sets are ever obtained, they will be able to merge into one group of proteins ready for working together in a living system.*

14. For our present purpose, assume *that the age of the earth is five billion years, and that the age of the universe is fifteen billion years.* From an evolutionary standpoint, these rounded figures are more or less standard at the present time. (As we will see, evidence is growing for a *much* younger age.)

With the extreme concessions listed above it might be thought that chance should easily arrange many protein chains in the course of earth's history. On the contrary, we will find it otherwise.

The reader will recognize that many of these concessions are either definitely impossible or else have a probability that is "vanishingly small," to put it mildly. They are made merely to offer chance such a favorable opportunity that its failure to produce should be conclusive.

Using All the Atoms on Earth for Making Proteins by Chance

In the list of concessions, it was assumed that all of the appropriate atoms on earth's surface, including air, water, and crust of the earth, were made into amino acids and arranged conveniently in sets to make it easier for chance to come up

---

stantially below the freezing point of water at the time of the origin of life." (The freezing point of water is 0° C.) This is very interesting.

[20] A difficulty with many theories on the origin of life is that hope depends on postulating many unusual conditions. As will be seen, however, even this concession will not bring success in seeking a chance origin of proteins.

with a usable protein. It can be estimated that there would be about 10^{41} such sets available.[21]

With each of these sets making a total of 10^{24} different chains per year as assumed in concession 11, that gives a total of $10^{24} \times 10^{41}$ chains produced on earth in a year's time, which is 10^{65}. Under concession 14, the total chains made since the earth began would be 5×10^{74}, which we will round off to 10^{75}.

The Odds Against an Average Protein by Chance Since the Earth Began

We have just seen that chance could have made 10^{75} different protein-length chains at the speed assumed during the entire time the earth has existed. Using the formula from the alphabet, we can now estimate how many of those might be considered usable protein molecules.[22] First, we should allow for one substitution per chain. This would have the effect of changing that $1/10^{240}$ formula to around $1/10^{236}$. The probability, then, for usable protein molecules in this total of 10^{75} produced since the world began is $10^{75}/10^{236}$. Simplifying the fraction, we get 1 in 10^{161} as the probability that even one would be usable, on the average.

Therefore, *the odds are 10^{161} to 1 that not one usable protein would have been produced by chance in all the history of the earth,* using all the appropriate atoms on earth at the fantastic rate described. This is a figure containing 161 zeroes.

It might be well to recall that even if one molecule *were* obtained, it would not help at all in arranging the second protein molecule unless there existed an accurate duplication process. Even if there were such a process, there are many other *kinds* of proteins needed before there can be a living organism.

---

[21] There are about 2.5×10^{44} nitrogen atoms and 9×10^{44} carbon atoms thus available. Since there is considerable variation in the data from which this can be figured, it will help chance if we use totals calculated from the most liberal estimates, namely: 9.35×10^{44} nitrogen atoms (C. C. Delwiche, "The Nitrogen Cycle," *Scientific American* [September, 1970], p. 140), and 4.6×10^{45} carbon atoms (Morowitz, *Energy Flow in Biology*, p. 69) available on earth. Since 1.35 nitrogen atoms are required per average amino acid in some bacteria, nitrogen would run short in supply before carbon, of which around five atoms are needed per amino acid.

To provide one of each of the 20 amino acids at each point in the desired 400-length chain, there will be enough nitrogen and other required elements for around 10^{41} sets.

[22] The total of possible arrangements 400 amino acids long is 20^{400}, which is the same as 10^{520}. The percentage of usable ones, 1 in 10^{240}, being smaller, is the figure to be used for the first protein. (This figure comes from the alphabet analogy just described.)

In Morowitz' minimal cell, the 239 protein molecules required include *at least 124 different protein species.*[23]

To Obtain a Set of Protein Molecules for Minimal Life

It has just been calculated that the probability of a single protein molecule being arranged by chance is 1 in 10^{161}, using all atoms on earth and allowing all the time since the world began. What is the probability of getting *an entire set* of proteins for the smallest theoretical living entity?

The second protein molecule will be far more difficult than the first, because it has to be part of a matching set. The protein molecules of a cell are quite specifically adapted to work together as a team. We assumed that the first protein could be *any* usable protein that might be good somewhere. Once that first one is specified, the rest of the set has to match it exactly. It is like assembling a car from a crate of automobile parts. Once the kind of automobile is determined by the first component used, then all the other items must be of that same matching group. Nothing else on earth will fit, in most cases, except the part made for that particular purpose.

After the first protein molecule is obtained by chance (if it ever happens), then the others must be quite specific in the same way as the automobile components.

The Second Protein Molecule Is More Difficult

The probability of getting the first protein molecule was influenced by the formula taken from the alphabet analogy. The second one is more difficult to obtain, we have just seen, because it has to be more exact to match the first one, instead of being just any protein.

The total number of possible orders in a chain of 400 amino acids of 20 kinds is 20^{400}. (The formula is: the number of kinds to the power of the number of units in the chain.) As stated above, 20^{400} is the same as 10^{520}.

Considering the first one as already obtained, we need 238 more. The second one could be any one of those 238. The probability is therefore $238/10^{520}$. The third one could be any of the 237 still needed, so its probability would be $237/10^{520}$. Calculating all of these, and allowing for one substitution per chain,

[23] Morowitz, personal communication, October, 1971.

we arrive at a probability of 1 in 10^{122470}. (See note 24 below.) Even if almost a trillion different sequences might work in each protein, the probability resulting is 1 in 10^{119614}. (See note 25 below.)

This figure represents the second through the 239th protein molecules. Multiplying in the first one, which was at a probability of $1/10^{236}$, we arrive at the final figure for the minimum set needed for the simplest theoretical living entity, namely, 1 chance in 10^{119850}.

Earlier, we obtained the figure of 10^{75} which was the total number of chains made since the earth began. In order to allow for overlapping sets of 239 each, we will use that same figure to represent the total protein sets formed. Dividing into the big figure just calculated, we learn that *the odds against one minimum set of proteins happening in the entire history of the earth are* 10^{119775} *to 1.* (See note 26 below.)

Even if such a set could be obtained, we would not have life. It would simply be a helpless group of nonliving molecules alone in a sterile world, uncaring and uncared for, the end of the line. In chapter 10 we will see that even if unlimited substitution is allowed in 9/10 of all the positions, the odds against one minimum set of proteins are still beyond comprehension.

No Conceivable Chance of Success

The odds against such a correctly ordered set of proteins for the smallest conceivable living entity are thus hopelessly large beyond understanding. The next chapter will make it easier to realize the gigantic size of even the smaller figures with which we have been dealing.

Chance was given every possible concession in this investigation. Its failure was miserable beyond power to describe. Yet chance is the only natural way that the first proteins could have been arranged. In all of the careful efforts of Oparin and his

---

[24] For one substitution, we again use the formula $\frac{(a-1)n+1}{a^n}$, adapting it to the situation just described.

[25] The calculation of this was $\frac{7601^{238} \times 238! \times 10^{12 \times 238}}{10^{520 \times 238}}$ yielding approximately $1/10^{119614}$. (The 238! means 238 *factorial* and signifies that we must multiply 238 x 237 x 236 . . . x 1. Actually, we used an over-simplification in this instance, which helps chance even more. Instead of all 239 being different kinds, which would require the use of the factorial, the 239 protein molecules include around 124 different protein species.)

[26] The number 10^{119850} divided by $10^{75} = 10^{119775}$.

followers in their attempts to get life from nonlife, *no real way has been found to get away from chance. It is the only possible source of the sequence, in the absence of planning,* in spite of the millions of words and the valiant efforts expended in the attempts that have been made.

There is no real reason at present to believe that any living thing has ever existed that is simpler than the *Mycoplasma hominis H39,* which is the smallest living entity known.[27] Although some viruses may be smaller, they do not qualify as autonomous self-replicating systems. A virus cannot duplicate itself without the help of a host cell whose machinery it must use to manufacture its proteins and nucleic acids. Instead of being an earlier step on the ladder of evolution, viruses are now thought by some scientists to be just the opposite, a deterioration or setback rather than part of the line of progress. Could it be that they are intimately involved with the curse that the Bible describes as having come upon the earth as a result of man's sin?

Both the *Mycoplasma hominis H39* and the theoretical smallest living thing have proteins averaging at least 400 amino acids of the 20 common varieties.[28] Dr. Morowitz' eminent work on the lower limits of size and complexity for living things was done, in part, for the National Aeronautics and Space Administration. Obviously the reason was to enable space missions to recognize any possible forms of life that might be simpler or different from our own. There seems to be no actual scientific evidence that would indicate a more primitive, simpler method of duplication than the one in use in existing living things.

Neither is there any adequate reason to think that there was ever a lesser number of amino acid types used in proteins. Many vital functions require proteins with all the twenty kinds included. Even viruses use all twenty. The same twenty are part of the theoretical minimal cell.

It is significant that the Yale team working on this subject has revised its figures upward at least twice. As research has progressed, it has become clear that the minimal living thing requires more parts than was at first thought. From 45 different proteins estimated as the lowest minimum in 1967, the number

---

[27] Harold J. Morowitz, "Biological Self-Replicating Systems," *Progress in Theoretical Biology,* ed. Fred M. Snell, Vol. 1 (1967), pp. 52, 54.

[28] Morowitz, personal communications, November, 1970, and November, 1971.

needed has risen to at least 124 different protein species. The average molecular weight per protein has also been revised upward slightly.[29]

If words are adequate, the situation appears utterly hopeless for a random linkup in a usable order. Even the hormones which the modern Lamarckian theory requires are likewise outside the realm of reasonable probability, as we saw in the case of insulin. Some hormones are complex proteins much larger than insulin.

Another Extreme Concession to Help Chance, but All in Vain

Just suppose that there are only ten kinds of amino acids, all left-handed. Imagine further that the average protein requires only twelve units per chain,[30] and that one substitution is allowed in any of ten of those twelve positions. Let it be granted that a living cell requires only ten proteins. Assume a speed of polymerization of one chain in three seconds, or 10,000,000 per year per set. Let all the other extreme concessions listed earlier remain in effect (use of all atoms on earth, automatic joining, the initial chain qualifying as "usable" under the formula developed on page 104, etc.).

Even with these preposterous assumptions, the probability of one set being produced during the history of the earth is only 1 in 10^{32}. The odds, therefore, are 100 million trillion trillion to 1 that not one set of even this simple kind of "proteins" would have been obtained by chance since the earth was born. So chance fails again.

This section should be remembered in connection with any further research, if, for example, it is ever discovered that more substitution in regular-length proteins is allowable. *The margin by which chance fails is so vast that no conceivable amount of new discovery along this line could change the basic conclusion* that complicated working systems do not arise by chance. In order to obtain and continue to have certainty, one must remember and apply this key principle whenever new challenges are met.

---

[29] Calculated by data from Morowitz, personal communication, November, 1971.

[30] Actually, a protein could not be that short, so this is an extreme concession. According to A. D. McLachlan of the Laboratory of Molecular Biology at Cambridge in England, "There is probably also a critical length of about 50 amino acids below which it is difficult to form a protein structure which is stable in solution under normal conditions." (A. D. McLachlan, "Repeating Sequences and Gene Duplication in Proteins," *Journal of Molecular Biology*, Vol. 64 [March 4, 1972], p. 431.)

A More Realistic Calculation

Those extreme concessions we listed on page 105 and following were used to show that it is useless to expect a protein to result from random linkups even under such artificially ideal conditions. Before leaving this subject, it may prove helpful if we now cut some of those concessions down to a more realistic picture (while remaining generous to chance so that there will still be no doubt about its failure).

When refigured thus, these conclusions can be reached:

The probability of a protein molecule resulting from a chance arrangement of amino acids is 1 in 10^{287}. A single protein molecule would not be expected to happen by chance more often than once in 10^{262} years on the average, and the probability that one protein might occur by random action during the entire history of the earth is less than 1 in 10^{252}.

For a minimum set of the required 239 protein molecules for the smallest theoretical life, the probability is 1 in 10^{119879}. *It would take 10^{119841} years on the average to get a set of such proteins. That is 10^{119831} times the assumed age of the earth and is a figure with 119,831 zeroes, enough to fill sixty pages of a book this size.*[31]

We are again prompted by the evidence to realize that Some-

---

[31] We suspect that some readers will not be eager to check the calculations for this section, after all the other figures in this chapter. Just for the individuals who may wish to do so, this brief summary of adjustments in the concessions which lead to the above figures is given: Concession 2, estimate $1/10^6$ probability that *all* would occur and in proper proportions. Cancel concession 3 because amino acids formed in a primitive environment would be racemic (see chapter 3 and appendix 1). Figuring at 400 length, 32 glycine, 32 following glycine or first in the chain, 336 others at 3/4 preference for the same hand, the probability of all being left-handed is $1/10^{51}$. (This, when multiplied by the $1/10^{236}$ obtained under the extreme concessions, produces the $1/10^{287}$ figure above.) Concession 5, 1/10; concession 6, $1/10^3$; concession 7, $1/10^4$; concession 8, 10, and 11 together, $1/10^{26}$ as follows: $1/10^{16}$ to adjust from our enormous speed down to normal top speed in bacteria; then $1/10^{10}$ to adjust to nonenzymatic speed (". . . . 10^{10} times as long, this being a rough estimate of the ratio of reaction rates with and without enzymatic catalysis. . . ." —Henry Quastler of Yale, in his *Emergence of Biological Organization*, [New Haven, Conn.: Yale University Press, 1964], p. 6). The total of these adjustments (not counting concession 3 made earlier) is $1/10^{40}$. Multiplying by the $1/10^{287}$ and dividing by rate per year from extreme concessions (10^{65}), the result is 10^{262} years. Dividing by 10^{10} as a rounded figure of assumed earth-age, the conclusion 10^{252} times the age of the earth.

Regarding sets, adjust concession 13 by $1/10^{10}$, and concession 12 by $1/10^2$. Totalling all the adjustments on all the concessions, we have $1/10^{103}$. This, when multiplied by the $1/10^{119776}$ obtained under extreme concessions, gives $1/10^{119879}$, the "realistic" probability of one set by chance. Dividing by 10^{38} as the realistic rate per year, we get 10^{119841}, which is 10^{119831} times the age of the earth.

Regarding concessions 1 and 14, although there is insufficient evidence to require them, they were left in effect, since materialists must have them, and, as we discovered, chance failed completely anyway,

one bigger surely had to be on the scene. Even one small protein molecule the size of insulin cannot be accounted for otherwise.

In the following chapter, the implications of these odds will be considered. Understanding the gigantic size of these numbers (of even the smallest figures we've discovered) is vital to the certainty toward which we are moving.

7

How Large Numbers Can Help You

Although we must keep all our confidence in our science, we must not blindly believe in its actual almightiness.[1]

—Pierre Lecomte du Noüy

SERIOUS REASONING MAY require effort. It is the delightful sort of effort that may reward the thinker with valuable insights about the nature of things.

Why Understanding Large Numbers Is Important

If one wishes to arrive at a high degree of certainty regarding the question of evolution, either for himself or in order to help others, it is vital to grasp the real meaning of the kind of numbers we are encountering.

It is easy to be careless in this regard. Many people see little difference between a billion and 10^{287}, for example. They figure some rare possibility just might actually happen, whether the probability is one in a billion or one in 10^{287}. After all, some men live to be 105 years of age. Ordinary people do win the Irish sweepstakes in spite of large odds against them.[2] So they think that, even if it is improbable, maybe life could have started by chance.

The vital difference is in the size of numbers. Let's look now more closely at a figure we obtained in the chapter just ended.

---

[1] Pierre Lecomte du Noüy, *Human Destiny* (New York: Longmans, Green & Co., 1947), p. 38.

[2] A moment's thought shows that in the case of the sweepstakes, it is *certain* that *someone will win*. This is an entirely different type of situation from the kind we are studying.

The probability of one average protein molecule arranging itself by chance in correct order was first computed. Then we assumed that all the needed atoms available on earth were gathered in convenient sets. Each set was trying out 30 million billion new arrangements every second. If chance could be expected to produce one protein molecule that would function anywhere, it would be considered a success. The probability of this happening even once since the earth began was less than 1 in 10^{161}. Let's compare that figure with some large numbers we can more easily comprehend.

Examples of Large Numbers

Take the number of seconds in any considerable period. There are just 60 in a minute, but in an hour that increases to 3,600 seconds. In a year, there are 31,558,000, averaged to allow for leap year. Imagine what a tremendous number of seconds there must have been from the beginning of the universe until now (using 15 billion years, which is one of the standard estimates by evolutionists). It may be helpful to pause a moment and consider how great that number must be.

When written down, however, it appears to be a small figure: less than 10^{18} seconds in the entire history of the universe.

The weight of our entire Milky Way galaxy, including all the stars and planets and everything, is said to be "of the order of 3×10^{44} grams."[3] (A gram is about 1/450th of a pound.) Even the number of atoms in the universe is not impressive at first glance, until we get used to big numbers. It is 5×10^{78}, based on present estimates of the radius at 15 billion light years and a mean density of $1/10^{30}$ grams per cubic centimeter.[4]

Suppose that *each one of those atoms* could expand until it was the size of the present universe so that each had 5×10^{78} atoms of its own. The total atoms in the resulting super-cosmos would be 2.5×10^{157}.

By comparison, perhaps the figure for the odds against a single protein forming by chance in earth's entire history, namely, 10^{161}, is now a bit more impressive to consider. It is 4,000

[3] *Encyclopaedia Britannica,* (1967), s.v. "galaxy."

[4] According to Jesse L. Greenstein, who was then head of the Astronomy Department at California Institute of Technology (personal conversation, November, 1971), 10^{78} was the figure based on a 10-billion-light-year radius. Since 15 billion light years is now the accepted view, we calculate that the number of atoms is around 5×10^{78}. (The earlier 10^{78} was "approximate.") Current estimates of radius range from 10 to 20 billion light years, although there is still uncertainty of measurements beyond a few hundred light years.

times larger than the number of atoms in that *super* universe we just imagined.[5]

A Number Too Big to Imagine

Try as we may, that slender probability for the chance formation of a protein is a number too large to grasp. Let's ponder it awhile. That big figure, 10^{161}, represents the odds against one protein in five billion years. We can now calculate how long a period would be required in which we could expect one success on the average.

We should bear in mind that all of the constituent atoms on the surface of the earth—on land, in air, in seas—are considered as made up into sets of amino acids conveniently available for each point on every potentially forming protein chain. In *each* of these 10^{41} sets, experiments are going on constantly at the rate of 30 million billion per second.

By simple mathematics, we discover that, on the average, a single usable protein might hook up correctly once in 10^{171} years, rounded.

The Case of the Traveling Ameba

Imagine an ameba. This microscopic one-celled animal is something like a thin toy balloon about one-fourth full of water. To travel, it flows or oozes along very slowly.

This ameba is setting forth on a long journey, from one edge of the universe all the way across to the other side. Since the radius of the universe is now speculated by some astronomers to be 15 billion light years, we will use a diameter of double that distance.

Let's assume that the ameba travels at the rate of one inch a year. A bridge of some sort—say a string—can be imagined on which the ameba can crawl. Translating the distance into inches, we see that this is approximately 10^{28} inches. At the rate of one inch per year, the tiny space traveller can make it across in 10^{28} years.

The ameba has a task: to carry one atom across, and come back for another. The object is to transport the mass of the *entire universe* across the entire diameter of the universe! Each round trip takes 2×10^{28} years. The ameba must naturally be presumed to be imperishable and tenacious!

To carry all the atoms of the universe across, one at a time,

[5] $10^{161} = (2.5 \times 10^{157}) \times (4 \times 10^{3})$

would require the time for one round trip multiplied by the number of atoms in the universe, 5×10^{78}. Multiplying, we get 10^{107} years, rounded. That is the length of time for the ameba to carry the entire universe across, one atom at a time.

But wait. The number of years in which we could expect one protein by chance was much larger than that. It was 10^{171}. If we divide that by the length of time it takes to move one universe by slow ameba, we arrive at this astounding conclusion: *The ameba could haul 10^{64} UNIVERSES across the entire diameter of the known universe during the expected time it would take for one protein to form by chance, under those conditions so favorable to chance.*

But imagine this. Suppose the ameba has moved only an inch in all the time that the universe has existed (according to the 15-billion-year estimate). If it continues at that rate to travel an inch every 15 billion years, the number of universes it could carry across those interminable miles is still beyond understanding, namely, more than 6×10^{53}, while one protein is forming.[6]

Sooner or later our minds come to accept the idea that it's not worth waiting for chance to make a protein. That is true if we consider the science of probability seriously. Missile scientists, like Wernher von Braun, use the same multiplication rule which is the basis of these calculations.[7] It helps get our astronauts to the moon and back.

Why Some Probabilities Are So Small

Charles-Eugène Guye was one of the most brilliant thinkers of this century. This noted physics professor at Geneva called attention to the rapidity at which the number of outcomes can increase: "It is sufficient to recall that a hostess can arrange 20 diners round a table in more than two million million million ways. What would it be if it were necessary to place one thousand?"[8]

If you have 20 guests, the first one can be seated in any of the 20 places. While that one is in any one of those 20 places, the next person can be seated in any of the remaining 19, and the same way, the next person in any of 18 seats not

---

[6] 10^{64} divided by 15 billion $(1.5 \times 10^{10}) = 6.6 \times 10^{53}$.

[7] Wernher von Braun, *Space Frontier*, New Edition (New York: Holt, Rinehart and Winston, 1971), pp. 108, 109.

[8] Charles-Eugène Guye, *Physico-Chemical Evolution* (New York: E. P. Dutton & Co., 1925), p. 164.

occupied. The total possible arrangements in such a situation comes to 20 x 19 x 18 x 17 x . . . x 1, called 20 *factorial,* and written in this interesting notation: 20! That is why, incidentally, we have not put exclamation points after some of the amazing figures we have computed. The exclamation point would change the meaning to factorial.

In the experiments mentioned so far, it has been assumed that all of the different amino acids were available at each point. The total of equally probable outcomes is gotten then by multiplying by itself the number of the available types, to the power of the length of the chain desired. When considering only L-amino acids, it was 20 x 20 x 20 x . . . x 20. The product number soon becomes astronomical.

Consider what a great change it makes when you barely increase an exponent of 10. If you start with 10^{101} and change it to 10^{102}, you are, in effect, *adding* $10^{101} + 10^{101} + 10^{101} + 10^{101} + 10^{101} + 10^{101} + 10^{101} + 10^{101} + 10^{101}$ to the original 10^{101}.

The Laws of Chance Are Dependable

Pierre Lecomte du Noüy, noted French scientist who escaped Nazi occupation in 1942 and came to the United States, wrote,

> The so-called "laws of chance" borrow their accuracy (which is considerable on our scale of observation) from the fact that no privileged atoms exist (from the particular point of view considered) and that, on an average, they all behave in the same unpredictable, disorderly manner.[9]

In other words, we can expect things to average out according to those laws, and we are not to think anything is likely to behave contrary to the law of large numbers, if it depends on chance alone. Throughout science, engineering, and business, you find almost absolute dependence upon these laws. It is logical that the same principles which are used in planning skyscrapers can be trusted when we apply them to the probability of proteins forming by chance.

Calculations Can Be Scientific—a Repeatable Study

Remember that the essence of the scientific method is the repeatable experiment with the same outcome if the experiment is carried out in the same way, no matter who does it. Anyone can check on the reality of the multiplication rule and the

[9] du Noüy, *Human Destiny,* p. 41.

mathematical formulas we have used. If doubts recur, one can go back and recheck until he is assured they are correct. The principles of probability are known and unhesitatingly trusted by engineers, astronauts, and all who use mathematics.

Certainty on this subject grows as one becomes convinced of the accuracy of the law of averages, and as he then considers the things that now exist. When one goes at this from the inductive scientific route, he can then by deduction see the logic of the Bible's position in crediting creation rather than chance. But why should anyone want to improve on the Bible? It contains the truths man needs. Without it, modern man cannot find his way in this vast, mysterious cosmos.

Modern Atheism's Substitute for God

In April, 1967, the international magazine, *Réalités,* printed an interview with French philosopher-scientist-theologian Claude Tresmontant, whom we have quoted earlier. The magazine, in its introduction to the interview, referred to Tresmontant's book, *The Problem of the Existence of God Today,* using these phrases: "closely argued reasoning," and "the almost overwhelming mass of learning with which it is weighted."[10] In the interview, Tresmontant, after stating that Plato, Aristotle, and others "thought that the world was a great living being, a Divine Animal," said, "Modern atheism still maintains that the world is the only Being." He then elaborated on what that would mean as to the nature of matter:

> Since it is assumed that this matter is increate and eternal . . . it must have produced, from its own resources, everything that has appeared in the universe, both life and thought.
>
> The total amorphous mass has been able to organize itself, to become animated and to endow itself with consciousness and thought. It is clear that if matter is to be looked at in this way it has to be credited with very great resources, great wisdom and positive genius, since great genius was needed for the independent invention of the large molecules which are part of the makeup of any living creature, however humble, as well as for the invention of the major functional systems that characterize higher forms of life—the digestive, circulatory, reproductive and nervous systems.[11]

With incisive reasoning, Dr. Tresmontant points out the implications of this substitution of the material universe for God.

---

[10] *Réalités,* Paris, April, 1967, p. 45.
[11] Ibid., p. 46.

In the end, the same qualities would be required as those that describe the God of the Bible. He says, if matter has thus been able to accomplish such wonders, then:

> I maintain that it must be gifted with great wisdom and incomparable genius. I would even say that matter must be credited with all the attributes that theologians specify as belonging to God: autonomous being, ontological self-sufficiency and creative genius.[12]

By this he shows that atheists cannot expect to escape the need for God—the same kind of God as described in the Bible—as the only rational explanation of the universe.

The general rule on the way things are is becoming clearer as we go on. Chance cannot create complex, orderly, operational systems. Neither can it account for beauty. To attribute to blind chance the perfume of a rose or the playfulness of a lamb is to ignore all logic.

Practical Impossibility

Speaking of large numbers, Lecomte du Noüy commented, "It is evident that exponents of over 100 lose all human significance. The nearest star is 40×10^{21} microns from us."[13] (A micron is one thousandth of a millimeter, which itself is about one twenty-fifth of an inch.)

Regarding probabilities involving numbers of large magnitude, the same author wrote:

> If the probability of an event is infinitely slight, it is equivalent to the *practical* impossibility of its happening *within certain time limits.* The theoretical possibility . . . can be so small that it is equivalent to a quasi-certitude of the contrary.[14]

We have seen that *an ameba could transport six hundred thousand trillion trillion trillion trillion universes, an atom at a time, across the diameter of the entire universe, travelling at the rate of an inch in fifteen billion years, during the time in which chance could be expected to arrange one average protein molecule.*[15] Perhaps the reader would agree that a proba-

---

[12] *Réalités,* Paris, April, 1967, p. 46.
[13] du Noüy, *Human Destiny,* p. 32.
[14] Ibid., p. 30.
[15] Note that all through this chapter, the figures we used were those obtained under those tremendous concessions to make it easier for chance to succeed. Under realistic figures, the odds would have been even greater against its success.

bility so slight as this surely qualifies, in Lecomte du Noüy's phrase, *as a quasi-certitude of its practical impossibiilty.*

The logic of these words of Scripture is now more easily evident: "Thou art worthy, O Lord, to receive glory and honour and power, for thou hast created all things, and for thy pleasure they are and were created" (Revelation 4:11).

8

DNA—"The Most Golden of All Molecules"

In terms of an analogy, [human DNA is like] a very large encyclopaedia of forty-six volumes, 20,000 pages each. Every cell in the human body is provided with the whole encyclopaedia.[1]

—John C. Kendrew

THE GREATEST DISCOVERY in the history of biology was that of the structure of DNA. It captured the imagination of the general public, particularly those already interested in science.[2] Understanding it is a key part of our progress to certainty.

That there should be a "language of life," as Crick called it,[3] which is a universal code, is very mysterious and intriguing.

The code has been found to be precisely the same in the cells of the smallest known living thing and in the nerve cells of the human brain. Yeast cells and the eye-retina cells of an eagle contain the exact same code with identical letters, arranged to spell different "words." Abundant research indicates this universal nature of the code to be the same in all creatures studied (with possibly very rare minor variations).

Size of the DNA Molecule

DNA, like protein, is a long slender thread in its primary structure. In fact, a DNA molecule may be hundreds of times

---

[1] John C. Kendrew, *The Thread of Life* (Cambridge, Mass.: Harvard University Press, 1966), p. 104.

[2] Codiscoverer Watson, as noted earlier, termed this fascinating chemical "the most golden of all molecules!"

[3] *1969 Yearbook of Science and the Future* (Britannica), p. 123.

as long as the diameter of the cell of which it is a part. This requires it to be doubled up and coiled or twisted around so it can fit into the cell.

A multicelled plant or animal will have more DNA per cell, since more coded information is needed. In the human cell, the DNA is divided into 46 *chromosomes*. The total length of all this DNA in *one* cell is about six feet![4] It is estimated that the total DNA content in your body would span the solar system![5]

A Quick Way to Understand the Plan of the Code

We can get a clear idea of how the DNA code is arranged by designing one of our own. Suppose we form a code in which only four symbols are to be used, the numerals 1, 2, 3, and 4. It is to be translated later into the 26 letters of our alphabet.

If we decide to put the numerals in groups of three, then we will have more than enough triplets of digits to match the 26 letters. In fact, we will have 64 different trios (111, 112, 113, 114, 121, 122, etc.). Because of the excess of these trios as compared to 26 letters, we can assign several different groups of three to the same letter, in most cases.

Let's let the letter "A" be coded by any of the following groups of digits, 111, 112, 113, 114. "B" can be represented by 121, 122, 123, or 124. For "C," we will assign only two triplets, 131 and 132. This will give us enough for the moment.

Now, using our simple code, let's write the word "Cab." It could possibly be 132114122.[6] To translate it, all we need do is divide it into groups of three, beginning at the correct starting point. Then, by referring to our code key or dictionary, we can easily decipher it.

It would work just the same if other symbols were used instead of the numerals 1, 2, 3, 4. For example, we could use a circle, a square, a triangle, and an oval. We could, as another alternative, use four different types of tree leaves, or even four chemicals. In the latter case, our code would be much like the DNA code, as we will see. DNA, however, does not translate to our alphabet but to the 20 amino acids, indicating the proper order for their joining, to make a specific protein that is needed. Biological life consists, to a great extent, of making the correct

---

[4] Philip Handler, ed., *Biology and the Future of Man* (New York: Oxford University Press, 1970), p. 134.

[5] Kendrew, *The Thread of Life*, p. 63.

[6] We could, of course, have used any of the alternates, when more than one group stands for a particular letter.

proteins with the proper timing and amounts.[7] Once formed, these various proteins can do many wonderful things.

Now that we have the main idea of the code plan, let's examine the way it actually exists in living things.

The Exotic DNA "Double Helix"

Watson and Crick and their co-workers discovered that this marvelous *deoxyribonucleic acid* molecule (DNA) consisted of a special type of spiral, a *double helix.* The long molecule continuously winds like the threads of a screw. Together the two sides of the double helix form a spiral staircase or ladder. (See Figures 5 and 6.)

When studying proteins, we found that a protein molecule is formed from smaller amino acid molecules, of which there are 20 kinds. DNA is likewise made of simpler molecules, but there are only six kinds. Four of these carry the message and the other two protect and hold them in place.

FIGURE 5

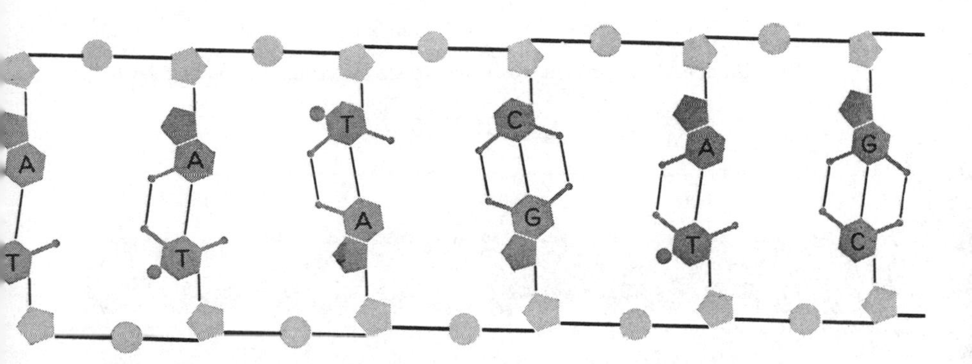

The above diagram depicts a short section of the DNA molecule in flattened form to show the ladderlike sides with steps or rungs consisting of the four "bases" which are the letters of the genetic code. Each base is connected to another by hydrogen bonds in the center of the ladder, thus forming a "base pair." The letters A, C, G, and T are the first initials of the four bases: adenine, cytosine, guanine, and thymine. In the sides of the ladder, the round molecules are phosphates, and the pentagonal ones are sugar molecules. Diagram is from same source as Fig. 6. See next page.

[7] Handler, ed. *Biology and the Future of Man,* p. 146.

FIGURE 6

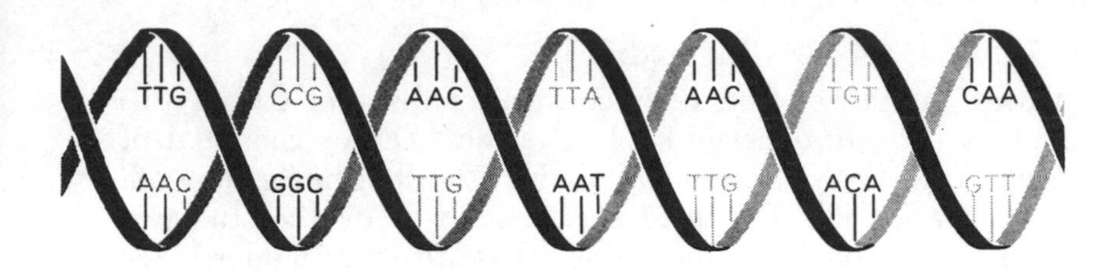

Shown above schematically is the DNA double helix in its natural coiled configuration. This is primarily to show the twisting of the ladder, and does not show the base pairing except to list letters of complementary bases in triplets or codons. In an actual DNA molecule, there are ten base pairs for each complete corkscrew turn of the double helix.

 Dr. Nirenberg's important work led to deciphering the genetic code.

FIGURE 7

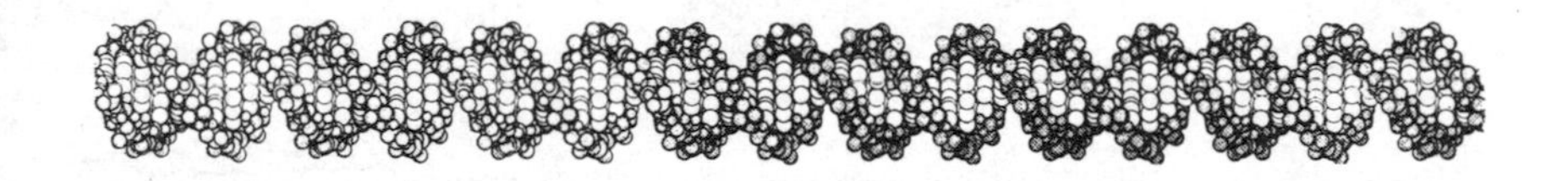

The coiled representation shown here is drawn more closely to scale than are the two preceding diagrams. This shows a section of the DNA molecule containing about one hundred base pairs or letters. The bases almost completely fill the space between the coiled sides of the twisted ladderlike double helix. This small section would be less than a ten-thousandth as long as the complete DNA molecule of a bacterium if drawn to the same scale. This picture is by Francis H. C. Crick, codiscoverer of the DNA structure.

FIGURE 8

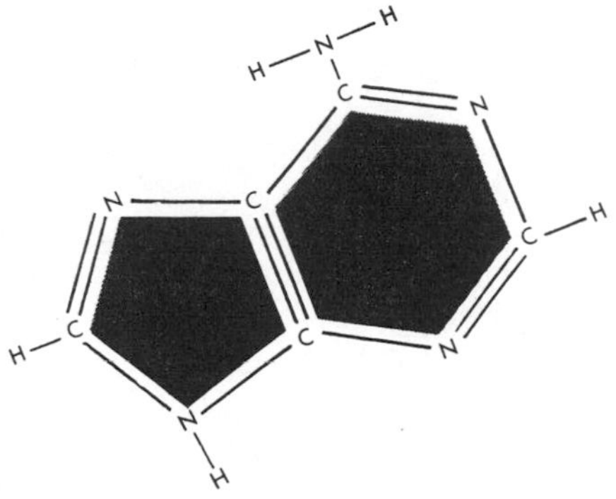

Adenine

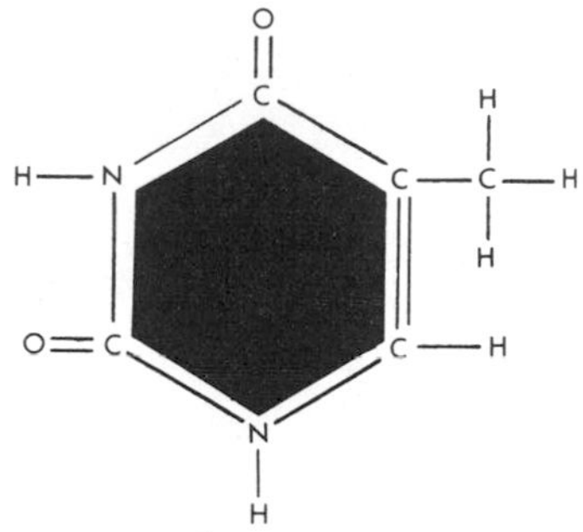

Thymine

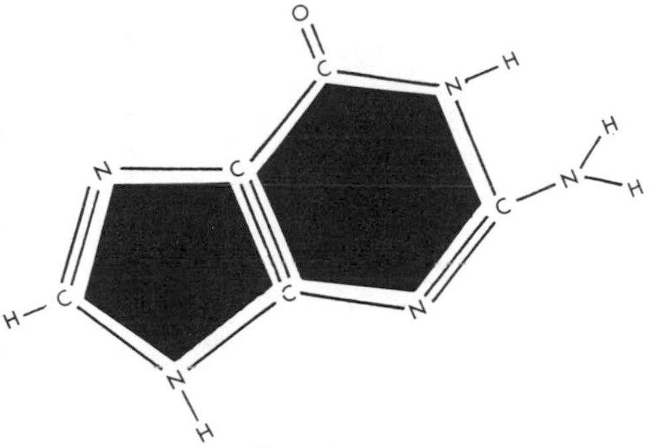

Guanine

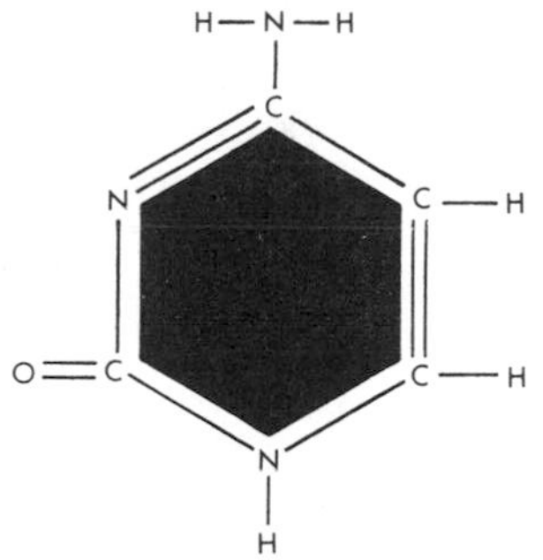

Cytosine

The four chemical bases which serve as letters of DNA. Figures 8 and 9 are from same source, given after Figure 9 on following page.

First, let's consider the sides of the staircase or spiral ladder. Each side is quite simple. It consists of only two kinds of molecules, alternating in regular fashion. One is a type of sugar, called *deoxyribose* (the D in DNA). The other component of the ladder's sides is a small molecule called a *phosphate*. It contains one atom of phosphorus, along with oxygen atoms. These two kinds of molecules join together in a very long chain —sugar-phosphate-sugar-phosphate-sugar—in regular order. The entire length of each side of the DNA double spiral is formed on this simple plan. These sides of the ladder may be thought of as frames to hold the letters in place.

The rungs or steps of the ladder are the all-important "letters" of the language of life. These are nitrogen compounds which

FIGURE 9

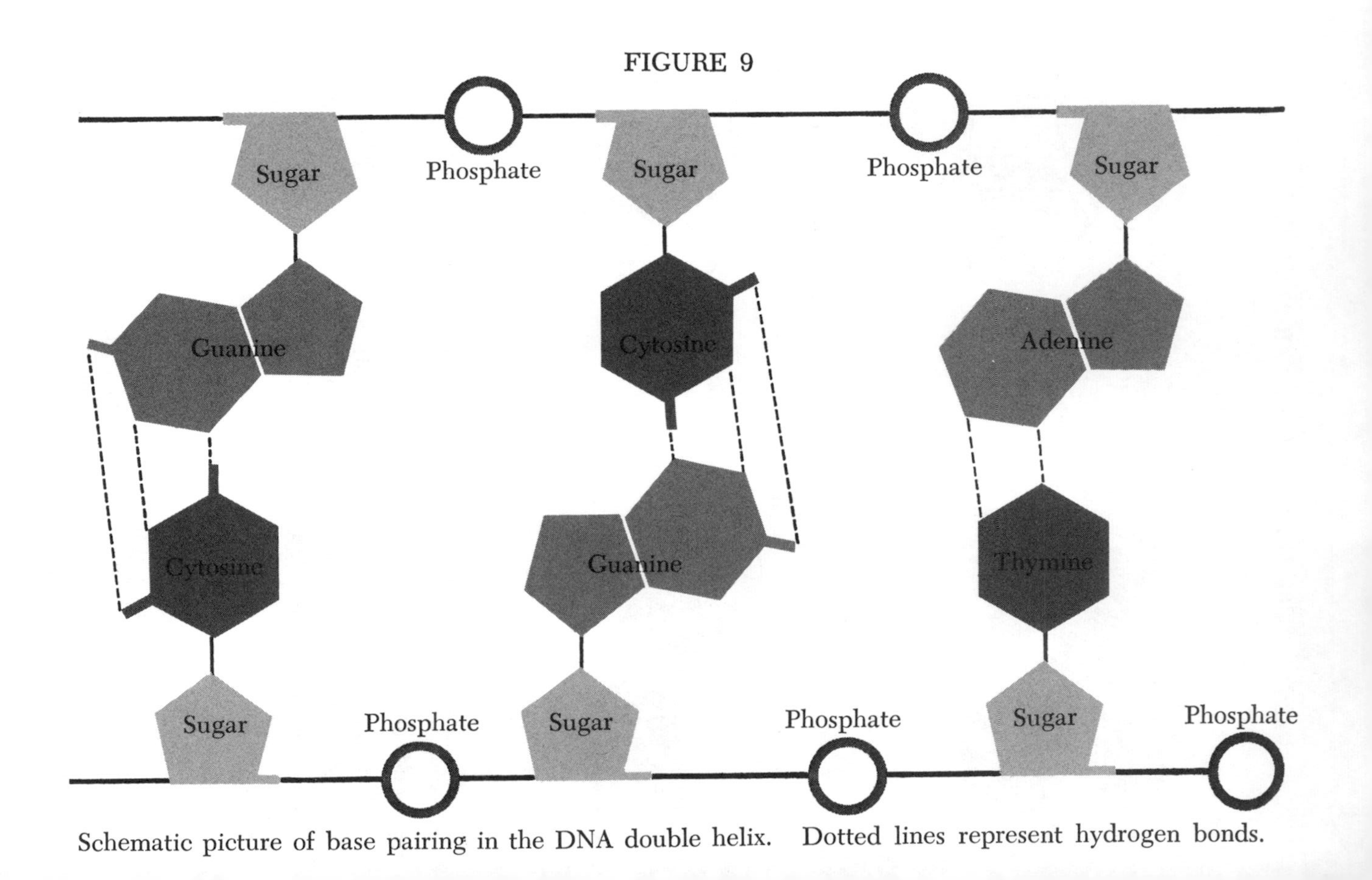

Schematic picture of base pairing in the DNA double helix. Dotted lines represent hydrogen bonds.

Figures 8 and 9 are adapted from "How Cells Make Molecules" by Vincent G. Allfrey and Alfred E. Mirsky. Copyright © September, 1961, by Scientific American, Inc. All rights reserved.

also contain oxygen, hydrogen, and carbon. There are four kinds of these in DNA. They are called *bases*.

A base is joined to each sugar molecule of the sides of the ladder. Each base extends halfway across to the other side of the helical ladder and connects with another base which is similarly projecting from the opposite side of the ladder. Together the two bases make a *base pair*. They can be pictured as steps of the spiral ladder.

These four bases are the all-important symbols or letters of the code. The names of the bases are: *adenine, guanine, thymine,* and *cytosine*. (In biochemistry, usually names which end with "-ine" are pronounced as if spelled "-een"; thus, adenine is pronounced "adeneen.")

A base pair consists of two *different* bases, joined together loosely by *hydrogen bonds* where they meet in the middle of the helix. Adenine always pairs with thymine, and guanine pairs only with cytosine, in DNA.

Watson and Crick discovered this *complementary pairing* mechanism of the bases. By this discovery, if you know what base is on one side of the spiral, you will know also the base that connects with it. Just a certain one will pair with it to complete that base pair. Using initial letters of the four bases, we say that "A" always pairs with "T," and "G" always pairs with "C."

A single base with its own section of one side of the ladder makes up a complete unit called a *nucleotide*. It consists of a base, a deoxyribose sugar molecule, and a phosphate. A base pair with its sections of both sides of the ladder is a *nucleotide pair*. A nucleotide pair has more than 60 atoms. "The exact order of these pairs constitutes a *genetic message* which contains all the information necessary to determine the specific structures and functions of the cell."[8]

This completes a look at the building blocks that form the DNA double helix.

Letters of the Universal Language

The all-important part of the DNA helix consists of the letters or bases that make up the code. Just as in our language the order of the letters spells out an endless variety of messages, so with DNA. Abbreviated as above, these letters are A, C, G, and T.

[8] Roger Y. Stanier, Michael Doudoroff, and Edward A. Adelberg, *The Microbial World*, 3rd ed. (Englewood Cliffs, N.J.: Prentice-Hall, 1970), p. 267.

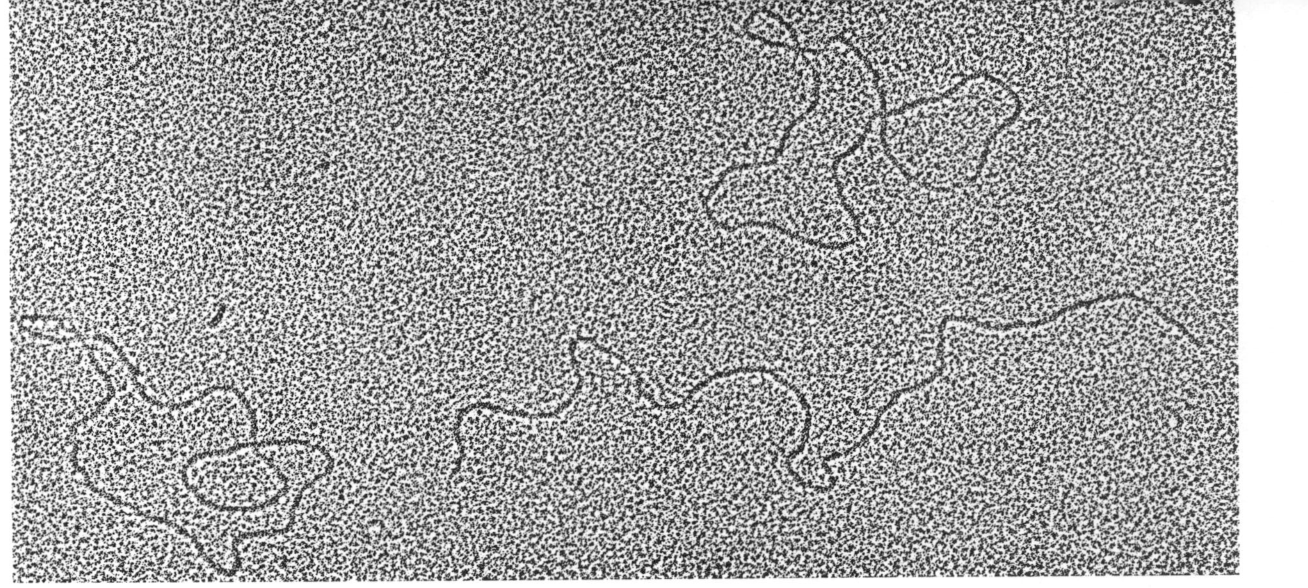

FIGURE 10

Courtesy of Dr. Arthur Kornberg.

Shown above are three DNA molecules. In the two "circular" molecules, the long slender thread of DNA is connected in the form of a loop, which is the normal situation in bacteria and viruses. The molecules shown contain perhaps 5,000 base pairs or code letters, which is quite short for DNA. (The DNA molecule of a bacterium may be a thousand times as long, and would be difficult to show in one picture.)

The electron micrograph above depicts double-stranded DNA formed in a famous experiment by Arthur Kornberg of Stanford University, and for which he is a Nobel laureate. It consists of synthetic double-stranded DNA, obtained by first making a hybrid of one strand from a bacterial virus and a synthetic strand formed by base pairing with this pattern strand. Activated nucleotides which are the precursors or building blocks of DNA and an enzyme(s) produced by living bacteria were used. Each thread in the picture is actually a double helix ladderlike chain, too small to see in detail even at the high magnification shown (around 78,700 diameters).

It is their order in the chain that carries the message, just as the order of letters in this line of type carries the thought.

Each base always has the same complementary base opposite it. In a sense, this might seem to narrow down the number of letters to only two if the base pairs could be read from either side. From research to date, it seems that the code is read from *only one side* of the double helix. That one side carries the message to be transcribed, and the other is called the "nonsense" side. There are, therefore, four letters instead of two in the usable alphabet. (The so-called "nonsense" side has at least two very important functions, as we will see, making possible the *replication* or duplicating process, and also enabling the cell to repair injured DNA.)

Changing From Four Letters to Sixty-four "Triplets"

At first thought it might seem impossible for only four symbols to carry much variety in messages. The DNA system solves this in the same manner as our code using the four numerals. The symbols of the code are read in groups of three. Each triplet of bases is called a *codon*. This system, employing only four letters to be read in groups of three is a marvelously simple plan. Intelligence sometimes combines simple things to get complex results.

Always DNA appears to be read three letters at a time, in the same direction, without overlapping. The reading must begin from a certain starting point, of course.

The code in the double helix has no divisions between these triplets. If we print it as translated into these four initials, it might look like this, for a certain section of DNA: AGTCAAG-CAGGGTCTCCC. As can be seen, it is important to know where to start so that the reading of the triplet codons will be in correct frame.

Translating to Proteins

Through long, patient investigation, biochemists figured out which codon, or trio, is translated into which amino acid in making a protein chain. It was found that in many instances several different triplets are assigned to the same amino acid. Three of the 64 codons indicate "end of chain." These serve as punctuation to signal the completion of a protein.

Research is still going on as to whether there are reasons for more than one codon to indicate the same amino acid. There are four such codons that code for glycine, for example. Hints are being discovered that there is good reason for having several.[9] Duplicate codons are thought to have something to do with the rate or speed of making proteins. Some amino acids are coded by as many as six different codons—each of which translates into the same amino acid as the others. On the other hand, the amino acid methionine has only one codon, as does tryptophan. Duplicates may be "a regulatory factor in some cases."[10]

How DNA Duplicates Itself

Let us now quite briefly consider the amazing process of the *replication* of DNA itself. This is the vital process on which all heredity depends. It is reproduction at the molecular level. Without this DNA copy-making process, life could not be passed along with continuity, if at all.

Francis Crick a few years ago described a preliminary problem:

> There are still a number of things about the process we do not understand, not the least of which is the fact that the two chains are not lying side by side, but are wound round one another, and that in order for the replication to take place they must be at some stage unwound. . . . In addition, the process appears to be one of great precision.[11]

Those who have examined electron micrographs of DNA have noticed the coiled, doubled, knotted twisting and turning that, from our point of observation, appear common in DNA molecules. Anyone who has ever tried to untangle a microphone cord or lamp cord will wonder how on earth the DNA thread ever can manage this intricate feat. It must progressively divide, making two double-helix chains in place of one along the entire length of the molecule. The DNA, remember, is much longer than the diameter of the cell, sometimes about a thousand times as long![12] Ideas on how the unwinding may occur

---

[9] James Kan, Marshall W. Nirenberg, and Noboru Sueoka, "Coding Specificity of *Escherichia coli* Leucine Transfer Ribonucleic Acids," *Journal of Molecular Biology*, Vol. 52 (1970), pp. 179-193. Also:

Joseph Ilan, "The Role of tRNA in Translational Control of Specific mRNA during Insect Metamorphosis," *Symposia on Quantitative Biology* (Cold Spring Harbor Laboratory, Long Island, N.Y., 1969), Vol. XXXIV, pp. 787-791.

[10] Marshall W. Nirenberg, National Institutes of Health, personal telephone conversation, October, 1971.

[11] Francis H. C. Crick, *Of Molecules and Men* (Seattle: University of Washington Press, 1966), pp. 39, 40.

[12] *Ibid.*, p. 37.

by rotation as the replication proceeds are feverishly under study. In fact, it is reported that the rotation during this unwinding occurs at the rate of more than seventy-five turns per second per growing point in bacteria.

Pictures have been taken of the DNA molecule of the smallest living thing, to which we have referred before, the *Mycoplasma hominis H39*. This DNA is in the form of a long threadlike molecule, joined together in a circle. Actual replication in process was photographed by H. R. Bode and Harold Morowitz at Yale.[13]

The molecule begins dividing into two threads at a certain point, and the division apparently continues until there are two circular loops of DNA instead of one. These then separate and become the DNA for two daughter cells. This is an unbelievable "miracle" when you look at the seeming tangles of the long thread during the duplicating process. Somehow it happens successfully, with a built-in wisdom which at this stage we cannot fathom. The mechanism involves a *growing point* complex, containing special proteins and possibly RNA. This complex may be attached to the cell membrane.

Complementary Pairing Is the Secret of Replication

The replication process seems to work in this way. When the two strands begin to split apart, this leaves each half of the ladder separate. (See Figure 11.) Each "base" is thus left with no partner.

Floating around in the "juice," there are various cell parts which have already been made on instructions from the DNA. These free-floating parts include nucleotides, ready to be fitted together to form a strand of the DNA spiral. The nucleotides are in an activated condition, with extra phosphates added to give them energy for uniting.

From the multitude of free-floating nucleotides, the correct matching ones come alongside the divided strands of the DNA which is duplicating. As we recall, each base will match none but its one-and-only opposite type. These then link up to the existing strand and to each other, with the aid of enzymes. When the process is completed, the DNA is again a ladderlike, *double* helix. Each half of the original is replicating at the same

---

[13] Hans R. Bode and Harold J. Morowitz, "Size and Structure of the *Mycoplasma hominis H39* Chromosome," *Journal of Molecular Biology*, Vol. 23 (1967), p. 198.

FIGURE 11

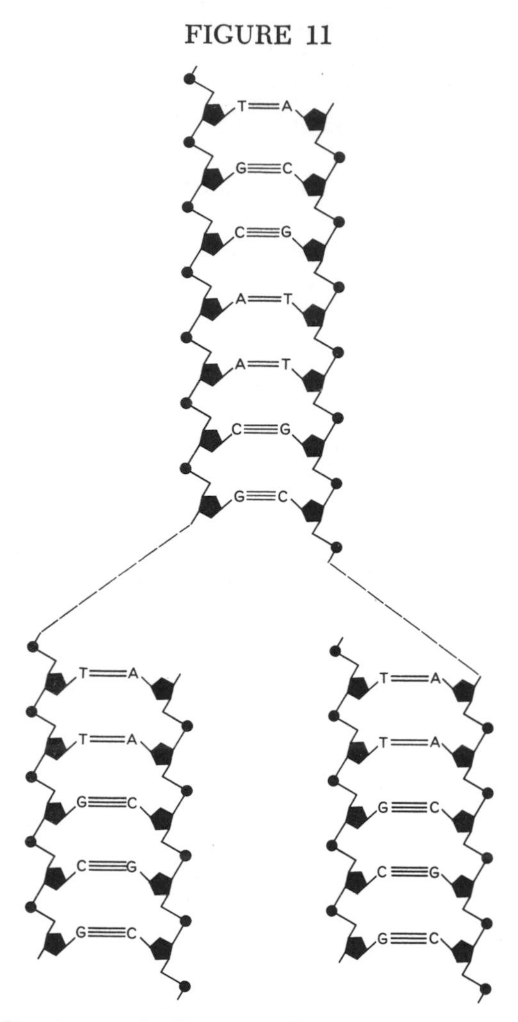

DNA replication or duplication takes place when the ladder-like double helix divides down the center and a new strand forms alongside each of the divided halves, thus making two complete ladders. By the rules of base pairing, the new strand in each case will be identical to the side it replaces. The nucleotide units from which it is assembled are preformed and available in activated form in the cell. The linking is done by enzymes at a very rapid rate, in opposite directions on the two strands—continuously on one and perhaps in short sections on the other near the fork.

time. Each finally becomes a complete double spiral. Complementary pairing insures that it will be identical to the original.

This is the secret of heredity. This is the ingenious method by which like begets like, and life is passed on to the next generation with continuity and exactness. We still scarcely realize how greatly everything depends on DNA, the only means of duplicating life.

While joined, the two sides of the helix protect the bases between them. When replicating, each half can make a complementary copy. That is why there are two sides instead of one.[14] When Watson discovered this, he said it was "too pretty not to be true."[15] It has been described as "this exquisite capability of nucleic acids to direct their own replication."[16] This duplication is so accurate that it would correspond to a rate of error of less than one letter in an entire set of the Encyclopaedia Britannica.[17]

Summarizing the Language of Life

Since we have had to get rather technical, let's pause and summarize the code and its message. The letters A, C, G, and T are strung along the spiral DNA thread. The letters are read three at a time. Each triplet or codon of letters tells which amino acid is to be placed next in order in arranging a protein molecule. Three of these codons are assigned as punctuation to indicate "end chain."

This marvelously simple code is the language of life. Thomas H. Jukes in his monumental work *Molecules and Evolution* tells about one type of special protein (cytochrome *c*) which is common to all forms of life except some of the simplest. In cytochrome *c*, the order of letters is the same for certain parts of the chain in all species which have been examined. We will

---

[14] It also allows an ingenious repair mechanism if one side is damaged, as we intimated earlier. (Philip C. Hanawalt and Robert H. Haynes, "The Repair of DNA," *Scientific American*, Vol. 216 [February 1967], pp. 36-43). This procedure is so complex that some scientists now believe that at least four different genes are required to control just the first step. (Akira Taketo et al., "Initial Step of Excision Repair in *Escherichia coli*," *Journal of Molecular Biology*, Vol. 70, No. 1 [September 14, 1972], pp. 1-14).

[15] James D. Watson, *The Double Helix* (New York: Atheneum Press, 1968), p. 210.

[16] Handler, ed., *Biology and the Future of Man*, pp. 34, 38.

[17] Calculated from the following estimate: "The average probability of an error in the insertion of a new nucleotide under optimal conditions may be as low as 10^{-8} to 10^{-9}." (James Watson, *The Molecular Biology of the Gene*, 2nd ed., [Menlo Park, Calif.: W. A. Benjamin, Inc., 1970], p. 297.)

look into this in chapter 12. He concludes that these "could scarcely have persisted for several hundred million years unless the code remained unchanged and identical in all the species involved."[18]

Many other biologists have commented on this astounding fact that the DNA code appears to be universal, the same language in every creature on earth, whether virus, elephant, or pine tree.[19]

In all earthly life, "the sequence of these nucleotides constitutes the set of instructions for the biochemical machinery of the cell."[20]

Before we go on to see how this intriguing language is translated through a very exact and beautiful process, it may be helpful to pause and reflect.

A Language Indicates an Intelligent Source

Let us consider this question: By all the rules of reason, could there be a code which carries a message without someone originating that code? It would seem self-evident that any such complex message system, which is seen to be wise and effective, requires not only an *intelligence* but a *person* back of it.

Who wrote the DNA code? Who is the author of this precise language? There is no evolutionary explanation that even begins to be an adequate answer. Professor Carl R. Woese put the situation frankly when he wrote, "We have to be content with a few naive conjectures to fill in the great gap of the code's evolution."[21]

The only logical thing to do is to listen to the voice of reason and to acknowledge that only God, the infinite Person, could author that amazing *living language!*

---

[18] Thomas H. Jukes, *Molecules and Evolution,* (New York: Columbia University Press, 1966), p. 73.

[19] Viruses could not operate successfully if it were otherwise. The code words in a virus give orders to the "host cell" which it has invaded. These coded instructions are carried out in the same way as if the *host* had given the same order with *its* DNA. (In passing, we might note that viruses may be one result of the curse brought upon the world by sin, as described in Genesis 3:17, 18. This was intimated briefly in an earlier chapter.)

[20] Handler, ed., *Biology and the Future of Man,* p. 32.

[21] Carl R. Woese, "The Biological Significance of the Genetic Code," *Progress in Molecular and Subcellular Biology,* ed. F. E. Hahn (New York: Springer-Verlag, 1969), p. 27.

9

The Remarkable Way Cells Translate DNA

...to duplicate that which only God could conceive.[1]
—Diane Rothstein

PERIODICALLY NEWSPAPERS REPORT in bold headlines and in a variety of wordings that scientists have succeeded in "synthesizing life" in laboratory experiments. What has usually happened, however, is that living cells have been taken apart, and then some of their components have been reassembled or combined with other chemicals. In all such experiments to date, a vital part of success has depended upon one or more complex parts that grew in actual living cells. (Even if the production of life from nonliving chemicals could be accomplished in the laboratory, it would be a product of intelligence, not chance.)

C. L. Strong has said (1970), "No one has created life in the laboratory. The possibility is vanishingly small that a viable organism can be compounded. Yet that slender chance continues to intrigue some experimenters. . . ."[2] It was of these experiments that Diane Rothstein wrote in the above quotation.

To bring our knowledge of the DNA system to the maximum needed before applying probability theory, this chapter will outline the fascinating process by which DNA translates information into action.

DNA Directs the Cell's Activities

John Kendrew uses this fitting comparison:

> Any living thing can be likened to a giant factory, a factory

1 Diane Rothstein, Letters, *Science Digest* (January, 1970), p. 9.
2 C. L. Strong, "The Amateur Scientist," *Scientific American* (January, 1970), p. 130.

> producing chemicals, producing energy and motion, indeed reproducing itself too (which most factories cannot do!) and if one thinks of the way in which assembly lines are organized in factories one realizes immediately that all this complex of operations could not be carried out unless they were in some way organized, separated into compartments, not higgledy-piggledy. In other words, there must be some kind of organization in the structure of an animal to enable it to carry out these processes in an orderly way.[3]

In that parallel, the DNA would be like the manuals and blueprints that prescribe in detail just how each operation is to be done, and in what order of timing.

The coded information in DNA, then, would obviously be absolutely essential. It would also be absolutely helpless unless it had the entire system of the manufacturing plant, including people or computers *to read and put into action* its instructions.

Transcribing From DNA to RNA Working Copies

We will follow Kendrew's analogy of an industrial plant. The DNA master copy of the production blueprints must be kept protected. What is required first of all is a way to make *working copies* of just the sections needed at the moment. These temporary copies can then be taken out into the rough-and-tumble of the production area, leaving the DNA original safely in the office. When no longer needed, the copies are destroyed.

The temporary copies of parts of the DNA are called *RNA*, or, more properly, *messenger-RNA*, usually written *mRNA*. RNA is quite similar to DNA. In fact, it is identical in structure to one-half of the DNA double helix, except in two respects.

The difference in name comes from a very slight difference in the sides of the chains. RNA is the abbreviation for *ribonucleic acid*. DNA is *deoxyribonucleic acid*. The small sugar molecules used in RNA are ribose sugar. Those in DNA are *deoxyribose*, with one less oxygen atom. (This slight difference is very important to life. It keeps the DNA from being dismantled by the enzyme "ribonuclease," which takes apart mRNA chains when their temporary job is completed.)

There is one other difference. The four RNA bases are the same as those used in DNA, except that in place of *thymine*, RNA always has *uracil*, which is quite similar. RNA's four bases

---

[3] John C. Kendrew, *The Thread of Life* (Cambridge, Mass.: Harvard University Press, 1966), p. 15.

are, therefore, adenine, cytosine, guanine, and uracil—A, C, G, and U.

The translation of DNA into proteins is done indirectly, via RNA. The reason, as we have indicated, is that DNA, the vital carrier of hereditary information from generation to generation, must be kept safe from damage at all times. This master copy of the instructions is therefore retained in the cell nucleus or otherwise protected. The wisdom of this is apparent.

The Transcription Process

When a section of DNA is to be *transcribed* into RNA, the DNA double helix divides at that location into two strands. Then, an RNA chain forms alongside one of those strands, in the same way that DNA replication takes place.

In the cell fluid are large numbers of the individual parts which can be used to form RNA chains. These are called *ribonucleotides* or RNA nucleotides. Each individual nucleotide will match one specific type of base in the divided DNA.

The same complementary base-pairing plan works here as when DNA duplicates itself, as described earlier. It must be remembered, however, that RNA uses uracil intsead of thymine. When RNA is forming alongside the DNA strand, the DNA adenine will pair with the RNA nucleotide uracil. Here are the pairing possibilities:

DNA Adenine	pairs with	RNA Uracil	(A - U)
DNA Cytosine	pairs with	RNA Guanine	(C - G)
DNA Guanine	pairs with	RNA Cytosine	(G - C)
DNA Thymine	pairs with	RNA Adenine	(T - A)

Since DNA is transcribed into RNA in order to accomplish work in the cell, the code designations are usually written in the mRNA form, rather than the DNA. The DNA version, in one regard, may be considered as the "negative" from which positive prints are made, meaning RNA copies. Code lists are therefore printed in the RNA form, as on page 144.

In chapter 8, it was seen that the DNA code apparently is read from only one side of the double helix. That side is the one which serves as the pattern strand when RNA is formed alongside it by base pairing.

As the RNA nucleotides line up opposite the matching DNA bases, they are connected together by a special enzyme. This enzyme is found in virtually all cells,[4] and is called *RNA polymerase.* It is responsible in large measure for the precision and fidelity of the copying process. There is evidence that this copying accuracy is so exact that it might correspond to a typist's making only one error in from 7 to 700 pages.[5] As to speed, *as many as 30 or 40 nucleotides per second* may be added to the forming RNA chain, in bacteria.

As the RNA copy is formed along the DNA pattern strand or *template,* it immediately separates progressively from the DNA. The two DNA strands then join up again, thus returning to their normal double helix condition.[6]

Before proceeding to what happens next with the RNA copy, two questions arise. When are copies made, and where do they begin on the DNA template?

Turned-Off Genes and Sophisticated Controls

Although much remains to be learned, it is now clear that an elaborate and precise control system governs the timing and location of RNA transcriptions.

That portion of DNA which encodes the sequence of one particular protein chain is called a *gene.* Genes must be switched off when not needed or there would be utter chaos from overproduction of items. While research is continually adding information, it is now clear that many genes are kept in the switched-off position by *repressor* molecules which are in turn coded for by *regulator* genes. The job of a repressor is to fasten to the DNA at an *operator* site, thereby preventing any copying

---

[4] James D. Watson, *Molecular Biology of the Gene,* 2nd ed. (Menlo Park, Calif.: W. A. Benjamin, Inc., 1970), p. 338.

[5] This is calculated from information by Carl R. Woese. He says it would seem that the bacterial cell, in order to function normally would require a low error frequency in transcription in the range of 10^{-6} and 10^{-4} per base pair, which means no more mistakes than 1 every 10,000 to a million letters of the code (10^{-6} is the same as $1/10^{6}$). (Carl R. Woese, "The Biological Significance of the Genetic Code," in *Progress in Molecular and Subcellular Biology,* ed. F. E. Hahn [New York: Springer-Verlag, 1969], p. 24.)

RNA polymerase (or *transcriptase*) works only if there is a DNA pattern strand present. It is therefore often called "DNA-dependent RNA polymerase." Multiple types of RNA polymerase have been discovered.

[6] RNA transcription is quite rapid, as just noted (although Watson says that DNA *replication* may be 100 times faster—*Molecular Biology of the Gene,* p. 528). In chapter 6, it was noted that many scientists think that at the time of the assumed natural origin of life, temperature would have been below freezing. Without enzymes, under those primitive conditions, it can be calculated that it might take a billion years *just to transcribe* the DNA of the smallest known cell into one mRNA copy. All that time, it would be subject to breakage and dismantling. Even if preserved, it would be helpless without all the machinery of protein synthesis about to be described.

of that gene into the form of RNA. This complex system involves two or more methods of operation. One technique employs molecules known as *inducers,* of which there are many kinds.

An inducer molecule will combine by weak bonds with a specific repressor, and this keeps the repressor from fastening to the gene. As a result, the repressor cannot turn off the gene, and so RNA polymerase begins transcribing that gene, by starting at a place on the DNA called the *promoter.* Here is one example. Suppose lactose sugar starts arriving outside of the cell of an *Escherichia coli* bacterium. An inducer will then fasten to the repressor that controls the genes which produce enzymes for processing lactose. As a result, the genes are transcribed into RNA, and proteins are formed for bringing lactose into the cell and processing it as food for the cell. It is much more complicated than this, but in this intricate way, the transcription begins at the proper place at the start of a gene and continues for the length of one or more genes.[7]

An alternative system works in this way: When there is on hand enough of a specific type of molecule used by the cell, one of those molecules will combine with a repressor, thereby causing it to fasten to the DNA at the operator site and keep the gene turned off because its product is not needed due to the supply already on hand. In this case, the molecule which fastened to the repressor is a sample of the type that is in plentiful supply or a related metabolite, and this molecule is termed a *corepressor.*

There is also a remarkable feedback system which exists in metabolic chains, preventing overproduction without involving the repressor system at the gene level. This works by what is called *allosteric inhibition* of enzymes in the chain. An end-product molecule from that chain may react with an enzyme at the start or at a key juncture of the chain, causing the enzyme to change its shape. As a result, it is no longer able to function in its usual capacity as an enzyme catalyst to keep the chain going.[8]

---

7 Related genes which are grouped together along the DNA chain are called an *operon.* One operon may control the making of several enzymes needed to complete one particular process, such as the assembling of a specific amino acid from other chemicals in the cell. This may require more than half a dozen genes. The RNA transcription may run for an entire operon, so that all these needed enzymes are made about the same time.

8 Existence of sophisticated controls for the cell's multiple complex production systems is unthinkable without intelligent design to account for it. The lack of

FIGURE 12

The Genetic Code in Alphabetical Order[9]

The 64 Codons and Their Amino Acid Assignments

AAA	Lysine	CAA	Glutamine	GAA	Glutamic acid	UAA	End chain
AAC	Asparagine	CAC	Histidine	GAC	Aspartic acid	UAC	Tyrosine
AAG	Lysine	CAG	Glutamine	GAG	Glutamic acid	UAG	End chain
AAU	Asparagine	CAU	Histidine	GAU	Aspartic acid	UAU	Tyrosine
ACA	Threonine	CCA	Proline	GCA	Alanine	UCA	Serine
ACC	Threonine	CCC	Proline	GCC	Alanine	UCC	Serine
ACG	Threonine	CCG	Proline	GCG	Alanine	UCG	Serine
ACU	Threonine	CCU	Proline	GCU	Alanine	UCU	Serine
AGA	Arginine	CGA	Arginine	GGA	Glycine	UGA	End chain
AGC	Serine	CGC	Arginine	GGC	Glycine	UGC	Cysteine
AGG	Arginine	CGG	Arginine	GGG	Glycine	UGG	Tryptophan
AGU	Serine	CGU	Arginine	GGU	Glycine	UGU	Cysteine
AUA	Isoleucine	CUA	Leucine	GUA	Valine	UUA	Leucine
AUC	Isoleucine	CUC	Leucine	GUC	Valine	UUC	Phenylalanine
AUG	Methionine	CUG	Leucine	GUG	Valine	UUG	Leucine
AUU	Isoleucine	CUU	Leucine	GUU	Valine	UUU	Phenylalanine

Amino Acids in Alphabetical Order With Their Code Assignments

Alanine	GCA, GCC, GCG, GCU
Arginine	AGA, AGG, CGA, CGC, CGG, CGU
Asparagine	AAC, AAU
Aspartic acid	GAC, GAU
Cysteine	UGC, UGU
Glutamic acid	GAA, GAG
Glutamine	CAA, CAG
Glycine	GGA, GGC, GGG, GGU
Histidine	CAC, CAU
Isoleucine	AUA, AUC, AUU
Leucine	CUA, CUC, CUG, CUU, UUA, UUG
Lysine	AAA, AAG
Methionine	AUG
Phenylalanine	UUC, UUU
Proline	CCA, CCC, CCG, CCU
Serine	AGC, AGU, UCA, UCC, UCG, UCU
Threonine	ACA, ACC, ACG, ACU
Tryptophan	UGG
Tyrosine	UAC, UAU
Valine	GUA, GUC, GUG, GUU
End chain	UAA, UAG, UGA

---

controls leads to chaos in any organized human endeavor and in the organized processes of organisms. Consider this comment on the importance of controls, by one of the discoverers of the DNA structure, who has not yet accepted the implications as to design involved in the DNA molecule which so fascinated him and us all: "Thus, the only useful distinction is that the cancer cell is less subject to the normal control devices which tell a cell not to divide." (Watson, *The Molecular Biology of the Gene*, p. 591.) For more complete details of the corepressor system described above, see this same reference, pp. 438-442. Dr. Watson also discusses the evidence for there being timing sequences between some genes, (p. 528).

[9] Adapted from data by Francis H. C. Crick, "The Genetic. Code: III," *Scientific American,* Vol. 215 (October, 1966), p. 57.

"Ribosomes" Which Process the RNA Copy

When the mRNA copy of a gene or of an operon is made, the work has only begun, just as when the office staff of an industrial plant makes copies of the blueprints at the request of a shop foreman. The instructions must then be read and put into action at the cell's assembly lines. The correct amino acids must be brought in proper order and fastened together to form the needed protein chain.

We may picture the next key figure as a production foreman with a complex assembly machine. He arranges for various workers to read the copy of the instructions and to bring the items in proper order so the foreman can link them together, using the machinery which he has on hand for that purpose.

In the cell, this key figure is known as a *ribosome* (pronounced rye-bo-sohm). It fulfills the job just described—of the foreman with the assembly machinery. A ribosome is a very small object made of proteins and RNA. It looks somewhat like a volleyball pressed against a basketball. As to purpose,

> This particle coordinates the translation of the genetic information in the sequence of the nucleotide bases in the messenger RNA (transcribed from the DNA molecule, the gene) to the sequence of amino acids in each protein manufactured in the cell.[10]

As the mRNA copy is made alongside the DNA, one or several ribosomes are positioned at the start of it. Then as each ribosome traverses the length of the mRNA, the RNA triplets or codons are translated so that they indicate which amino acids are to be assembled and attached in the same order as the coded sequence. This amazing and efficient operation occurs at each ribosome assembly machine.

If a particular codon happens to be GGC, for example, a glycine molecule (smallest of the amino acid types) would be brought to the ribosome. It is as if the ribosome foreman admits into the assembly area a worker who handles glycine stock and who is carrying one glycine molecule, because the instructions in the code specify that the next amino acid to be attached should be glycine.[11]

---

[10] Masayasu Nomura, "Ribosomes," *Scientific American*, October, 1969, p. 28.

[11] As we will see, the process is much more complicated. There are important intermediates now to be described. Some oversimplification may serve to give the general idea, with details to be filled in later.

Ribosomes consist of about 60 different kinds of proteins combined with a spe-

Transfer RNA, Delivery Vehicle for Amino Acids

While the mRNA is being processed by the ribosome in order to assemble amino acids into a protein, how will these amino acids actually be brought into the proper order? There does not seem to be any innate attraction or affinity between an amino acid and the RNA letters which code for it.

In the early research after the Watson-Crick breakthrough, it became apparent that there must be intermediates to bring the amino acids to the ribosome in proper order. Two such vital go-betweens were finally located. One serves as a transport molecule. It is called *transfer-RNA,* which is a different form of RNA from that which has been described. Transfer-RNA, written *tRNA,* is a comparatively short chain of RNA containing some seventy-five or eighty ribonucleotides. The RNA strand doubles back on itself, and base-pairs with its own chain in some places. The overall shape of the tRNA molecule in some ways resembles a key or a cloverleaf. If tRNA is to do its job properly, the shape must be very precise, and this seems to depend in part upon the right temperature and the correct concentration of certain ions (e.g., magnesium and sodium) in the cell fluid.

Transfer-RNA is perfectly fitted for its mission. First of all, each tRNA type attaches to only one variety of the twenty amino acids. Secondly, the particular tRNA delivers that amino acid in the proper sequence for the forming protein. This is possible because the tRNA molecule has at one end a special RNA triplet of code letters which match the mRNA codon which specifies that particular amino acid. When these complementary codons come together by base-pairing, the amino acid being transported by that tRNA is thus in position to be linked to the growing protein chain in the correct order. All this takes place at the ribosome, which is like a mobile assembly machine as it moves along the mRNA strand (or as the mRNA tape passes through the ribosomes).

---

cial form of RNA–*ribosomal,* or *rRNA.* There is more RNA than protein by weight in a ribosome ordinarily. The ribosome has two sections (designated the 50-S and 30-S particles) which can exist separately but which come together to read the mRNA message. According to Watson, there may be up to 15,000 ribosomes in a single bacterium. In contrast, at a given time, there are only about 1,000 mRNA molecules in a single cell of some bacteria, because the mRNA is short-lived, being broken down into its parts to be used again in forming new mRNA messages. (Watson, *Molecular Biology,* pp. 368, 369, 395, 452, 455.) The ribosomal subunits are called 50S and 30S in bacteria, for example; whereas the main ribosomes of higher cells contain 60S and 40S sections.

There must be enough tRNA species to match each of the twenty types of amino acids. Further, there ought to be enough to read each of the sixty-one codons which signify amino acid types. Recent research is filling in the gaps in this direction. In fact, there are indications that there may be more than enough to equal the number of codons.[12] There is one instance known where two different kinds of tRNA are used for the same codon, but for a special reason. One of these two serves only to *initiate* a protein chain—in bacteria, where it has been found.[13] A tRNA may read multiple codons (wobble theory).

The Enzyme "Interpreter"

The second intermediate which is involved in bringing amino acids for proper assembly is perhaps even more vital. There seems to be no natural attraction between an amino acid and its own transfer-RNA, so something must bring them together. It is as if there were two languages, and neither party understands the other except when there is an interpreter to bridge the gap. This essential task is done by a special group of enzymes which match the different tRNA's and amino acids. One part of each such enzyme fits just its own particular kind of amino acid and no other. Another part of the enzyme interacts with its own type of tRNA. In plain language, it can be pictured as follows: the enzyme grasps its amino acid and its tRNA and fastens them together.[14]

Summarizing the Translation Process

Connecting all the parts of the protein-forming complex into an abbreviated simple description, we begin with DNA which is the master original containing the instructions for cell activities. When there is need, parts of the DNA instructions are copied and sent out into the cell in the form of messenger-RNA.

---

[12] Marshall Nirenberg, personal telephone conversation, October, 1971.

[13] The amino acid, methionine, is coded by the RNA letters AUG. Two different tRNA forms will recognize this codon. One of these responds only when the AUG occurs at or near the start of the mRNA strand. This tRNA places a modified ("formylated") form of methionine in the starting position for protein synthesis. Such a form is adapted for this initial site. When AUG occurs internally, however, it is read by the other (standard) form of tRNA, and places a regular unmodified methionine in the chain. (The formylated tRNA for methionine will also read GUG at the start of mRNA. When that codon occurs internally, it is read by the regular tRNA for the amino acid valine.) (Brian F. C. Clark and Kjeld A. Marcker, "How Proteins Start," *Scientific American* [January, 1968].)

[14] This, too, is oversimplification. The amino acid must first be put in an activated state by reaction with ATP, the universal power molecule of all known cells. This activation is catalyzed by the same enzyme just described.

This mRNA tape then passes through one or more ribosomes which "read" the coded instructions with the aid of transfer-RNA molecules which bring the particular amino acids called

FIGURE 13

Translation, or Protein Synthesis

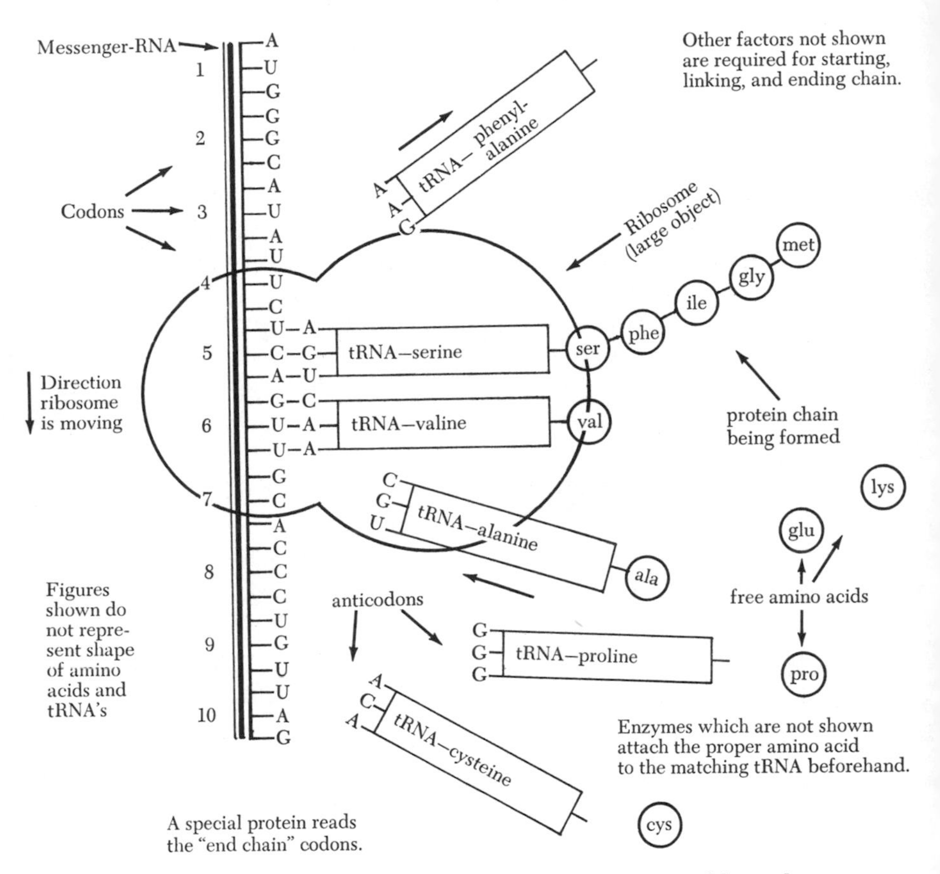

Messenger-RNA being translated into protein as it is traversed by a ribosome

As each codon or triplet of letters is read, a transfer-RNA molecule approaches which has an anticodon that will base-pair with those letters. This tRNA carries its matching amino acid which has been attached to it by its interpreter enzyme. As the tRNA is processed by the ribosome, the amino acid is joined onto the forming protein chain in the order called for by the mRNA sequence of code letters, which in turn was transcribed shortly before from the DNA master copy. This complex process takes place with fantastic speed and precision, and is remarkably similar in all living things known, from amebas to human beings. Recent evidence indicates that both transcription and replication may often be associated with cell membranes, including the *endoplasmic reticulum.*

for in the code. These tRNA's were charged beforehand with specific amino acids by the aid of matching interpreter enzymes.

As the ribosome continues along the mRNA tape, the amino acids are linked into a protein chain in the sequence called for by the RNA triplets. The resulting protein is then released for its specific duty in the cell, having been made as ordered originally by the codon sequence in the master DNA blueprint.

The protein that is thus formed may be an enzyme to perform tasks like the job done by the special enzymes just described, to join together two specific types of molecules. It may, instead, be a structural protein, or perhaps a hormone, or a specialized protein like hemoglobin. DNA carries out practically all of its work of running the cell by ordering the manufacture of different kinds of proteins and different kinds of RNA molecules. These, in turn, are so cleverly formed that they automatically arrange themselves in proper shape and position, and then carry out their task in the ongoing processes of cell life. Around 5,000 different kinds of molecules may exist in a single cell, many of them proteins.

New Discoveries Reveal Even More Complex Precision

To anyone with an interest in biology, the protein synthesizing mechanism which has been described is fascinatingly intriguing. One can hardly wait for further experiments that may explain gaps in present knowledge. As research continues, the plan of cell operation becomes more amazing than ever.

For one example, in 1969 biochemists at the Weizmann Institute of Science in Israel reported that multiple special enzymes are required to bind the messenger-RNA to the ribosome before protein synthesis can begin. They called attention to "the complexity of this scheme . . . the mechanism which ensures correct protein chain initiation, and, thereby, accurate translation of the genetic code."[15]

Further, two other researchers gave evidence that one or more special proteins are also involved in protein *termination.*[16]

Furthermore, many other special factors are involved during the main process of protein synthesis. These include an enzyme

---

[15] M. Revel, M. Herzberg, and H. Greenshpan, "Initiator Protein Dependent Binding of Messenger-RNA to the Ribosome," *Cold Spring Harbor Symposia on Quantitative Biology,* Vol. XXXIV (1969), pp. 261 ff.

[16] M. R. Capecchi and H. A. Klein, "Characterization of Three Proteins Involved in Polypeptide Chain Termination," *Cold Spring Harbor Symposia on Quantitative Biology,* Vol. XXXIV (1969), p. 469.

for binding the tRNA to the ribosome at its first or "A" position, and another "transfer factor" to move this tRNA to the second or "P" position. Between these two events, the vital joining of the forming chain onto the new amino acid by the formation of the peptide bond is brought about at the "A" position by a special enzyme which apparently exists in only one copy per ribosome and is part of the larger (50-S) ribosome particle. Magnesium, GTP (similar to ATP), and several other agents are found to be involved also in protein formation. Much of the process remains to be clarified, but the above gives some idea of the picture as it seems to date.

Highly Organized Efficiency in an Intricate System

It becomes increasingly clear what a highly integrated, complex, effective system is involved in living things. This is true in the simplest known living cell, as well as in cells of the human body. In scientific literature one encounters the highest praise of this marvelous system by some of the scientists who know it best.

Atomic physicist George Gamow was involved in attempts to solve the DNA code after the first Watson-Crick breakthrough. He even obtained the help of two cryptologists who were government experts at solving secret codes. Gamow waxed eloquent over what he called in popular terminology "gene molecules":

> Indeed, considering on the one hand the remarkable permanence of genes, which carry almost without any deviation the properties of a given species through thousands of generations, and, on the other hand the comparatively small number of individual atoms that form one gene, one cannot consider it otherwise than as a well-planned structure in which each atom or atomic group sits in its predetermined place.[17]

It is tragic that such a brilliant man as George Gamow could never let himself admit that there must have been a *Planner* behind the "well-planned structure."

In connection with Gamow's admiration of the remarkable stability of the coded message making possible accurate heredity, it is interesting to note that Professor Thomas Jukes, an ardent evolutionist, stated: "The purpose of life is the perpetuation

---

[17] George Gamow, *One, Two, Three . . . Infinity* (New York: Viking Press, 1966), p. 264.

of a base sequence."[18] At the conclusion of his book, *Molecules and Evolution,* he waxed religious in the manner of a dedicated materialist. Jukes seems to make DNA his object of worship, expressing the following poetic sentiment in prose form. After crediting evolution (by random changes and natural selection) for the development of life to the present stage, he said:

> MAN: Five hundred million years ago, a billion years ago, the long molecules were joined together in the pools of tepid water.
>
> Phosphate, sugar; phosphate, sugar, phosphate; A, C, T, and G; C, A, G, and T. . . .
>
> (Five hundred million years, a billion years, the long rods, immortally never-changing, mortally ever-changing, reached the day, when, through what they had wrought, they saw themselves as in a mirror.)[19]

Source of the System

How did this amazing system come to be? The only answers which an evolutionist has are vague and unsatisfying when examined closely. Crick did the best he could with the problem, considering that he clearly did not want to acknowledge any supernatural element being involved. Here is his explanation:

> It is the next steps that seem difficult, and that may not be easy to study. At the moment when natural selection started, was there only nucleic acid and no protein? Or, on the other hand, was there only protein and no nucleic acid? The difficulty of these alternatives is that if we had protein alone it is not easy to think of a simple replication process, whereas if we had nucleic acid alone (which would make the replication easy) it is difficult to see how nucleic acid could provide the necessary catalytic activity. A third possibility, which to my mind is rather promising, is that when natural selection began both nucleic acid and protein existed, and that the synthesis of protein was crudely coupled to nucleic acid in the same sort of way as it is today. At first sight it seems highly unlikely that this complicated mechanism could have arisen by chance, but it is really quite possible that some primitive version of it started in that way and although not perfect was sufficiently accurate to enable the system to get going.
>
> The real difficulty about the origin of life is that the experimental evidence showing what happened has long ago

---

[18] Thomas H. Jukes, *Molecules and Evolution* (New York: Columbia University Press, 1966), p. 4.

[19] Ibid., pp. 264, 266.

> disappeared. All we are left with is a certain amount of frozen history in the organisms as we see them today. This is going to make it scientifically very difficult, because it is inevitable that there will be more theories than there are facts to disprove them.[20]

A little careful rereading of that quotation and thoughtful consideration of the subject will reveal that his statement that it is "really quite possible" is merely whistling in the dark. Dr. Crick has more recently attempted at greater length to come up with an evolutionary plan for the origin of the code and protein synthesis.[21] After diligent effort, he leaves the reader with no plausible scheme.

Oparin's books take into account the need for a detailed model. The entire hope of success in his plan, however, rests upon natural selection. This was to occur *before* there was any process for making accurate copies of components. Only a vague and inexact sort of chance dividing is mentioned at that stage. As we have seen, natural selection is impossible without accurate duplication of all necessary components.

Biologist Gary E. Parker uses the following apt analogy:

> None of the parts of an airplane can fly by itself. Only the whole airplane can fly. An airplane, it seems, is a bunch of non-flying parts *organized* to fly. . . .
>
> None of the molecular parts of a living cell can live by itself. Only the whole cell can live. A living cell, it seems, is a bunch of non-living molecules *organized* to live.
>
> Organization, not substance, seems to make the difference between life and non-life.[22]

Evolution Has No Solution for the Origin of Life

Professor Parker explains the reason why life could not have started spontaneously, whether one considers proteins first or DNA first, or both.

> There's one thing protein molecules can't do: reproduce. Reproduction is the function of DNA. DNA can reproduce itself . . . and DNA can reproduce proteins. . . .
>
> DNA, however, can neither reproduce itself accurately nor make protein without a host of helpers, including several

---

[20] Francis H. C. Crick, *Of Molecules and Men* (Seattle: University of Washington Press, 1966), pp. 69, 70.

[21] Francis H. C. Crick, "The Origin of the Genetic Code," *Journal of Molecular Biology*, vol. 38 (1968), pp. 367-379.

[22] Gary E. Parker, "Origin of Life on Earth," *Bible-Science Newsletter*, Vol. VIII, No. 12 (December 15, 1970), p. 4.

> already existing protein molecules. So, life really depends upon the relationship between DNA and protein—DNA (or related nucleic acid) for reproduction and protein for structure and function. This DNA-protein relationship is basic to life in viruses and all known life forms.[23]

Another impossible dilemma in trying to account for life beginning naturally is the one described in detail on page 106 in footnote 17. The reader may wish to refer again to that description, because no real solution exists to the problem. To review it quite briefly, the first task would be to form amino acids. This requires a different, primitive atmosphere with no oxygen, and with ultraviolet rays reaching earth's surface. Ultraviolet rays, however, are deadly to proteins and also to DNA (and RNA). Even if somehow life could start and there eventually were algae or plants to produce oxygen (and ozone, formed from oxygen), it might require millions of years to get the ozone shield formed. It now exists in the upper atmosphere miles above the earth and is a vital safeguard for living things on earth's surface.

Furthermore, algae tend to live at or near the surface of the water, and would be in the lethal path of those rays. The photosynthetic bacteria which sometimes live at a safe depth in the water of narrow lakes have a simpler form of photosynthesis *which does not produce oxygen,* and hence would not help in forming an ozone shield. Even these bacteria would be subject twice a year to water circulation when such lakes passed through the temperature at which water is most dense: 4° C.

Yet another possible problem, described on page 107, footnote 19, is that some scientists now believe the temperature at that period was below freezing, below the temperature at which living cells can grow at all (although they might be able merely to survive at that temperature).

In concluding this chapter, it can be noted that there is no reason to believe, from the standpoint of any actual evidence or logic, that any living thing has ever existed that was less complex or less organized than the simplest living cell known today.

In the next chapter, when we apply the laws of chance to the golden molecule of DNA, we will make it as easy as possible for chance to succeed. Instead of using the smallest known cell,

---

[23] Gary E. Parker, "Origin of Life on Earth," p. 4.

we will again use the smaller theoretical "minimal living system" resulting from Morowitz' research for the National Aeronautics and Space Administration.

When we remember that chance strains itself in making over five trillion attempts in order to spell "evolution" once, it seems almost ludicrous even to proceed in asking whether such amazing items as the DNA code could have started by chance. The odds against a gene sequence will be too astounding to comprehend.

10

Could Chance Arrange the Code for One Gene?

> *At the present time, there is no satisfactory hypothesis to explain the evolution of the protein-synthesizing mechanism.*[1]
>
> —from *Biology and the Future of Man* (1970)

The DNA System Excites Admiration

The main job done by DNA is to give the instructions for synthesizing proteins. In the preceding chapter, we saw that the mechanism by which these instructions are carried out is in some ways even more astounding than the code itself.

Almost two hundred of America's best biologists cooperated in writing the outstanding volume quoted at top of this page. Their purpose was to give a complete account of the status of knowledge in the entire field up to the time of writing, and to point out areas where more research was most needed.

The wonderment and admiration of scientists for the DNA system is frequently expressed in that book. "Although we can see the basic design in the process, a chemical understanding of certain remarkable features has thus far eluded us."[2] They praise "the high fidelity we know exists in the overall process."[3]

Considering the system, it is natural to agree with a sentiment expressed by missile expert Wernher von Braun. He said he found it as difficult "to understand a scientist who does

---

[1] Philip Handler, ed., *Biology and the Future of Man*, (New York: Oxford University Press, 1970), p. 187.
[2] Ibid., p. 45.
[3] Ibid., p. 48.

not accept the presence of a superior rationality behind the existence of the universe as it is to comprehend a theologian who would deny the advances of science."[4]

It is strangely true that a number of scientists and many other people do try to explain everything without reference to any intellect back of what exists. Without a Designer, however, the materialist is left with only one source, namely chance, to do it all.

In spite of desperate attempts by some to introduce natural selection long before actual life existed, it has become quite evident that such a control was utterly impossible without an accurate duplication system for all the essential parts.

The Only Duplication System

There has been no indication found of any system for such duplication other than the precise DNA-mRNA-ribosome-enzymes-tRNA-twenty amino acid plan described in the preceding chapter. For this reason, Morowitz postulates it as part of the minimal theoretical living entity.[5] Could such a system come about by random association of molecules?

The all-important central component would have to be DNA (or possibly RNA) with a coded message. The message would give instructions for making the necessary parts for the living system, including the enzymes that govern the duplication of the code molecule itself.[6]

---

[4] Wernher von Braun, quoted in Associated Press dispatch in *The Cleveland Plain Dealer* of July 19, 1969, p. 5.

[5] Harold J. Morowitz, "Biological Self-Replicating Systems," *Progress in Theoretical Biology*, ed. Fred M. Snell (New York: Academic Press, 1967), Vol. 1, pp. 35 ff.

[6] The speed of replication of DNA is inconceivably fast, ranging apparently to 750 or 1,000 nucleotides *per second* added to each strand for each growing point in some cases. The duplication process involves a growing point complex consisting of proteins and perhaps RNA. Several reports indicate the growing point may be closely associated with the cell membrane. Investigation proceeds at a furious pace, and anything we record is therefore subject to revision as more knowledge of the process is revealed by research.

Robert E. Bird and co-workers report that bacterial replication generally involves a bidirectional fork, with movement of the fork in opposite directions simultaneously at the same velocity. ("Origin and Sequence of Chromosome Replication in *Escherichia coli*," *Journal of Molecular Biology*, Vol. 70, 1972, pp. 549, 563.) Roger Y. Stanier, et al., describe multiple forks, apparently occurring when two daughter DNA double-helix molecules begin replicating before the original forks have completed their cycle—making possible a cell division time of twenty minutes. (*The Microbial World*, 3rd ed. [Englewood Cliffs, N.J.: Prentice-Hall, Inc., 1970], pp. 294 ff., 374 ff.). The circular DNA molecule in the bacterium *Escherichia coli* has perhaps five million nucleotide pairs. Its usual cell division time under good conditions is forty minutes without multiple forks. If this involves bidirectional movement of the fork, the number of nucleotides added

In addition to the coded message, there would have to exist *at the start* the minimum machinery to produce what the code specified. One or more copies of each component of the system would have to exist, or else the code message would be absolutely powerless to get life moving. Among those items required at the beginning would be ribosomes, amino acids, RNA polymerase, ATP for energy, and all the other enzymes and vital factors recently discovered that are necessary for any protein production whatever.

Let's now apply the laws of chance to *just one facet* of the operation—the probability that code letters might ever become arranged in any usable order fortuitously (if, of course, code letters were already existing). In other words, could chance conceivably account for a correct sequence for just one set of genes for minimal life, or even for a single gene? Any arrangement at the start would have been random, if creative design is ruled out. First, we need to understand exactly what a gene is.

A Gene Is a "Paragraph" of the DNA Message

We have seen that DNA carries the instructions of heredity in the form of bases or letters strung along the middle of a double spiral molecule. This message can be thought of as divided into sections or paragraphs which are called genes. Usually, a single gene will code for a single protein chain. The average gene in the smallest theoretical living thing would have over 1,200 letters or nucleotide pairs.[7]

A gene may contain from a few hundred to a few thousand base pairs or nucleotide pairs. The smallest known cell has about 600 genes.[8] A set of human chromosomes, containing the

---

per strand per fork movement would be just over 1,000, for each of the two forks moving apart from each other. *E. coli* can replicate in twenty minutes, but at this speed, multiple forks may be involved.

John Cairns reported a replication speed requiring 15,000 turns per minute in unwinding the double helix. ("The Bacterial Chromosome," *Scientific American*, Vol. 214, [January 1966], p. 42.) For unwinding, it is now thought that enzymes make nicks in one side of the helix. As the fork moves along, one strand is polymerized continuously in the same direction as fork movement. The other strand is apparently formed in the opposite direction in short fragments, later to be joined into a complete circular daughter molecule. Many mysteries remain in this amazing process. (This, or some such process, is necessary because nucleotides join only onto the 3′ end of a new forming strand. In the DNA double helix, the strands are polarized oppositely to each other, with the 5′ end of one strand across from the 3′ end of the other.)

[7] Morowitz, personal communication, November, 1970.

[8] Morowitz, personal communication, November, 1970.

cell's DNA, consists of over two million genes.[9] If a chain could link up, what is the probability that the code letters might by chance be in some order which would be a usable gene, usable somewhere—anywhere—in some potentially living thing?

Using All the Atoms in the Universe

From the calculations in previous chapters, it could be guessed that to obtain a gene would be at least as difficult as to obtain a protein molecule. Instead of using all the atoms on earth, therefore, this time let us assume that *all the atoms of the entire cosmos* have been made into sets of nucleotides, and that these are activated, ready for linkup. (Nucleotides are made of atoms of carbon, nitrogen, hydrogen, oxygen, and phosphorus.)

It will be presumed that each chain will polymerize or link up at the swiftest speed of atomic processes (of which the limit is said to be around 10^{16} per second as noted earlier).[10] With each nucleotide being added at such a speed, the number of complete chains (genes) per second is 8.3×10^{12} in any one set. In a year, a set of nucleotides would produce 2.6×10^{20} genes, which we will round off to 10^{21}.

Chance is trying for the first gene in the universe, so there is no pattern strand of DNA or RNA existing. The four different nucleotides will occur only in random order in the chain. If just one side of the ladder or double helix is obtained, it will be considered sufficient, in the thought that if one is obtained, the other side might form by base pairing.

From standard estimates of the cosmic abundance of the elements,[11] it can be found that phosphorus is the limiting element in forming activated nucleotides. There are estimated to be 1.5×10^{72} phosphorus atoms in the universe.[12] Three atoms of phosphorus are needed for each activated nucleotide. This

---

[9] Considering the human genome (DNA per cell) as three billion nucleotide pairs averaging 1,200 per gene.

[10] Harold J. Morowitz, *Energy Flow in Biology* (New York: Academic Press, 1968), pp. 12 ff.

[11] Philip Handler, ed., *Biology and the Future of Man*, p. 168.

[12] This figure is based on a ratio of 115/10,000 phosphorus atoms to silicon atoms (ibid.), and on the radius and mean density used earlier on page 118.

Dr. George Preston, of the California Institute of Technology's Hale Observatories, has pointed out that one should not now put undue confidence in tables of cosmic abundance. There are many uncertainties and variables. The universe is not static in this regard. Elements are constantly being formed from other elements in the interior of stars. These elements may then be scattered by supernova explosions. A small percentage of certain classes of stars now indicate unexpected proportions of some elements on their surfaces, including phosphorus. Interior

will make 10^{68} sets, so that one copy of each of the four kinds of nucleotides is present at each point of the 1,200-unit chain being formed.

If each set is producing 10^{21} sequences per year, that will be a total of 10^{89} different chains annually, using all of the appropriate atoms of the universe. As in the case of proteins, it is assumed that each chain will be dismantled immediately and another one built until there is a usable gene. This is done at the prodigious speed of eight trillion chains per second.[13]

The Number of Possible Orders in a Gene

There are three different ways to determine the number of possible sequences in a DNA chain. The general formula, it may be recalled, is: the number of kinds to the power of the number of units in the chain. If each order is equally likely, the probability of a particular sequence will then be one in the total of possible orders.

With four kinds of nucleotides, and a chain 1,200 long, the total of possible arrangements would be 4^{1200}, which is approximately 10^{722}.

The letters of a gene, however, are read in triplet codons (comprising sixty-four kinds of triplets) of which there are 400 in this size chain. If computed in this way, there would be a total of 64^{400} possible orders, and this turns out to be the same as when figured by individual letters, namely 10^{722}.

The reader may recall, however, that many of the twenty amino acids are coded by more than one triplet. The duplicate codons are thought by some to be "a historical accident." Others believe they may be "perhaps a regulatory factor in some cases,"[14] since nature is "seldom redundant" for very long.[15] As mentioned in the preceding chapter, evidence is accumulating that these seeming duplicates may serve the vital purpose of *regulating*[16]

---

composition is uncertain. (George Preston, California Institute of Technology, personal telephone conversation, December, 1971.)

For our purpose, however, the figure used above is reliable enough. Chance will fail this test by such a margin that it would not matter if the number of phosphorus atoms had to be changed, regardless of extent.

[13] Eight trillion per second *in each set!* That is 10^{81} *per second* for all the sets.

[14] Marshall W. Nirenberg, National Institutes of Health, personal telephone conversation, October, 1971.

[15] Philip C. Hanawalt, Stanford University, personal telephone conversation, November, 1971.

[16] Joseph Ilan, "The Role of tRNA in Translational Control of Specific mRNA During Insect Metamorphosis," *Symposia on Quantitative Biology* (Long Island, N.Y.: Cold Spring Harbor Laboratory, 1970), pp. 787-791.

the synthesis of proteins. If that turns out to be true, then there would be no useless duplicates among the 64 codons,[17] and the total real sequences would be the 10^{722} figure.

Since research is not yet final on that point, however, let's again give chance the benefit of the doubt and figure it as if all the duplicates were useless extras.

There are only twenty-one different possible primary outcomes for each codon position. Those potential outcomes which are signalled by codons are the twenty amino acids plus "end of chain." We will therefore figure on the basis of twenty-one kinds, for a chain 400 amino acids long. The figure 21^{400} is approximately 10^{528}. If we allow one substitution per chain[18] (without limiting it to the active site—another boost for chance), then the equivalent total of different sequences is 10^{524}

Chances of One Gene in the Entire Universe

Using again the formula obtained from the alphabet analogy, it can be assumed that $1/10^{240}$ is the proportion of orders that might be usable somewhere. Since 10^{240} is less than 10^{524}, the probability of getting a usable gene on any one try is $1/10^{240}$ for the first gene. Allowing for one substitution has the effect of reducing the figure to $1/10^{236}$.

The total orders produced in a year by all the nucleotide sets from the entire cosmos was 10^{89}, as seen on page 159. The probability of getting a usable gene in a year is therefore $10^{89}/10^{236}$, which is $1/10^{147}$. *With all the concessions given, one could expect a usable gene in 10^{147} years, from the tremendously rapid efforts of all the nucleotide sets of all the atoms of the universe.*

Professor Warren Weaver in his book on probability states the rule we are using in these words: "If two events are independent, the probability that they both will occur is the product of their respective probabilities."[19] This is that same central principle, the multiplication rule. By "independent" is meant

[17] C. Thomas Caskey, Arthur Beaudet, and Marshall W. Nirenberg, "RNA Codons and Protein Synthesis," *Journal of Molecular Biology*, Vol. 37 (1968), pp. 99-118.

[18] For discussion of substitution limits, see footnote 9 in chapter 6, p. 100. Substituting one amino acid for another is thought to be usually lethal or deleterious. Since there are evidently some substitutions that can at least be tolerated if limited to about one substitution per chain on the average, not in the active site, we are again figuring it with chance getting the advantage.

[19] Warren Weaver, *Lady Luck, Theory of Probability* (Garden City, New York: Doubleday, 1963), p. 111.

that they do not interfere with each other. In nucleotide linkups, apparently there is equal probability and no interference.

In this model experiment, the entire chain is formed by the random action at each position in sequence independently. The rule therefore is to multiply the probabilities of all the positions. In this way, one obtains the "product of their respective probabilities." This is the method we have used.

How Long Is 10^{147} Years?

Dr. Weaver told this interesting story which may be used for comparison with our time of "once in 10^{147} years":

> In the lore of India there is a tale about a stone, a cubic mile in size, a million times harder than a diamond. Every million years a holy man visits the stone to give it the lightest possible touch.... Removing one [atom] every 10^6 years then indicates that 10^{51} years would perhaps be required.[20]

He is referring to the time needed to wear the stone completely away by this feather touch which removes one atom every million years. Now it is quite evident that 10^{51} years, though *exceedingly* long, is nothing compared to the length of time in which we may expect one success in getting a usable gene, which is 10^{147} years.

We might remind ourselves what each added zero does to a number. Instead of adding 10 or a billion, it *MULTIPLIES everything before it by 10.* For example, suppose we had one less zero, namely, 10^{146}. When we add the final zero, we multiply the entire 10^{146} by 10, in order to get 10^{147}.

Random Occurrences Governed by Rules

Irving Adler in his book *Probability and Statistics* said, "Random occurrences, like fully determined events, are governed by certain rules."[21] Those carefully researched rules, which are depended upon so widely in science and industry today, are the ones being followed in our calculations. The results should be as trustworthy as the Golden Gate Bridge or the Eiffel Tower, both built in dependence on the principles of probability theory. (In such construction, not every piece of steel and not every rivet is tested, nor is every act by every workman. By the use of sampling tests, however, the probability is calculated that

---

[20] Ibid., pp. 235, 236.

[21] Irving Adler, *Probability and Statistics for Everyman* (New York: John Day Co., 1963), p. 13.

any particular component would be defective or inadequate as to allowable limits of stress. By the multiplication rule, the chance of failure of, say, two components which augment each other can be known. The overall probability of the structure can likewise be calculated as to stability.)

Our "margin of safety" is exceedingly greater than engineers ever would consider necessary for complete assurance.[22]

The Fallacy That Time Can Produce the Extremely Improbable

Those intent on getting life from nonlife sometimes put their hope in life forming on distant worlds by chance, throughout the vast galaxies of the universe during several billions of years. Surely in all that time and all that amount of matter, they suppose life would happen many times.

French paleontologist André de Cayeux quoted a Russian scientist, Kostitzin, as saying that in the totality of the universe, "the development of an improbable condition is not impossible, and the nondevelopment of such a condition is not very probable."[23] Another example of this sort of assumption is expressed in noted medical researcher George Wald's epic article "The Origin of Life" when he wrote:

> The important point is that since the origin of life belongs in the category of at-least-once phenomena, time is on its side.

---

[22] It might be mentioned that the probability of at least one usable gene is even less than the impossibly remote chance we calculated. There is a rule called Poisson's formula which can be used when the number of tries is very large and the probability very small. If the probability is, on the average, one in a huge number, actually one would have a 37% probability, rounded, that not even one would occur in that number of trials. There would also be a 37% chance of exactly one, 18% chance of exactly two occurring, 6% chance of three, and 1% chance of four, and a small fraction of a percent for five. (Émile Borel, *Probabilities and Life* (New York: [Dover Publications, 1962], pp. 73, 74.)

This formula arises from the fact that in any series of tries, you will not always get exactly the *average* expected result, but sometimes more, sometimes less. For example, in drawing from ten numbered coins, the average probability is to get the number one once in ten draws. If a person does several different series of ten draws each, he will find that in some series he does not get the number one at all, and in some he obtains it twice or even three times. If, instead of a 1/10 probability, the number is quite large, like 1 chance in 10,000 or 100,000, then the expected percent of the series with zero, one, two, and three times can be calculated by use of Poisson's formula. It involves a mathematical symbol, *e*, which is 2.718. . . . If the average probability is one in a number like, for example, 10^5, the chance of getting none at all in a given series is $1/e$, which is 36.788 . . . %. The same formula tells the chance of getting exactly one. For the chance of getting two or more, the formula becomes $1/e2!$ or $1/e3!$, etc. ($e3!$ is 2.718 x 3 x 2 x 1). We have checked this out in experiments involving large numbers and it proved true.

With the size of the odds we have found for one gene, even dividing it by five would make little difference, since it would reduce it less than one zero.

[23] André de Cayeux, *Three Billion Years of Life* (New York: Stein and Day, 1969), p. 208.

> However improbable we regard this event, or any of the steps which it involves, given enough time it will almost certainly happen at least once. . . .
>
> Time is in fact the hero of the plot. The time with which we have to deal is of the order of two billion years. What we regard as impossible on the basis of human experience is meaningless here. Given so much time, the "impossible" becomes possible, the possible probable, and the probable virtually certain. One has only to wait: time itself performs the miracles.[24]

If this "logic" held true, it would be an easy way for materialists to get this miracle of the origin of life performed. *The fallacy lies in the size of the figures.*

When one looks at it mathematically, he might suspect that Dr. Wald, like Kostitzin, just didn't get around to extensive calculating on this problem. Also, we should remember, knowledge about the DNA system (and proteins) was quite limited at the time he wrote, compared to the present. Note that he referred to a time of about 2×10^9 years, in which he supposed that the entire present milieu of living things evolved from nonliving chemicals.

By contrast, compare the figure arrived at by calculations in the preceding pages, namely, 1 chance in 10^{147} years of trials under conditions that were so extremely advantageous to chance. One chance of what? Getting just *ONE* usable gene. It takes, however, a minimum of at least 124 genes to code for the *different kinds* of proteins for Morowitz' minimal living entity described earlier. With all 124 genes required, it will never be a case, then, of merely obtaining a complex molecule "at least once."

It would be discouraging to wait those 10^{147} years for one gene, since 10^{147} is a thousand billion billion . . . (till the word billion is used sixteen times). Even if it *could* happen "just once," we would not be out of the woods at all. It would be just one of the many complex parts that must *all* be in position before the smallest living thing could live. To get the probability of all of these parts, the chances of each one would have to be computed together.

Wasting "Cerebral Horsepower"

Trying to get complex order out of random arrangements is

[24] George Wald, "The Origin of Life," *Scientific American* (August, 1954), p. 48.

to waste time. Sooner or later, logic calls reasonable minds to realize that there are here too many virtual impossibilities. Dr. Joseph L. Henson, biologist, says that to believe in evolution, one has to have "faith to believe that the statistically improbable is going to happen again and again and again."[25] When the statistically improbable is *as improbable* as $1/10^{236}$ for just the first gene,[26] consider what kind of unfounded faith would be required!

Kenneth K. Landes, in an article entitled "Illogical Geology" in *Geotimes*, used an interesting phraseology on another subject which might correctly be appropriated here. He spoke of "the cerebral horsepower now being wasted on futile attempts to explain away the truth. . . ."[27]

Surely it is wasted intellectual effort to try to coax chance into producing precise and intricate order.[28]

Slowing the Ameba to One Angstrom Unit in Fifteen Billion Years!

How long is this time that it will take for one gene to occur by chance, on the average? With a probability of once in 10^{147} years, the ameba described in an earlier chapter could transport many complete universes the entire distance of the diameter of the cosmos while chance is still working on one random gene that will be usable.

It is interesting to contemplate the slowest speeds our minds can grasp. The diameter of a hydrogen atom is about one Angstrom unit. Suppose our ameba from chapter 7 has travelled only that distance since the universe began, using the assumed fifteen-billion-year figure again. If the tiny traveller continues to move at that snail's pace of all snail's paces, it will take *3,810,000,000,000,000 years to span the distance of ONE INCH!*

Traveling that slowly, the ameba would complete the task

---

[25] Joseph L. Henson, Bob Jones University, personal correspondence, December, 1971.

[26] The ratio of $1/10^{236}$ is the probability, and 10^{147} is the number of years it would take, as calculated on p. 160.

[27] Kenneth K. Landes, *Geotimes*, Vol. III (March, 1959), p. 19.

[28] Dr. Morowitz has described the interesting fact that a degree of order is sometimes produced by energy flow. (Morowitz, *Energy Flow in Biology.*) The extent of such naturally produced order is quite different from the degree of order required for the simplest living thing. As an example of order from energy flow, we might consider the wind bringing a degree of order in autumn leaves. The limitations of order produced in this manner are clearly quite confining, in the absence of intelligent planning, regardless of the amount of energy flow.

of carrying the entire universe across in about 4 x 10^{125} years. *In this leisurely fashion, the little space crawler would have time to convey 2 x 10^{21} complete universes, one atom at a time, all the way across the thirty billion light years of the assumed diameter of the cosmos, during the time that chance could be expected to arrange one gene in any usable order, trying at the unbelievable speed noted earlier, using all the atoms in the universe!*

If all the people living on earth—men, women, and children of all ages—were put to work counting rapidly day and night, it would take them five thousand years just to *count* the number of complete universes that this ameba could *transport* during the average time that chance could produce one lonesome gene! Remember that chance was using all the atoms in the universe in this test.

The Second Gene Would Take Interminably Longer

As with proteins, if the first gene was on hand, all the others for a minimum set would have to match, like the parts of a particular kind of watch. The second gene, therefore, would be much harder to get than the first, because it would have to match. After obtaining the first gene, the aim would then be to get any one of the other 123 genes needed to complete the set. For that second gene, this would mean that we would have to overcome odds of 10^{524} to 123.

Even if the most fantastic advantages were given to chance, the situation would still be hopeless. Suppose, for example, that it is allowed that for each gene, as many different sequences would be acceptable as there are atoms in the universe. With such an extreme concession, the ameba could still transport more than 10^{57800} complete universes across that thirty-billion-light-year distance, traveling at the rate of one Angstrom unit in fifteen billion years, during the time that chance could be expected to get the sequence in correct order for a minimum set of genes for the smallest theoretical living thing.

Just to print the figure for the number of those universes carried by the ameba would require around twenty-eight pages.

Looking at it another way, let us suppose that substitution is freely allowed in *nine-tenths* of the loci or positions in the chain. That is, such a tremendous degree of variation is permissible that in a chain of 400, only 40 need be correct and the others can be anything. This would be a similar situation whether one considers a protein chain, or a gene of 400 codons. It is like an exam where all that matters is that you get 40 out of 400 right.

With this extreme amount of variability, the odds against success in a chance arrival at a usable set of either genes or proteins are still fantastic. This is true even at the speed postulated and using all the atoms of the universe in the attempt. Let's consider the length of time in which just one-half of the required set of genes (or of proteins) might occur by random alignment. We will again measure that time by the number of complete universes the ameba can transport across the diameter of the universe one atom at a time at the unbelievably slow speed described a bit earlier. That number of universes is so large that if all the atoms of the universe were people counting steadily, it would take them 5,000 years just to count those universes which the ameba could carry during the average waiting time for one-half of a minimum gene or protein set to align in usable sequence.

The formula for probability with multiple substitutions allowed, just in case you happen to be curious, is:

$$\sum_{i=0}^{s} \frac{n!}{i!(n-i)!} \cdot \frac{(a-1)^i}{a^n}$$

where n is the number of units in the chain (amino acids or codons), a is the number of kinds of units, s is the number of substitutions allowable, and i is the variable for summation from zero to s. The large symbol is the Greek letter sigma, which represents summing up the results, from all the values of i as the number of substitutions ranges from zero up to s. Here $n = 400$, $s = 360$, $a = 21$ (21 different codon outcomes).

The Single Law of Chance

Émile Borel, a distinguished French expert on probability, stated what he called "the single law of chance," or merely "the law of chance," in these words: "*Events whose probability is extremely small never occur*"[29] He calculated that probabilities smaller than $1/10^{15}$ were negligible on the terrestrial scale, and, he said:

---

[29] Émile Borel, *Elements of the Theory of Probability* (Englewood Cliffs, N.J.: Prentice-Hall, Inc., 1965), p. 57.

> We may be led to set at 10^{-50} the value of negligible probabilities on the cosmic scale. When the probability of an event is below this limit, the opposite event may be expected to occur with certainty, whatever the number of occasions presenting themselves in the entire universe.[30]

By "opposite event," he means *no* event, or failure to occur. Under the single law of chance, therefore, even a single gene would never be arranged in any usable order in the entire universe, if we apply this statement by the eminent mathematician. One need only to compare the probability of one gene (10^{-236}) with Borel's 10^{-50} which he said is the limit of meaningful probabilities on the cosmic scale. What would he say to the figure we got for the minimum *set* for smallest life, namely, a probability of 10^{-57800}? The ameba's journeys have made it clear that our minds cannot grasp such an *extremely* small probability as that involved in the accidental arranging of even one gene (10^{-236}). By the single law of chance, it will never occur.

Logic Requires Belief in a Designer

This old analogy is as reasonable now as ever: We intuitively know that a watch requires a watchmaker. It has many parts that must be precision-adapted to match other parts that are useless alone. Why would anyone attempt to circumvent this principle in science? We will look into the reasons for this in the next chapter.

The conflict is basically between chance, disorder, and chaos on the one hand, and God, order, and organization on the other. Of him it is said that he "sustains the universe by his word of power."[31] Nothing else gives any adequate explanation of what we ourselves can observe.

There is a type of evidence which may be far more convincing to an individual than the mathematical proof we have been considering, as weighty as we have found that to be. It is the assurance which God has promised to all who will take him up on the following offer:

He said, through Christ, "Whoever has the will to do the will

---

[30] Émile Borel, *Probabilities and Life* (New York: Dover Publications, 1962), p. 28.

Regarding Borel's use of the minus exponent, the reader may recall that this means the same as writing the number as a fraction with the figure 1 on top. 10^{-50} is the same as $1/10^{50}$, or 1 chance in a figure with 50 zeroes.

[31] Hebrews 1:3 NEB

of God shall know whether my teaching comes from him. . . ."[32] Such a person will be given inner assurance that Christ was who he claimed to be: the Son of God by whom the worlds were made.[33]

---

[32] John 7:17 NEB
[33] Hebrews 1:2

11

Why Has Evolution Been Widely Accepted?

Neo-Darwinism has become an established orthodoxy, any criticism of which is regarded as little less than lèse-majesté.[1]

—C. H. Waddington

IN THIS CHAPTER, we will briefly examine a persistent question: If evolution is not true, why does it occupy such a dominant place in modern education and how has it gained such wide acceptance? (The reader is referred by way of review, to thoughts on this subject at the beginning of chapter 6, pages 95-98.)

The domain of science involves accurate observation of evidence and controlled experimentation. Of the latter, Aimé Michel wrote, "Experimental science is completely based on one single principle. In its entirety, and by definition, it proceeds from one single process, *which is the reproducible experiment with a single solution*"[2] (Michel's italics).

In dealing with the subject of evolution, most proponents in the field of science have been *endeavoring to sell a philosophy rather than to present scientific evidence.* The harm is done when this philosophy is proclaimed as if it were scientific fact backed by experimental or observational evidence.

Scientists Are Fallible Human Beings

The public tends to believe that *every* scientist is 100 percent

---

1 C. H. Waddington, "Towards a Theoretical Biology," *Nature.* Vol. 218 (1968), p. 527. Note: *lèse majesté* means crime against the sovereign; treason.

2 Aimé Michel, in preface to André de Cayeux' *Three Billion Years of Life* (New York: Stein and Day, 1969), p. 23.

correct in *every* pronouncement. It is almost unbelievable to some people that scientists could be subject to human errors. James Watson, who discovered the pairing mechanism of DNA, made the following observation (which he has no doubt regretted because of its impolitic nature): "In contrast to the popular conception supported by newspapers and mothers of scientists, a goodly number of scientists are not only narrow-minded and dull, but also just stupid."[3] (Watson may have been facetiously attributing this viewpoint to his colleague.)

This extreme appraisal is certainly not correct for most scientists. In the field of science are some of the finest people on earth. Watson's comment may serve to alert us, however, to the fact that scientists, being human, show a great variety of beliefs, attitudes, and character, just as do politicians, teachers, and salesmen.

"Modern man," said George Charles Roche III, "does not seem to understand that science can harbor illusions on the image of nature and thus mislead."[4]

Any scientist will try to fit the evidence into his general philosophy of the nature of things. Sometimes this natural tendency overrides logic and leads one to look at only the favorable evidence. Take the study of proteins that do the same job in various organisms. The idea is that in closely related organisms, the sequences of the amino acids in such proteins should match more closely than sequences from organisms which diverged farther back on the "evolutionary tree." Enthusiasm for this popular idea easily leads to ignoring sequence data which contradict evolution.[5]

Degrees of Commitment to Evolution

There is great variety among scientists and others who believe evolution. Some, like Simpson, Wooldridge, and Oparin, are crusaders for the doctrine. This is logical—if a person really believes in a philosophy, he likely will spread it.

Others echo it gladly, and a great multitude simply go along because it seems to be the thing to do. Many of the latter

[3] James D. Watson, *The Double Helix* (New York: Atheneum Press, 1968), p. 14.

[4] George Charles Roche III, *Legacy of Freedom* (New Rochelle, N.Y.: Arlington House, 1969), p. 9.

[5] This important subject will be discussed briefly in the next chapter, and some such sequences will be compared.

have serious doubts about evolution, but they keep their reservations to themselves. And, of course, a great many people are honestly confused on this question.

Not because of evidence, but because of presumed evidence—this is a major explanation for the prevalence of evolutionary belief. It is the subject of the next chapter, where the assumed proofs will be examined briefly.

A Fashionable False Idea

William Randolph Hearst, Jr., once wrote about pressures from "fashionable ideas . . . which are advanced with such force that common sense itself becomes the victim." A person under such pressure may then act, he said, "with an irrationality which is almost beyond belief."[6]

It is exactly thus with the overwhelming pressure to accept evolution.

"I regard evolution as a major myth of our time," said John G. Read, "—a myth in the name of science."[7] An aerospace engineer for Hughes Aircraft, and a former evolutionist himself, Read made this comment after he cited the uncertainties and assumptions involved in accepted radiocarbon dating techniques. The power that the "myth" of evolution has gained over the public, through the human desire to conform, amounts almost to mass hypnosis. It has its effect because people have been led to think that it is the "orthodox" view among those whom they consider to be scientific and worldly-wise.

An individual thus affected is reluctant to examine the evidence open-mindedly. The problem is emotional. One can easily become committed to what appears to be a fashionable philosophy, the "in" thing among his peers. The deciding factor is the pressure to conform, right or wrong. It always takes courage and intentional honesty to seek truth in the face of the compulsion to be considered "in" because of being "like."

Even some who profess faith in God tend to shy away from looking into evidence such as that to which attention has been called in these pages, lest the facts, if accepted, cause them to lose favor with nonbelievers in Christianity whose approval they value. Seldom would such a person venture far into a book on a theme like this.

---

[6] William Randolph Hearst, Jr., "Editor's Report," *The Herald-Examiner* (Los Angeles, Nov. 14, 1971), p. A-4.

[7] John G. Read, interviewed on "And God Created," KBBI-FM Radio, Los Angeles, February 7, 1971.

When a fashionable idea has the center of the stage in a society, it tends to drive off opposing viewpoints. Some readers may find, as we have, that it is difficult to locate in some university libraries certain serious scientific works critical of evolution. Books of this type have a way of ending up not in the science section but in the religious section of city libraries! Many inquiring students thus never hear the other side as part of their scientific studies. While most universities perhaps try to be fair to all thoughtful viewpoints logically deriving from the evidence, occasionally a school will refuse a degree apparently as a result of prejudice against nonconformity, with regard to belief in this popular doctrine. These factors contribute to an understanding of why evolutionary belief is so widespread.

Scientific works which fail to support evolution may sometimes run into difficulty getting into print. When Immanuel Velikovsky's controversial theories, which threatened orthodox solar system evolutionary dogma of the time, were scheduled for publication by a major textbook house, even prominent scientists were involved in the storm of protest that caused the publisher to back down. This display of human prejudice and efforts to stifle true academic freedom resulted in a book entitled *The Velikovsky Affair* which documents the whole story.[8]

Columbus and the Indians: the Matter of Overview

Columbus sailed with the outlook of discovering India by a new route. When he reached the new world, he did not recognize it as such, but thought it must be part of India, or islands near India. He named the natives "Indians."

It is like that with some evolutionists. They have their minds set with the idea that there is no Creator. Things had to happen *without supernatural intervention.* Having determined this in their thinking, nothing—*nothing*—can cause them to consider anything that is not a materialistic explanation. No matter how

---

[8] Alfred DeGrazia, ed., *The Velikovsky Affair* (Hyde Park, N.Y.: University Books, Inc., 1966).

Quoting from page one of that book: "What must be called the scientific establishment rose in arms, not only against the new Velikovsky theories but against the man himself. Efforts were made to block dissemination of Dr. Velikovsky's ideas, and even to punish supporters of his investigations. Universities, scientific societies, publishing houses, the popular press were approached and threatened; social pressures and professional sanctions were invoked to control public opinion."

This was an extreme case and not the rule, of course, but it does indicate that radical prejudice for conformity is possible by some recognized scientific "authorities."

hard-pressed such a person may be for lack of evidence or logic, he must search around for some way to explain things without an intelligent inventor. This is a primary reason for the persistence of evolution. It is a chosen *overview* or philosophy of life, rather than science.

Without a strong advance commitment to the philosophy of evolution, would any reasonable person ever stretch logic so far as to believe, for example, that the ponderous jaw bones of reptiles evolved into the delicate, intricately matched bones of the inner ear, whose exact length and precise hinged motion transmit sound to the inner eardrum? Those who thus believe should at least refrain from ever criticizing the most unreasoning devotee of any religion for his persistence in finding explanations which fit his belief, even if his particular religion happens to be a false one.

The Christian may not now be able to give ideal answers to some questions, but the evolutionist is in far worse shape when it comes to solutions for difficult questions. In fact, only belief in an intelligent Creator can provide a really adequate world view or cosmic philosophy that can encompass the whole range of things. Although there are still problems, recent discoveries have, for the Bible believer, solved several that formerly had no explanation. For any mysteries remaining, consider this statement by Pierre Lecomte du Noüy:

> Mystery for mystery, it seems wiser, more logical and more intelligent to choose the one which explains, thus satisfying our need to comprehend; the one which opens the doors to hope, rather than the one which closes those doors and explains nothing.[9]

Fear of Teleology As a Threat to Human Conceit

Many materialists seem to fear the idea that there may be purpose or design in nature (teleology). This fear appears to be based on aversion to considering that there may be *Someone in charge* of the universe, to whom we would be responsible.

Even intelligent people will sometimes resist the sensible but humbling knowledge "that they are parts and not masters of the awesome mystery called creation."[10]

The new company vice-president who likes to give the im-

---

[9] Pierre Lecomte du Noüy, *Human Destiny* (New York: Longmans, Green & Co., 1947), p. 84.

[10] Hearst, "Editor's Report."

pression that he owns the company is an example. The night custodian who relaxes with his feet on the boss' desk exemplifies also this human tendency to want to exalt ourselves.

The pride of man is a well-known fact to all students of human nature. If there is no God, man can take all the credit or give it to something less than himself, such as "chance." He can then do as he pleases, without being limited by ideas of a future accounting, a judgment, heaven and hell.

Those who close their minds to considering God are like the small boy who shut his eyes and told others, "You can't see me." By deciding there is no God, man thinks he is rid of Him.

The loss is enormous. It is a poor substitute when man turns to chance as his god. To depend on mutations as the raw material of evolution, for example, is to postulate "creation by mistake," because the assumed development would arise from errors and injuries involving DNA. Evolutionary scientists, nevertheless, spend lifetimes searching for the reasons for various organs and life processes—never doubting that there are such reasons.

Evolution As a Religious Faith

Robert T. Clark and James D. Bales have written an excellent small book entitled *Why Scientists Accept Evolution.* In it they show with careful documentation that Darwin, Huxley, Spencer, and other early evolutionists did not start in that direction primarily because of scientific evidence, but because of emotional and spiritual bias against God, the Bible, and Christianity. Holding such an attitude, it was easy for them to interpret physical evidence as favoring a materialistic explanation of things. Evolution became their substitute for God.[11]

Bolton Davidheiser was an evolutionist for many years. He received his Ph.D. in zoology at Johns Hopkins University, specializing in genetics. Eventually he turned from evolution to Christianity. His first book, *Evolution and Christian Faith* (1969), is one of the most complete and scholarly studies yet made and covers a wide scope.

Dr. Davidheiser goes into considerable detail on this subject of evolution as a faith. It is often overlooked that a logical faith

---

[11] Robert T. Clark and James D. Bales, *Why Scientists Accept Evolution* (Grand Rapids, Mich: Baker Book House, 1966).

is involved in accepting some scientific precepts, but to believe evolution requires a different kind of faith without basis:

> Many phenomena have been observed so regularly to occur under certain conditions that they are taken for granted, and it is not realized that faith in the uniformity of nature is being exercised. But the situation is quite different with regard to the theory of evolution, for many alleged phenomena in the evolution of life are mysterious, and to accept them requires faith.[12]

Evolution, it has been said, requires of its devotees a higher degree of faith in the unknown than does creation. Evolutionary doctrine is based on a long series of assumptions, many of them groundless and the others uncertain. Each of these assumptions is treated as if proved as soon as the writer or speaker goes on to the next step. The result is something like building a house at the top of a structure of straws.

Bias Against the Supernatural

A highschool textbook in wide use in public schools is entitled *Molecules to Man.*[13] Its *entire theme* is the theory of evolution. Around 1967, we searched an earlier edition of this textbook in vain for even a hint that anyone anywhere ever believed in creation. The authors did not hesitate to discuss other opposing theories, as long as these did not involve a supernatural being to be considered seriously. They spoke freely, for example, of spontaneous generation, an earlier belief that small mammals and insects originated from decaying matter.

The evidence of bias in that textbook was slightly modified in the edition in use in 1973. However, about the only mention of creation is in a couple of quotations, one of them from Darwin.

Francis Crick commented about British schools. He says, "Personally, I myself would go further, and think it is also regrettable that there is so much religious teaching." He disapproves the "tremendous institutional support given to religion by such a body as Cambridge University. . . ." One wonders, however, if the alternative he suggests would not in effect be *another religion:* "I think it is difficult to overemphasize the importance of teaching natural selection, both in schools and

---

[12] Bolton Davidheiser, *Evolution and Christian Faith* (Nutley, N.J.: Presbyterian and Reformed Publishing Co., 1969), p. 153.

[13] *Molecules to Man,* Blue Version, Revised, Biological Sciences Curriculum Study (Boston: Houghton Mifflin Co., 1968).

in universities, so that every member of our culture has a clear and firm grasp of the principle. . . ."[14]

He admits that there are "intelligent people who sincerely believe in vitalistic ideas,[15] even though they are fully acquainted with the scientific knowledge on the subject," but thinks it "highly unlikely that there is anything that cannot be explained by physics and chemistry." Regarding those who disagree, he has this comment: "A lunatic fringe always remains. There are still people alive today who believe that the earth is flat. . . ."[16] It is always a good idea to be alert when ridicule like this is used, to find if it is unconsciously employed as a substitute for proof or logic.

"Holding to evolution is unbelief, faith only in a negation," wrote T. Robert Ingram. He says that while materialistic evolution is often characterized as a religion, by looking deeper, one finds that it is more accurately an "unfaith."

> Evolution is properly categorized as systematic denial that God has Created us. The evolutionist cannot agree with anyone as to what he believes: but all are at one as to what they don't believe.[17]

Theistic Evolution a Compromise?

Since this book is primarily on probability and evolution, we are not going deeply into other subjects, including theistic evolution (evolution involving God). The reader is referred to the excellent and complete study of this theory by Dr. Davidheiser in his book mentioned earlier (footnote 12, page 175).

We have seen before that the pressure of the *assumed* evidence forces many to come to terms with evolution. They don't want to be "unscientific," and they give undue credit to the proofs evolutionists claim. Some of the evidence which we now have was not known earlier. Adjustment to evolution is unnecessary after all.

It is regrettable that some scientists who believe strongly in God make this same weakening accommodation to evolution. They do not do this because of evidence. Doubtless the explanation lies in the following causes:

---

[14] Francis H. C. Crick, *Of Molecules and Men* (Seattle: University of Washington Press, 1966), pp. 89-91.
[15] vitalistic: involving more than just material factors
[16] Crick, *Of Molecules and Men*, pp. 97-99.
[17] T. Robert Ingram, Letter to Editor, *Creation Research Society Quarterly*, Vol. 8 (September, 1971), p. 116.

(1) Scientists can easily overestimate the supposed evidences of evolution outside their particular field. A physicist, for example, may be persuaded that the biologists have real proof of evolution, and as a scientist he respects the reports of other scientists.

Like the theologian described earlier (page 29), many professional people including scientists in other specialties may be mistakenly led to believe "that the scientists have proved evolution to be true, and they have to do the best they can with it." Doing the best they can, in such a case, they espouse the idea that God did it, but through gradual, natural processes.

(2) Some believers in God are not clearly aware that the Bible and evolution are not compatible. They suppose that theistic evolution is a philosophy acceptable to the Christian faith, not having thought through the contradiction involved. Among these are some great souls who started out as unbelievers, and have gotten as far as faith in God, but have not yet encountered or fully considered the Bible's teachings on this subject.

(3) Difficulties with the "geologic time scale," descriptions of early man, and astronomers' recounting the vastness of the universe—these may lead one to an unadvisable reinterpretation of the Bible account. In the next chapter, these subjects will be dealt with briefly.

Thomas Huxley said, "It is clear that the doctrine of evolution is directly antagonistic to that of Creation. . . . Evolution, if consistently accepted, makes it impossible to believe the Bible."[18]

Why God Didn't Make Things Unmistakably Clear

Why did the Creator leave room at all for anyone to doubt as to the truth about Himself?

If each of us is in this life as an opportunity to develop into a person—to develop character—then there must be the chance to choose. God therefore leaves room for personal decision.

There is plenty of evidence. God does not, however, grasp a person by the neck and force him to believe. We choose to open our eyes to the implications of the evidence or to ignore them. That's part of the plan, because character comes only by choice. Choice shapes one's character, and character determines

---

[18] In: Fred John Meldau, *Why We Believe in Creation, Not in Evolution* (Denver: Christian Victory Publishing Co., 1959), p. 8.

personal destiny. Choices that a person makes regarding the Creator are logically the most important of all choices.

The business manager who wants to get rid of the owner of the business is in trouble. The same is true of a human being who chooses to ignore his Creator. Unless we really want to find Him, we won't. "I have come in recent years," wrote Louis Cassels, "to the suspicion that God deliberately hides His reality from the casual inquirer."[19] *Casual* seeking is an insult to such a Being as the Creator, whose patent is on every blade of grass, on the nucleus of every atom, and throughout nature.

If Cassels' statement is true, consider how unlikely it is that the deliberate ignoring of God will produce evidence convincing to the skeptic. Henry Fairfield Osborn, a crusading evolutionist of the early twentieth century, expressed the rebellious spirit of human beings thus: "In truth, from the earliest stages of Greek thought man has been eager to discover some natural cause of evolution, and to abandon the idea of supernatural intervention in the order of nature."[20]

It is too bad that man—made in the image of God, given dominion over the earth, offered the privilege of sonship and co-creative work together with God—should abandon this high honor and the freedom that goes with so exciting an adventure, and instead rebel and try to get rid of the Owner by deciding He isn't there.

A character in one of Shakespeare's plays gave an incisive picture of a universal human tendency in these familiar words:

> But man, proud man,
> Drest in a little brief authority,
> Most ignorant of what he is most assured. . . .
> Plays such tricks before high heaven
> As make the angels weep.[21]

True Science Requires Courage

Scientists are often fearless in proclaiming new ideas as long as these do not question evolution. For one example, Dr. J. V. Smith of the University of Chicago, according to an Associated Press dispatch, announced some revolutionary views concerning the moon at a 1970 lunar conference. "Smith's theories were

---

[19] Louis Cassels, *The Reality of God* (Garden City, N.Y.: Doubleday and Co., 1971), p. 3.

[20] Henry Fairfield Osborn, *The Origin and Evolution of Life* (New York: Charles Scribner's Sons, 1917), Preface, p. ix.

[21] William Shakespeare, "Measure for Measure," Act II, Scene II.

greeted with gasps from some of the scientists attending," said the news report.[22]

"Physics often advances by shattering theories," said two physicists in an article in *Scientific American.*[23] Consider how much faster biochemistry, for example, might progress if the "cerebral horsepower now being wasted" in trying to support outmoded evolutionary doctrine were instead put into productive research on the challenging gaps in our knowledge of molecular biology.

As it is now, most biochemists seem to feel that they must relate all research to the evolutionary scheme of things. It will take courage on the part of individual scientists to break out of this inhibiting and restrictive straitjacket. Involved in this problem is the scientific integrity of those who advocate protecting the evolutionary viewpoint from an objective evaluation alongside creation.

Charles Darwin once accused some opponents of "the blindness of preconceived opinion."[24] One might wonder if those words fit some present-day scientists who have unwittingly been influenced to accept the unscientific notion that a purely material explanation must be found for all that exists.

If we may be permitted a sociological generalization, such a belief is not merely academic, but carries certain practical connotations as it reaches the public. The average person would reason that if all can be materialistically explained, it would mean that there is no God. If there is no God, why should not one forget others and do as he pleases (except when others can help toward his own happiness)?[25]

It can easily be seen how such a view might play a part in undermining the moral and social foundations of western civilization. It might even appear that nothing but totalitarian authority would suffice to guarantee order in the absence of character in individual citizens—character with its inner controls,

---

[22] "Was Moon Once a 'Molten Blob'?" Associated Press Dispatch, *The Herald-Examiner* (Los Angeles, January 5, 1970), p. A-1.

[23] Frederick V. Murphy and David E. Yount, "Photons as Hadrons," *Scientific American,* Vol. 225, (July, 1971), p. 96.

[24] *The Origin of Species,* Mentor Edition (New American Library, 1958), p. 444.

[25] Alan Radcliffe-Smith described evolution as "a theory which results in a grovellingly debased view of human origins . . . and which helps to spawn such grotesquely distorted pieces of literature as Marx's *Das Kapital* and Hitler's *Mein Kampf* . . ." (*Nature,* Correspondence, Vol. 241 [January 12, 1973], pp. 150, 151.)

resulting from "the fear of the Lord," as the Bible calls it. Such a "fear" consists of reverence and awe for a good and just Creator and a fear of invoking His displeasure. It does not necessarily involve the idea of "dread," unless one refuses to yield to His claims, and it is a strong incentive for proper conduct toward other people as well as toward one's Maker.

The growing evidence against evolution will eventually force American evolutionists to face the fact that the position is untenable. Some will then open-mindedly explore the idea of creation, while others will doubtless persist in materialism at any cost, and will turn to forms of Lamarckism or follow Oparin in the communist belief that matter intrinsically will develop of its own accord.

At present (1973), the controversy between evolution and creation is frequently in print in the scientific magazines of both England and America. The prestigious British science journal, *Nature,* widely read by scientists of all English-speaking countries, has included a large number of items over several months. Here are some ideas expressed:

A professor in the Department of Anatomy, University of Western Australia, described evolution as a "time-honoured scientific tenet of faith—for this is what evolution has become to many of us—rather like a theological doctrine, to be defended with some passion."[26]

Another professor, J. W. Fairbairn, of the School of Pharmacy, University of London, spoke of the highly speculative nature of evolution. He said, "It is now belatedly coming to be realized that evolutionary speculation has had a deleterious effect on practical taxonomy." On the subject of evolution's supposed help in shaping taxonomy, Fairbairn said: "There is a curious dishonesty about this in much biological writing." He said, "I treat the Genesis account of creation with as much respect as that of the biologist."[27]

Another correspondent delineated the problem facing nonconformists:

> There are more anti-Darwinists in British universities than you seem to realize. Among them is a friend of mine who holds a chair in a department of pure science "in a field

---

[26] David Allbrook, *Nature,* Correspondence, Vol. 241 (January 12, 1973), p. 150.

[27] J. W. Fairbairn, *Nature,* Correspondence, Vol. 241 (January 19, 1973), p. 225.

> bearing on the evolutionary question," to use your phrase. If his friends ask why he keeps quiet about his unorthodox views, he replies in words very like those used recently in another connexion by Professor Ian Roxburgh: "... There is a powerful establishment and a belief system. There are power seekers and career men, and if someone challenges the establishment he should not expect a sympathetic hearing."

The writer, A. T. J. Hayward, went on to say:

> The majority of biologists accept the prevailing views uncritically—just as a great many competent Russian biologists were once brainwashed into accepting Lysenko's quackery. Others have thought for themselves and come to realize the flaws in contemporary Darwinism. But for them to speak out would be to invite ridicule and would probably ruin their careers.

Hayward ended his letter by noting: "Anyone who thinks that only uninformed cranks reject Darwinism should read the whole of Thompson's *Introduction.* It will make him think again."[28]

He was referring to the noted entomologist, W. R. Thompson. Because of the high esteem in which he was held in the scientific world, Thompson was pressed to write an introduction for the Centenary edition of Darwin's *Origin of Species* (printed in 1956), even though Thompson was not a Darwinist himself. The result was no help to the cause of evolution. Hayward quoted thus from that *Introduction:* "This situation, where scientific men rally to the defense of a doctrine they are unable to define scientifically, much less demonstrate with scientific rigour, attempting to maintain its credit with the public by the suppression of criticism and the elimination of difficulties, is abnormal and undesirable in science."

Personal integrity is sometimes costly. This is true whether one is a scientist or not. To go where truth leads, however, has the advantage of yielding self-respect, as well as the feeling of being in tune with the real universe. Another value of being in step with true science is that it enriches those in one's circle of influence who may thereby also find courage to line up with the preponderance of the evidence.

---

[28] A. T. J. Hayward, *Nature,* Correspondence, Vol. 240 (December 29, 1972), p. 57. (We are not implying that all of these writers would agree with our position in every detail, of course.)

12

The Assumed Evidence of Evolution

In recent months the teaching of evolution has come under attack in a number of states . . . not by theologians but by scientists.[1]
—*Scientific American*

Persuasive Promotion of an Inferior Product

The situation is still as it was when evolutionist Henry Fairfield Osborn wrote these words with regard to efforts to find an adequate natural basis for evolution and avoid the supernatural: "There have been great waves of faith in one explanation and then in another: each of these waves of confidence has ended in disappointment. . . ."[2]

To consider an intelligent cause is out of the question for a dedicated materialist. Evolution is his life.

A person would never guess, by listening to those who cam-

[1] "Science and the Citizen: Creationism," *Scientific American*, Vol. 224 (January, 1971), p. 46.

In California, some scientists who attended a state textbook hearing in 1969 stated that special divine creation can be explained as a scholarly and scientifically valid doctrine, whereupon the State Board of Education ruled that evolution may no longer be taught as the only theory, declaring, "Scientific evidence concerning the origin of life implies . . . the necessity to use several theories." This was reported in *Bioscience*, Vol. 20 (October, 1970), pp. 1067-1069.

In October, 1972, the National Convention of the National Association of Biology Teachers, meeting in San Francisco, reserved much of one afternoon of the convention for presentations of creationist interpretations of origins, and other creation implications in biology.

Needless to say, many who espouse evolution are quite unhappy with such developments. Their current opposition takes the form of relegating creationism to the realm of religion and emotion since they refuse to consider seriously the scientific basis for believing in special creation as the most logical explanation of the phenomena of nature.

[2] Henry Fairfield Osborn, *The Origin and Evolution of Life* (New York: Charles Scribner's Sons, 1917), Preface, p. ix.

paign for evolution, that their case was weak in evidence. Exaggerated claims make it sound like solid science. These claims are so convincingly stated that most people conclude that evolution has really been proved. This explains, as was noted earlier, why many brilliant people have been led to accept some form of evolution. Not having access to all the supposed evidence themselves, they have been swept along with the overwhelming chorus of assertions by others who had more faith than facts.

It will be helpful to keep in mind that the aim of this chapter is *not* a thorough study of these assumed proofs of evolution. That would take an entire book in itself, and several excellent ones already exist. We will merely take up these subjects briefly to indicate whether the presumed evidence may be nonexistent, misinterpreted, or under a question mark.

Space will limit us to brevity, since this is, after all, supposed to be a shortcut. The idea is to include in this one volume not only the probability studies, but at least the gist of answers to other major questions which might otherwise cloud one's certainty about whether evolution could be true.

The Geological Time Scale

Without a lot of time, evolution is out of luck. *It is an article of faith that there must have been billions of years available* for it to happen. Scientists who accept evolution are quite slow to accept dating results that run contrary to that standard dogma.

Melvin A. Cook, while he was Professor of Metallurgy at the University of Utah, wrote: "... *There really are no reliable time clocks* despite an almost overwhelming contrary opinion"[3] (italics added). Cook, who received his Ph.D. in physical chemistry at Yale, in the remarkable book just quoted, gives extensive attention to techniques of dating the past. We highly recommend these studies.

Here is a strange incident Dr. Cook describes:

> In 1956 the author visited the Schefferville Mine of Iron Ore Company of Canada.... While there, he was shown and given samples of several fossil wood specimens that had been recovered from the iron ore (a pre-Cambrian deposit)[4] at depths in the mine of several hundred feet. The chief ge-

---

[3] Melvin A. Cook, *Prehistory and Earth Models* (London: Max Parrish and Co., Ltd., 1966), Preface, p. xi.

[4] In the evolutionary scale, pre-Cambrian is the vast period prior to 600 million years ago.

> ologist described the occurrence as strange and anomalous, explicable neither on the basis of overturns nor fissures that would permit sluff-off of vegetal matter into crevices in the ore body. He exhibited two independent and consistent radiocarbon analyses that rèvealed ages in the neighborhood of 4000 years. Specimens varied from bright, modern-appearing wood through darkened (some charred by heat) to typically fossil-appearing, rock-like wood. Analyses had demonstrated that this fossil wood was essentially uncontaminated and unchanged chemically, but still essentially ligno-cellulose of well preserved internal structure.[5]

An article in a 1968 issue of the *Journal of Geophysical Research* admitted tremendous errors in the dating of rocks by the *potassium-argon* method. Scientists carefully dated samples of volcanic materials with the known formation date of 1800 and 1801 for a flow at Kaupulehu, Hualalai Volcano, Hawaii. The dating, therefore, should have matched that time span, namely, around 168 years. Eight tests listed in the article, however, gave ages ranging from 160,000,000 to 2,960,000,000 (almost three billion) years![6]

Robert L. Whitelaw, Nuclear Consultant and Professor of Mechanical Engineering at Virginia Polytechnic Institute, concluded a scholarly article in *Creation Research Society Quarterly* with the opinion that the same much-trusted dating method may be completely untrustworthy, and that cosmic rays may have accounted altogether for the build-up of argon-36, as he phrased it, "well within the 7,000 years since Biblical creation."[7]

Froelich Rainey said concerning Carbon-14: "Unfortunately, the difficulties and complexities involved in arriving at a 'true' date for any event by this method are not so clear. . . . Many archeologists still think of radiocarbon dating as a scientific technique that must be either right or wrong. Would that it were so simple!" Rainey says that 1870 B.C. (±6) is "the earliest actual recorded date in human history." Few people realize how much uncertainty is involved in dates prior to that.[8]

The radiocarbon dating system was developed by Willard F.

---

[5] Cook, *Prehistory and Earth Models*, p. 332.

[6] John G. Funkhouser and John J. Naughton, "Radiogenic Helium and Argon in Ultramafic Inclusions from Hawaii," *Journal of Geophysical Research*, Vol. 73, Part 5 (July 15, 1968), Table 2, p. 4603.

[7] Robert L. Whitelaw, "Radio-Carbon and Potassium-Argon Dating in the Light of Recent Discoveries in Cosmic Rays," *Creation Research Society Quarterly*, Vol. 6, No. 1 (June, 1969), p. 73.

[8] Froelich Rainey, "Dating the Past," *1971 Yearbook of Science and the Future* (Britannica), pp. 390, 391.

Libby, for which he received the Nobel prize in chemistry in 1960. Professor Cook said, "It is very interesting indeed *that an exact application of Libby's methods and data* for the C^{14} method dates the atmosphere at around 10^4 years."[9] (That is just 10,000 years!) Cook also discusses the uranium-thorium-lead process, arriving at additional figures which dispute the standard long ages concept.

One does not often hear of these short-term dating results because evolutionists tend to ignore or reinterpret any results that do not match the preconceived scheme. To do otherwise would be considered extreme heresy. The evidence, nevertheless, supports Cook's conclusion quoted above: "There really are no reliable time clocks. . . ."

One of the best sources for documented current reports by scientists on the degree of accuracy involved in various dating methods is *Creation Research Society Quarterly*,[10] especially the June 1970 issue. It is surprising to find that there is strong evidence that the Mississippi River may be only about 5,000 years old—evidence based on a geological study of the delta, according to an interesting article in the same periodical (September 1972, p. 96ff.).

Ancient Man

The only types of definitely human fossils with enough bones to tell us much have been Neanderthal and Cro-Magnon men. Both have considerably *larger brain capacity* than modern man![11]

Note that the Neanderthals had these facial characteristics: "heavy, bi-arched shelf of bone over the orbits [eye sockets]; low, retreating forehead . . . receding chin." As you will recognize, this is the stereotype commonly put forward of the supposed primitive, dull cave man, whose likeness confronts school children from the pages of textbooks. Neanderthal man, however, *averaged* a brain capacity of 1450 cm^3 (cubic centimeters) to our 1350 cm^3 today.[12]

The "cave man" posture used in textbook and magazine pic-

---

[9] Cook, *Prehistory and Earth Models*, p. 10.

[10] This periodical may be ordered from 2717 Cranbrook Road, Ann Arbor, Michigan 48104. (1973 price, $11 per year.)

[11] Neanderthals had a brain cage which averaged 7.5 percent larger than present-day cranial capacity, "remarkable for its absolute size." Cro-Magnons, who are not thought to be descendants of the Neanderthals, had even larger brain capacity, ranging from 14 to 29 percent larger than that of modern man. (*Encyclopaedia Britannica*, 1967, Vol. 2, p. 51 and Vol. 6, p. 792).

[12] *Encyclopaedia Britannica* (1967), s.v. "anthropology."

tures of Neanderthal man is an interesting story. The *Encyclopaedia Britannica* of 1967 gave this explanation, embarrassing for evolutionists:

> The popular conception that these people were slouched in posture and walked with a shuffling, bent-knee gait seems to have been due in large part to the faulty reconstruction of the skull base and to the misinterpretation of certain features of the limb bones of one of the Neanderthal skeletons discovered early in the 20th century.[13]

Perhaps it is best to be skeptical of the recurring spectacular claims of important finds of ancient man that are always showing up in the news media. The dogmatic statements made by some anthropologists are sometimes withdrawn later. The scientist may change his mind, or new discoveries may prove his first pronouncement to be a wrong diagnosis. Initially, however, it is made to sound absolutely certain: "This is not a theory. It is a fact," one well-known anthropologist was quoted in a news report of a new find. We recalled that his father, also an anthropologist, had reversed himself after some similar dogmatic claims.

Ever since an eager young Dutch university lecturer named Eugene Dubois went to Java determined to find the "missing link," and discovered a few bones in 1891, the "Java man," now called *Homo erectus*, has been an evolutionary mainstay in the supposed descent of man, in spite of early controversy between scientists over interpretation of the find.

Upsetting news, however, has just been announced from Australia. Remains of 40 human beings were unearthed, whom scientists estimate were buried "a scant 10,000 years ago." *Scientific American* of October, 1972, relayed a report "that the overall skull form includes archaic features that preserve almost unmodified the morphology typical of *Homo erectus* fossils from Java, combined with elements reminiscent of early representatives of Homo sapiens" (p. 48).

But, we should remember, *Homo erectus* was supposed to be long departed from the scene at that recent period of the evolutionary timetable, having flourished instead around 700,000 years ago. Researchers studying the Australian fossils included A. G. Thorne, of the Australian National University, and P. G. Macumber, of the Geological Survey of Victoria, who co-authored

[13] *Encyclopaedia Britannica* (1967), s.v. "Neanderthal Man."

a report in *Nature*. Thus another stalwart among evolutionary "proofs" has been rendered virtually useless. (Check into the subject, and you may be surprised to find how little real evidence anthropologists have for "ancient man" and missing links.)

The various skull shapes *arranged in series* in some popular magazine articles and in museum displays are largely the result of artists' imagination. These presentations do not accurately reflect real evidence in many instances. As we have seen, skull shape seems not to affect brain capacity anyway. More than one thoughtful peruser of such pictures has later watched people with all of those same skull shapes walk by on some busy city street.

Since proponents of evolution *must* have gradual development of human beings through the ages, one can expect more spectacular evolutionary announcements. Just remember Columbus and the "Indians" and the matter of overview discussed earlier. Columbus had his mind set on India and so the people he discovered had to fit the theory. He named them Indians. Evolutionary crusaders like Dubois and L. S. B. Leakey tended to identify every bone and artifact in a way that would enhance their previous belief. That is human nature, of course, and scientists should not be expected to be less human than other people, in this regard.

There are men living in caves even today. One can imagine future evolutionary anthropologists some day puzzling over campfire remains where the author and a group of teenage boys lived in a large cave when trapped by a summer snowstorm in the California Sierras. Fortunately, we left no human bones.

In June, 1971, scientists found a primitive tribe living as cave dwellers in Tasaday Forest in the Philippines. "They are challenging the basic ideas about the life of man," said Manuel Elizalde, leader of an expedition which studied them. This discovery "could lead to a new understanding of prehistoric man," scientists said. These stone age people don't fit the cave man image of cartoons, and have been described as "brilliant," and having quick wit.[14]

Horses and Dinosaurs

Among long-vaunted citadels of evolutionary faith that are

---

[14] Wire service reports in the *Herald-Examiner* (Los Angeles, 3/27/72), p. A4; (3/29/72), p. A3; and (3/30/72), p. A15.

now beginning to quake is Old Faithful, the horse. For many decades, the horse has been a prize exhibit in biology classrooms to exemplify straight-line evolution. It was supposed to have evolved from the dawn horse, "eohippus," now called *hyracotherium.*

As the reader may know, to follow all the presumed stages of the fossil series required one to jump back and forth between America and Europe.

Growing questions have led some leading evolutionists to become a bit wary of this animal. For example, G. A. Kerkut (Southampton University, Department of Physiology and Biochemistry) pointed out areas of uncertainty when he wrote, "The actual story depends to a large extent upon who is telling it and when the story is being told. In fact, one could easily discuss the evolution of the story of the evolution of the horse."[15]

One difficulty, Kerkut says, is that "at present . . . it is a matter of faith that the textbook pictures are true, or even that they are the best representations of the truth that are available to us at the present time."[16] He indicates that it is very hard to track down how much actual fossil evidence exists for various stages.

Dinosaurs are supposed by evolutionists to have become extinct no later than 70 million years ago, and man is not supposed to have come on the stage earlier than one or two million years before the present. Yet fossilized footprints giving every appearance of being human have been found in the same stone as dinosaur tracks in the Paluxy River bed in Texas, both evidently made before the rock hardened.[17] Fossils of trilobites, assertedly extinct for 230 million years, are documented in sandal-shod human footprints in Cambrian rock at Antelope Springs, Utah.[18] (The Cambrian period refers to the time span of from 500 to 600 million years ago.)

Given a worldwide flood, as described in the Bible, in geological evidence, and in the folklore of tribes around the world,

---

[15] G. A. Kerkut, *Implications of Evolution* (New York: Pergamon Press, 1960), pp. 144, 145.

[16] Ibid., p. 148. Also, for a complete study on this subject: Frank W. Cousins, "A Note on the Unsatisfactory Nature of the Horse Series of Fossils as Evidence for Evolution," *Creation Research Society Quarterly,* Vol. 8 (September 1971), pp. 99 ff.

[17] C. L. Burdick, "Changing Concepts Concerning Evolution," *The Naturalist,* Vol. 16 (Spring, 1957), pp. 38-41.

[18] William J. Meister, Sr., "Discovery of Trilobite Fossils in Shod Footprint of Human in 'Trilobite Beds'—A Cambrian Formation, Antelope Springs, Utah," *Creation Research Society Quarterly,* Vol. 5 (December 1968), pp. 97-102.

the dinosaurs would have perished in great numbers. If a few survived via the ark of Noah (young ones would have been chosen!), these may have become extinct soon after, yet late enough to be described, as some Bible scholars believe, in the ancient book of Job, chapters 40 and 41. It is also conceivable that the "dragons" perpetuated in myth and tradition in many countries from Japan to England may have originated from descriptions handed down of certain types of dinosaur which they resemble.

Coal and Oil Deposits

On the evolutionary scale, most coal deposits were formed earlier than 250,000,000 years ago, some being 400,000,000 years old. Oil deposits as well are presumed to be very old, resulting from organic remains of ancient creatures. Professor Cook writes, however:

> Among the strongest arguments for a maximum age of less than 10^5 [100,000] years is the occurrence of abnormally high (in some cases actually geostatic) fluid pressures in deep well drill holes. Such high pressures require sudden deep burial. Moreover, to retain them for periods greater than 10^4-10^5 years is apparently impossible under the observed permeabilities of reservoir and trap formations. . . . Coalification and the occurrence of coal deposits also seem, from a consideration of basic facts, to require short history; *coalification in a few years is an observed fact* (italics added).[19]

On a related subject, Professor George Mulfinger has demonstrated by experiments at Bob Jones University that stalactite formation may require months or years rather than long ages of time for formation.

Several scientists have reported making oil and coal from organic matter in hours or less. Some of the methods might have produced such results *naturally*, in a few years time.

Fossils and the Flood

A catastrophic flood of the gigantic proportions described in Genesis would have provided the best known source of the observed arrangement of fossils. An excellent book mentioned earlier, *The Genesis Flood,* contains a very thorough scientific investigation of the evidence involved, as well as complete

---

[19] Cook, *Prehistory and Earth Models,* p. 341.

reports on many other matters such as the occurrence together of human tracks and dinosaur tracks.[20]

Few people realize how far from convincing the evolutionary story from fossils really is. For example, "some 25 major phyla are recognized for all the animals, and in virtually not a single case is there fossil evidence to demonstrate what the common ancestry of any two phyla looked like."[21] The same esteemed authors admit that "we still search for the ancestors of the dominant group of modern plants, the angiosperms."[22]

Concerning the evolution of algae, three other noted authors say, "The relationships *between* divisions are completely obscure. The primary origin of the eucaryotic algae as a whole is accordingly an unsolved (and no doubt insoluble) problem."[23]

These authors of the advanced textbook, *The Microbial World*, remind us that the best known method of classifying living things came about by "the restructuring of hierarchies to mirror evolutionary relationships. A taxonomic system in which this is an avowed goal is known as a *phylogenetic system*."[24] This is the system used in most textbooks on zoology.

They further state, however, that "the course that evolution has actually followed can be ascertained only from direct historical evidence, contained in the fossil record. This record is at best fragmentary and becomes almost completely illegible in Precambrian rocks. . . ."[25]

Of classifications other than plants and vertebrates, they write:

> For all other major biological groups, the general course of evolution will probably never be known, and there is simply not enough objective evidence to base their classification on phylogenetic grounds.
>
> For these and other reasons, most modern taxonomists have explicitly abandoned the phylogenetic approach in favor of a more empirical one: . . . quantification of similarities and differences.[26]

---

[20] John C. Whitcomb, Jr., and Henry M. Morris, *The Genesis Flood* (Philadelphia: Presbyterian and Reformed Publishing Co., 1961.) This book may be ordered from The Institute of Creation Research, 2716 Madison Avenue, San Diego, California 92116. (As of 1973, $6.95 cloth, $3.95 paperback.)

[21] Philip Handler, ed., *Biology and the Future of Man* (New York: Oxford University Press, 1970), p. 506.

[22] Ibid., p. 509.

[23] Roger Y. Stanier, Michael Doudoroff, and Edward A. Adelberg, *The Microbial World*, 3rd ed., (Englewood Cliffs, N.J.: Prentice-Hall, Inc., 1970), p. 99.

[24] Ibid., p. 528.

[25] Ibid., pp. 528, 529.

[26] Ibid., p. 529.

This new system is called *numerical taxonomy.* It provides a welcome release from evolutionary classifications. It is likely that its full acceptance will be slow for philosophical overview reasons described in chapter 11.

The fossil creature with the generic name *Archaeopteryx* has been widely used to prove that birds descended from reptiles. This interpretation is now beclouded, says the *1970 Britannica Yearbook of Science and the Future* (pp. 397, 398):

> Some years ago, the distinguished British anatomist G. R. de Beer made a plaster cast of this brain region and concluded from his examination that *Archaeopteryx,* for all its long tail and feathers, had a reptilian-type brain. Recently, however, a Stanford (Calif.) University zoologist borrowed de Beer's cast and reached a different conclusion. [Namely: that although small, it was a bird brain after all.]

The closest living relative of birds, in evolutionary belief, is the crocodile! Most people on first hearing of that idea are likely to think, "They must be joking." That is, however, the standard doctrine. Vertebrate paleontologist J. W. Ostrom, of Yale University, is a specialist on dinosaurs. In a 1973 conversation, he told the author interesting facts about pterosaurs (flying reptiles) and about *Archaeopteryx,* specimens of which he had recently studied. The latter, he believes, was carnivorous, and was a ground dweller, in some ways like the present-day secretary bird. Ostrom theorizes that *Archaeopteryx* evolved from an ancestor which was a coelurosaurian dinosaur.

There is much still unknown about this rare bird.[27] Only a few imperfect fossils have been found, in a quarry in Bavaria. In spite of some mysterious features, the creature is widely recognized as actually *avian* (bird), largely because the feathers and their arrangement on the wings are precisely as in modern birds. Also, the clavicles are fused into a "wishbone" and the foot has an opposable toe. Some other features are different from modern birds—teeth and a bony tail, for examples. Much has been made of its claws on the wings. Ornithologist Thomas

---

[27] The authors of the highly regarded volumes of *Avian Biology* wrote about *Archaeopteryx:* "Unknown are the links connecting this momentous find to its reptilian ancestors on the one hand and to its avian descendants on the other." Although tempted to draw conclusions, they said, "Without paleontological support . . . conclusions must remain hypothetical." (Ed., Donald S. Farner and James R. King, Vol. I [N.Y.: Academic Press, 1971], p. 20.) It seems clear that there is no real evidence or proof that *Archaeopteryx* evolved from *anything.*

R. Howell, of UCLA, assured me that there is a modern bird in South America, called the hoatzin, which also possesses claws when young, using them for climbing around on tree branches.

We may wonder if possibly the great Designer planned *Archaeopteryx* with a bit of humor, like that suggested by the elephant's high-pitched voice and the mixed-up features of the duck-billed platypus. Perhaps the Creator is just independent enough to do things His way, instead of as we would suppose.

Later in this chapter, there will be a list of excellent books (including some already quoted, like *The Genesis Flood*) which go deeply into many of these subjects of vital interest on which space allows us only a few paragraphs.

One interesting sidelight on the concept of a universal flood is this: in addition to water derived from volcanic action (when "the fountains of the great deep were broken up" as the Bible describes this in Genesis 7:11), some scientists believe such a flood as described would have involved the prior existence of some kind of "canopy"—perhaps water vapor—surrounding the earth several miles above the surface.[28] It is hypothesized that this would have screened out the ultraviolet rays, some of which now manage to filter through the ozone shield and which may be involved in the aging process. This would explain the long life-span of people who lived before the flood, according to the Bible. Immediately after the flood, the life span dropped by degrees, but rather rapidly, to present levels. Mutations caused by ultraviolet rays and perhaps other incoming radiation would have begun on a different scale without the protective canopy.

Evidence Accumulating for a Young Earth

A universal flood would also doubtless have affected rates and conditions of some or all of the methods of dating the past. It is even conceivable, though perhaps unlikely, that God utilized a near-collision of a comet that could also have affected timing on the moon at the same time as the flood, when the "windows of heaven were opened" (Gen. 7:11). Such a comet was suggested by Immanuel Velikovsky in his controversial book, *Worlds in Collision*.[29] (Velikovsky suggested that Venus was once a comet! This provoked much dispute.)

---

[28] Whitcomb and Morris, *The Genesis Flood*, pp. 399-405.

[29] Velikovsky, *Worlds in Collision* (New York: Doubleday & Co., Inc., 1950). As regards reliability of dating the past, Frederick B. Jueneman, a research director, recently wrote concerning the explosion which astronomers believe re-

Evidence is accumulating that it is not unscientific to consider that the earth may after all be quite young. The reader may already be aware of the "circular reasoning" upon which the geologic time scale was built. In simple terms, the age of the rock strata is determined by what kinds of *fossils* they contain. And how is the age of a fossil determined? By the *rock stratum* in which it is found!

Many believe God originally would have created things in operating condition. Entities such as living trees would have been created with some of them in mature form, especially in the garden of Eden, which "God planted." These would give an "appearance of age" even though freshly created, just as Adam and Eve were created as adults. These trees would have provided their first food. Distant stars would be made with light already spanning the distance to earth. Full-grown animals would look as if they had been living from birth or from the egg. This is a reasonable assumption, given an all-wise Creator. Even earthly architects plant half-grown and full-grown trees in front of new public buildings.

Pollen grains of "pine" trees and of flowering plants have been found in *pre-Cambrian* strata of the Grand Canyon.[30] Pre-Cambrian, the reader may recall, refers to very ancient times, more than 600 million years ago, in the geologic time scale. According to usual evolutionary views, there were practically no plants on land at that assumed distant time, except possibly some algae or mosses. Concerning the *Cambrian* period, which is supposed to have been more recent, a high school textbook of 1969 states this customary position: "There is little evidence of Cambrian life on the land surfaces. Only very low forms of plant life could have existed on the exposed rocks."[31]

---

sulted in a pulsar called Vela-X (PSR 0833-45) about 11,000 years ago and comparatively nearby: "Being so close, the anisotropic neutrino flux of the superexplosion must have had the peculiar characteristic of resetting all our atomic clocks. This would knock our carbon-14, potassium-argon, and uranium-lead dating measurements into a cocked hat! The age of prehistoric artifacts, the age of the earth, and that of the universe would be thrown into doubt." (*Industrial Research* [September, 1972], p. 15, as quoted by Duane T. Gish, "Speculations by a Scientist," *ICR Acts and Facts*, Vol. 2 [March, 1973].) The reason for such an effect, some physicists now think, is that neutrinos trigger the decay of radioactive atoms and such an explosion as that mentioned would produce a tremendous flux of neutrinos, thus speeding up some forms of radioactivity.

30 Clifford Burdick, "Microflora of the Grand Canyon," *Creation Research Society Quarterly*, Vol. 3, (May 1966), pp. 38, 39, 50.

31 William L. Ramsey, et al., *Modern Earth Science* (New York: Holt, Rinehart and Winston, 1969), pp. 394, 395.

Evidence of the existence of life as advanced as flowering plants and pine-related trees in that supposedly ancient period is startling to evolutionists. It is undeniable that such finds have been made in Cambrian and pre-Cambrian strata, even by scientists of evolutionary persuasion. S. Leclercq of the University of Liege, Belgium, reported on his research in an article in *Evolution.* He says, "Such a remarkable variety of spores[32] in Cambrian sediments is impressive and certainly unexpected."[33] From an evolutionary standpoint, this would mean, he indicates, that a lot of development had to take place far earlier than had been supposed.

Oparin, unable to deny the existence of such spores, says, regarding a subsection of the pre-Cambrian period:

> Sequence . . . greatly confused and distorted. In particular, in several cases we have had to recognize that the layers of Riphean formations sometimes contain plant fragments and spores of a considerably younger age than would be expected from the geological data of that location. Apparently they were sometimes carried there from overlying strata.[34]

That this is not the correct explanation is clear from the very thorough procedures used by Clifford Burdick in his Grand Canyon research, where pollen grains were found in pre-Cambrian and other strata. He concludes:

> Finding of spores of plants at least closely related to pines in the pre-Cambrian makes it extremely difficult to visualize any evolutionary development of these specialized plants. The undoubted occurrence of pollen of flowering plants is even more difficult to explain in usually accepted evolutionary concepts.[35]

It is clear that *the long ages of the geologic time scale are a matter of faith rather than evidence.* Davidheiser points out that frequently strata lie just above others believed to be much older where there is no evidence of erosion to account for the disappearance of the strata that should have been between them. He says, "This is a serious problem, but it is disregarded. Sometimes fossils are found in reverse order, with the older above

---

[32] Spores are plant reproductive cells capable of developing into complete organisms. They are encased in a hard outer shell to withstand environmental hazards.

[33] S. Leclercq, "Evidence of Vascular Plants in the Cambrian," *Evolution,* Vol. X, No. 2 (June, 1956), pp. 109, 111.

[34] A. I. Oparin, *Genesis and Evolutionary Development of Life* (New York: Academic Press, 1968), p. 190.

[35] Burdick, "Microflora," p. 50.

the younger. This is explained as due to thrust-faulting, where older strata have slid across the top of younger." There is no evidence, however, of the tremendous friction that would have occurred, he says, in such faulting.[36]

Further Indications of a Young Earth and Universe

John G. Read, quoted earlier, is another scientist who was formerly an evolutionist—also an atheist—who abandoned evolution after considering the evidence. Read has recently calculated the age of the oceans as indicated by their nitrate content with relation to the rate of addition from rivers annually. He says that only a small amount of nitrate is lost by return to the atmosphere, since nitrates in the seas are very stable.[37]

C. C. Delwiche estimates thirty million metric tons of nitrates and nitrogen in organic materials reach the ocean each year.[38] Most of the nitrates, according to Read, would remain and build up, thus making possible a "nitrate chronology" for the oceans. Read's conclusion is that the oceans, by this chronology, are approximately 6,000 years old.[39]

Other facts which seem to require a revision "of models of origin and interrelationships of species," as listed by Melvin A. Cook, are as follows:

> The helium content of the atmosphere, its exudation rate from the lithosphere, and the maximum possible rate of loss into the exosphere indicate a maximum atmospheric age at around 10^4-10^5 years.
>
> The uranium content of the oceans, the flux rate into the oceans, the relatively small uranium content of the ocean sediments and absence of any other uranium 'sink' suggest a maximum age for the oceans of 10^5 years.
>
> Isotopic ratios of lead and strontium seem to show that

---

36 Bolton Davidheiser, *Evolution and Christian Faith* (Nutley, N.J.: Presbyterian and Reformed Publishing Co., 1969), p. 286.

Many geologists accept the extreme assumption that the Matterhorn in the Alps was pushed more than thirty miles over younger rocks. Mythen Peaks, also in the Alps, must have been pushed all the way from North Africa, according to the theory.

Prominent Netherlands geologist J. H. F. Umbgrove wrote that Swiss geologists had generally accepted E. Argand's idea that much of the Alps came from "overthrusting Africa over Europe" (J. H. F. Umbgrove, *Symphony of the Earth* [The Hague: Martinus Nijhoff, 1950], pp. 27, 78).

Some, including Umbgrove, held that the movement was somewhat less distant. Apparently, evolutionists need this overthrust theory as a means of preserving the geological time scale because of fossils found in the Mythen, for example.

37 John G. Read, personal telephone conversation, 1971.

38 C. C. Delwiche, "The Nitrogen Cycle," *Scientific American* (September, 1970), p. 146.

39 Read, conversation mentioned above.

> the age of the earth is small relative to the half-life of corresponding radioactive sources. Uranium-thorium-lead chronometry is discordant and anomalous when interpreted conventionally, but the uranium-lead picture turns out to be remarkably consistent when re-interpreted in terms of possible (η, γ) reactions and the effects of leaching uranium ores in relatively recent times. Leaching has obviously occurred; it is the only explanation for extremely large Pb^{206}/Pb^{204} and Pb^{207}/Pb^{204} ratios. Under a leaching mechanism one cannot have large ratios without having all lesser gradations of enrichment. The Sr^{86}/Sr^{87} ratios also bear out a short history of the earth. . . .
>
> From the observed magnetism and rates of decay of natural remanent magnetization the upper limit of the age of lavas exhibiting paleomagnetism appears to be below 10^5 years.[40]

In view of such evidence, it would seem reasonable to keep an open mind toward the possibility that, after all, earth's past may be measurable in thousands rather than billions of years. Don't, however, expect any dedicated materialist to consider that possibility even in his wildest moments.

As to age outside of the solar system, one of the means of judging age is the measure of the distance and the speed of recession of stars and galaxies. This method is based on faith in the theory of uniformity, and does not take into account that a creation would *not* necessarily have had to originate in a "Big Bang" with all matter at the center of the universe, and with stellar progression beginning without diversity of phase. A Creator could create a river with water already present in all stages of descent from source to mouth from the moment of its creation. The same could be true in regard to light—it could already have been en route between distant stars and the earth, if part of His plan included the reception of that light on earth.

How Old Is the Moon?

Since the first Apollo moon landing at Tranquility Base, the public has often been given estimates of the age of the moon rocks, and these commonly are above four billion years. It is

---

[40] Cook, *Prehistory and Earth Models*, pp. 340, 341.

Dr. Cook, who is chairman of the board at IRECO Chemicals, said in answer to my inquiry that he had a limited number of copies of this book available. He may be addressed c/o IRECO Chemicals, Suite 726, Kennecott Building, Salt Lake City, Utah, 84111 ($6.50 postpaid, as of 1973). His book presupposes some knowledge of higher mathematics, geology, physics, and chemistry for full understanding, and contains exceedingly worthwhile information.

seldom realized how much the evolutionary overview may have affected such conclusions. Dr. Melvin A. Cook, and others since, have pointed out reasons why these dates cannot be trusted, referring particularly to data on moon samples documented in numerous reports in *Science* (Moon Issue), January, 1970. Most of the information in this section is from articles by Dr. Cook and personal conversations we had in late 1972.

The inert gases (helium, neon, argon, krypton, xenon) found in moon rock and soil samples are "surface correlated" rather than "bulk correlated." This means that the gases are not absorbed throughout the center of the rock or soil particle, but are instead *adsorbed* or attached to its surface.

According to the standard evolutionary view, the gases would have been produced for billions of years in the moon's surface, and should be found throughout the rocks, and this would be expected if these gases were indigenous or radiogenic, produced by radioactivity as postulated in dating techniques which measure these gases. This fact was not sufficiently taken into account. According to Cook, even the limited amount of gases remaining, after surface gases were removed by "acid etching" in some cases, cannot properly be concluded to be solely of radiogenic origin. Since "surface concentrations were thousands of times greater than bulk concentrations for all entrapped rare gases,"[41] this concentration gradient would tend to be a driving force for at least some diffusion into the rock from its surface. This diffused gas, if mistakenly considered as wholly radiogenic in origin, would produce inaccurate dating results.

If these surface-adsorbed noble gases were not from within the moon's surface, what was their source? Interestingly, the ratios of these rare gases on moon solids is remarkably similar to ratios of the same gases in the *solar wind* (which is a constant stream of particles from the sun). It is therefore quite possible or probable that their source on the moon samples is adsorption from solar wind, an explanation that would account for the surface correlation of the gases.

One would expect considerable "fractionation" of the entrapped gases if they were indigenous, during the billions of

---

[41] Melvin A. Cook, "Rare Gas Adsorption on Solids of the Lunar Regolith," *Journal of Colloid and Interface Science,* Vol. 38, No. 1 (January, 1972), p. 18.
Dr. Cook received the E. V. Murphee award from the American Chemical Society in 1968 while he was Professor of Metallurgy at the University of Utah, as well as the 1968 Nitro-Nobel Gold Medal.

years involved—that is, the lighter gases would have escaped from the rocks in greater degree than the heavier. Instead, the ratios hold remarkably well, being roughly proportional to the solar wind ratios.

A factor which renders all the clocks useless is that the moon has apparently been subjected in "recent" times to surface temperatures between 1000° and 1300° C. This is shown, among other things, by a "glaze" still remaining on its surface, and by the fact that moon samples are depleted in all substances which boil below about 1300° C as compared to the composition of comparable rocks of earth. (The similarity between earth rocks of corresponding type is quite close as to composition involving substances which have higher boiling points.) Moon samples were also somewhat depleted in lead, which melts at 327.3° C.

It can easily be seen what such heating would have done to the time clocks which depend on elements which boil or vaporize below that 1000-1300° C range. Potassium, the key element of the potassium-argon system of dating, vaporizes at 744° C, and rubidium, main element of the rubidium-strontium technique, boils at 688° C. Furthermore, uranium, starting element of the uranium series, melts at 1132.3° C, and therefore, like lead, might be expected to be less stable as to location under those high temperatures to which the moon was subjected. The consequent migration or movement of all these elements in vaporized or in melted form would be expected to give the divergent and anomalous dating results that are actually found.

The ages of moon rocks ranged (in the reports) from 2.2 billion to 8.2 billion years, which is a spread of over 6 billion years! "Exposure" ages included much shorter times, even down to 1,000 years. Scientists from the Departments of Geology and Space Science at Rice University were among those who were convinced that the rare gases were of solar wind origin. They wrote, "We conclude that most of the inert gases were implanted in the fragments from the solar wind and from cosmic rays of greater intensity." As to exposure ages, they said, "We estimate that the average 'hemispheral' exposure of a 250 [micrometer] fragment to solar wind of present-day intensity was [around] 10^3 years. . . . However, a calculation based on ^{84}Kr

gives [around] 10^4 years.... These times become much longer if solar cosmic rays were the source of the gas."[42]

If the moon's surface had been producing radiogenic gases such as helium for four billion years, this would create an unsolvable (at present) problem similar to that on earth, in the light of the geological ages view. Dr. Cook went into considerable detail on this matter in a 1957 article in *Nature*.[43] Attempts to account for the tremendous amount of helium that would have been produced on earth during that span of time leave a discrepancy of around "five orders of magnitude," or a factor of 10^5 times too little. That article is quite enlightening on the probable young age of the atmosphere. The question embarrassing to those who postulate the geological time scale is: Where is the earth's radiogenic helium? "The same dilemma," says Professor Cook, "now appears to arise for the moon!"[44]

While it is impossible for the reasons given to date the moon, Dr. Cook gives some indications, particularly in view of the helium situation just mentioned. He suggests that the moon's age (the age of its present surface condition at least) may be measured, as an upper bound, in tens of thousands of years rather than billions.

To summarize, the moon rock dates in billions of years cannot be maintained because:

1. The main elements used in dating techniques would have vaporized or melted during high temperatures that have affected the moon's surface in recent times. Since those elements would have therefore moved about, this spoils their use for accurate dating, and partially accounts for the widely differing dates.

2. The rare gases on moon rocks and soil particles cannot properly be used in dating processes, because these inert gases evidently did not come from radiogenic sources on the moon

---

[42] D. Heymann et al., "Inert Gases in Lunar Samples," *Science,* Vol. 167 (January 30, 1970), pp. 555-558.

In 1971, Leon T. Silver proposed that "volatization of materials on the lunar surface could be what was messing up the age-dating results. If material has lost rubidium, for example, it would appear older than it actually is." More recently, Paul W. Gast asked, "Where has all the rubidium gone?" and answered, "We don't know." (As reported in "A Solution to the Lunar Soil's Age Discrepancy," *Science News,* Vol. 103 [March 24, 1973], p. 182.) A new theory to save the long ages of orthodox dating is that bombardment of the lunar surface caused agglutinates, with loss of rubidium, but this theory has yet to be confirmed.

[43] Melvin A. Cook, "Where Is the Earth's Radiogenic Helium?" *Nature,* Vol. 179, No. 4552 (January 26, 1957), p. 213.

[44] Cook, *Journal of Colloid and Interface Science,* p. 18.

but most likely instead had their origin in the solar wind. This is indicated by the fact that gas ratios in the two are proportional, and that the gases are adsorbed on the surface of the rocks and particles rather than absorbed evenly throughout the samples. Since the main dating methods used for the lunar samples involve these gases, the dates are untrustworthy.

We are not suggesting that anyone *must* accept a young age for the universe. From experience we know that such a thought might at first strike a person as "incredible," in the light of what science supposedly has proved. As the evidence pointing to a young age continues to grow in quantity and quality, however, logic does seem to require that reasonable persons now give consideration to the possibility that it is not unscientific to question the geological age scale. It turns out to be rather exhilarating to think that the first chapters of Genesis may after all be interpreted literally and without the need to fit in the long ages somewhere.

Getting back to the moon, perhaps many who have been convinced that materialism is the only scientific philosophy were surprised at the emphasis on the Creator from astronauts on Apollo flights via television. First there was the reading of the Bible's creation narrative from moon orbit, commemorated on a U.S. postage stamp. After other such incidents, one astronaut was later interviewed while taking part in Christmas religious services in Jerusalem. He told of the unexpected "closeness of God" of which he was conscious during his three days on the moon. The news reporter credited this for his new "religiosity." The fact that astronauts are highly intelligent, well-educated, emotionally mature men added to the impact of what to many seemed to be a strange turn of events.

Life in Outer Space

Periodically there are reports that would lead a person to think that there is evidence that life must have evolved elsewhere in the universe, because, for example, amino acids or other "organic" compounds (carbon compounds) have been found in meteorites.

The presence of amino acids does not indicate life or its beginning. Living things use many compounds that exist also in nonliving nature—water, for example. Life consists, in part, of "nonliving molecules organized to live." The probability of getting the parts in right order, as we have seen, is utterly infinitesimal without first having the whole system of DNA and its complex array of precision machinery.

Life Created in the Laboratory?

Even if scientists ever manage to put together something which could correctly be described as "alive," it would be the result of their long, intelligent, purposeful effort. It would provide no evidence whatever that such a thing could ever have happened without conscious intelligence directing every condition. The Christian need not lose his balance over claims of such accomplishments. Exaggeration is nothing new either for the apologist for evolution or for the reporter who needs a story.[45] Both are only human like the rest of the people you meet each day.

Dr. Edward Teller, noted for his work on the hydrogen bomb, said at a 1970 Chicago meeting of the American Association for the Advancement of Science (regarding the exploits of scientists during World War II and after): "What scientists have gained in success, they have lost in modesty."[46] Of course, only a few of the outspoken ones are thus guilty.

Comparative Anatomy

What does it prove if there are similarities in the skeletal structure of different animals? Evolutionists interpret it as a sequence of development from lower types to higher, because that fits their overview. The facts fit even better in the framework of the overview of a Creator who used similar plans with variations adapted to the needs of the particular creatures. Henry Ford could have invented cars and trucks at the same time—vehicles that are similar, yet adapted to different purposes.

Proponents of evolution sometimes exaggerate wildly in this regard in the formation of museum and classroom displays for the purpose of providing gradual gradation from one type to another. Actually, however, the supposed sequence is plagued with gaps and discontinuities and other problems.

A better explanation is this: "Creationists believe that when God created the vertebrates, He used a single blueprint for the body plan but varied the plan so that each 'kind' would be

---

45 As explained at the start of chapter 9, no one has yet created "life" in the laboratory, and the likelihood is small that it will ever be done. Every synthesis of any main component of living cells has depended upon the use of one or more complex molecules which were made in an actual living cell.

46 *Science News,* Vol. 99 (January 2, 1971), p. 6.

perfectly equipped to take its place in the world." This logical statement is from the nonevolutionary high school textbook, *Biology, A Search for Order in Complexity.*[47]

Dr. George Howe, in a paper presented to the National Association of Biology Teachers, said, "The teacher who has a real interest in academic honesty and professional ethics will... present the creationist alternative adequately in both the classroom and the laboratory."[48]

Amino Acid Sequences in Proteins

It may be of interest to look at some actual sequences of the twenty common amino acids which make up all proteins and many other shorter molecules essential to life.[49] It is fascinating that the mere difference in the order of these units in the chain causes such varied products as human growth hormone and rattlesnake venom (which, by the way, enables the snake to capture prey and begins the digestion of it).

1. *Insulin.* The Alpha chain is identical in human, pig, sperm whale, dog, and rabbit. The Beta chain, on the other hand, is identical in human and elephant. For abbreviations of the amino acids, see Figure 3 on page 101.

Here is the sequence for human insulin. A dash indicates the start of the Beta chain.

> Gly Ile Val Glu Gln Cys Cys Thr Ser Ile Cys Ser Leu Tyr Gln Leu Glu Asn Tyr Cys Asn – Phe Val Asn Gln His Leu Cys Gly Ser His Leu Val Glu Ala Leu Tyr Leu Val Cys Gly Glu Arg Gly Phe Phe Tyr Thr Pro Lys Thr

2. *Apamine.* This is one of the several toxins in bee sting and consists of a very short chain of amino acids:

> Cys Asn Cys Lys Ala Pro Glu Thr Ala Leu Cys Ala Arg Arg Cys Gln Gln His

3. *Cytochrome c.* This is an important protein used in the energy cycle of apparently all organisms except certain pro-

---

[47] John N. Moore and Harold Schultz Slusher, eds., *Biology: A Search for Order in Complexity* (Grand Rapids: Zondervan Publishing House, 1970), p. 420. This is an excellent high school textbook. The publisher's address is 1415 Lake Drive, S.E., Grand Rapids, Michigan 49506.

[48] George Howe, "Homology, Analogy, and Innovative Teaching," presented at 1972 National Convention of the National Association of Biology Teachers at San Francisco on October 27, 1972.

[49] The data in this section are from Margaret O. Dayhoff, *Atlas of Protein Sequence and Structure 1972* (National Biomedical Research Foundation, Washington, D.C., 1972.) The interpretations are our own.

caryotes, simplest of organisms. It plays a key part in the reactions that take place in mitochondria to be described later.

When one compares the sequences of cytochrome *c* chains from various organisms, he discovers that although they differ, there are remarkable similarities. An identical section of eleven amino acids occurs in virtually all species examined to date. The sequence given below is that of human cytochrome *c*. We will compare it with the cytochrome *c* of Baker's yeast by italicizing the amino acids which are identical in both:

> *Gly* Asp Val Glu *Lys Gly* Lys Lys Ile *Phe* Ile Met Lys *Cys* Ser Gln *Cys His Thr Val Glu Lys Gly Gly* Lys *His Lys* Thr *Gly Pro Asn Leu His Gly* Leu *Phe Gly Arg* Lys Thr *Gly Gln Ala* Pro *Gly Tyr Ser Tyr Thr* Ala *Ala Asn* Lys Asn *Lys* Gly Ile Ile *Trp* Gly *Glu* Asp Thr Leu Met *Glu Tyr Leu* Glu *Asn Pro Lys Lys Tyr Ile Pro Gly Thr Lys Met* Ile *Phe* Val *Gly* Ile *Lys Lys* Lys Glu Glu *Arg* Ala *Asp Leu Ile* Ala *Tyr Leu Lys Lys Ala* Thr Asn Glu[50]

Sequence comparison is new as an assumed evidence for evolution. The idea is that more closely related organisms have fewer differences. Although this works for some comparisons, many others directly contradict that premise.

Rattlesnake cytochrome *c* is closer to human (14 differences) than to rhesus monkey (15), dog (21), penguin (30), or even a fellow reptile, the snapping turtle (22)! Human beings are closer to the pekin duck (11) than to a fellow mammal, the horse (12). Tomatoes and sunflowers appear closer to human than to other mammal, reptile, amphibian, fish, insect, or yeast.

Mammals are said to have evolved from reptiles; these came from amphibians, and they arose from fish. By cytochrome *c* comparison, however, the dog as one extreme example is closer to carp (a fish) than to rattlesnake (reptile) or bullfrog (amphibian).

The data show that in closely related organisms, the corresponding place in the chain may be occupied by amino acids which differ greatly in size, acidity, and electrical properties. Some of the differences, moreover, would have required multiple mutations in the same codon to evolve one from the other—

[50] There are thus sixty-four sites with identical amino acids. Baker's yeast has five additional sites preceding locus number one of human cytochrome *c* and it ends one site earlier.

in the face of the laws of probability.

As can be seen, sequence comparison apparently is no real help for evolution. Given a Creator, however, sequences would match the needs. Some similar organisms would require similar sequences. In other cases, organisms that appear far different may have cellular needs for similar cytochrome *c*.[51]

Vestigial Organs

Materialists used to belabor Bible believers with a long list of "useless" vestigial and rudimentary organs, supposedly left over from prior evolutionary stages. Now, however, functions or adequate explanations have been discovered for most of the list. Take one dramatic example, the appendix!

> *The human appendix,* that tiny anatomical curiosity whose importance to health has long been doubted and debated, *may all along have been protecting other organs of the body against the attacks of cancer.* Evidence to support this startling view was presented at a California medical meeting by Howard R. Bierman, Clinical Professor of Medicine at Loma Linda University . . . [after a] 20-year study . . . (italics added).

The article went on to give details and concluded:

> As a theory, the human appendix may be an immunologic organ whose premature removal during its functioning period permits leukemia and other related forms of cancer to begin their development. The appendix is composed of lymphoid tissue, suggesting that like such other lymphoid organs as the tonsils and spleen it may secrete antibodies which protect the body against attacking viral agents.[52]

And evolutionists used to say that the appendix was a useless vestigial organ.

(To prevent alarm, Dr. Bierman stressed the belief that the

---

[51] A common explanation of the origin of complex genes is that they began as short chains which later grew by accidental repeating of some sequences, the duplicate sections then diverging by mutations. Strongly disputing this view are the investigations of A. D. McLachlan of the famed Laboratory of Molecular Biology at Cambridge, England. He concludes, "There is, therefore, no necessity to postulate that gene duplication . . . has been a dominant influence in the recent evolution of proteins." (A. D. McLachlan, "Repeating Sequences and Gene Duplication in Proteins," *Journal of Molecular Biology*, Vol. 64, [March 14, 1972], p. 431.)

Watson, moreover, suspects that repetitive sequences of "spacer DNA between other genes sometimes might be used to count time," to match the order in time when two genes' products are needed to begin functioning. (James Watson, *Molecular Biology of the Gene* [Menlo Park, Calif.: W. A. Benjamin, Inc., 1970], p. 546.)

[52] *Medical Times, Journal for the Family Physician* (September, 1966), p. 263a. Published in East Stroudsburg, Pa.

great majority of people would not be in heightened danger after an appendectomy.)

Embryonic Recapitulation

According to the recapitulation theory, the developing embryo exhibits some of the stages of the evolution through which its ancestors ascended. This idea has fallen into disfavor, though many persist in trotting it out.

> In recent years the idea has been all but abandoned for several reasons. Researchers have shown that the stages through which an embryo passes are necessary for its development from one cell to a complex organism. The heart, for example, develops as the demands on it increase.[53]

Further Reading on Assumed Proofs of Evolution

Since we are merely touching briefly on many of these subjects, some readers may wish to know where they can research more deeply into them. Bolton Davidheiser's *Evolution and Christian Faith*[54] (1969) contains a wealth of documented and interesting information along this line on such problems as fossils, comparative anatomy, vestigial and rudimentary organs, embryonic recapitulation, and many others. This book has a helpful and thorough study of the matter of theistic evolution as well (pages 168 ff.).

The high school textbook, *Biology: A Search for Order in Complexity* (1970), includes much helpful material on these subjects, while fulfilling its role as an excellent biology textbook.[55]

A compact pamphlet containing a world of documentation is: *Evolution, Science Falsely So-Called,* which may be ordered for only thirty-five cents including postage (1973) by residents of the United States and Canada from the address given below.[56] Dr. Henry M. Morris has authored several fine books of various lengths, which we also highly recommend.[57]

There are many other excellent books concerning evolution.

---

[53] Moore and Slusher, eds., *Biology,* p. 424.

[54] This book may be ordered from Dr. Bolton Davidheiser, Box 22, La Mirada, California 90638, $5.25 postpaid ($3.50 paperback). Other excellent publications of his are also available.

[55] The publisher's address was given in footnote 47, page 203.

[56] Order from: International Christian Crusade, 205 Yonge St., Room 31, Toronto 1, Canada.

[57] Names and prices of excellent books by this prolific author, a scientist highly knowledgeable on the evolution question, may be obtained by writing him at: Institute for Creation Research, 2716 Madison Avenue, San Diego, California 92116. Also articles and books by Dr. Duane T. Gish, biochemist, are available at the same Institute.

Professor A. E. Wilder Smith of Switzerland writes with helpful clarity on evolution. He holds *three* doctoral degrees in Organic Chemistry, etc. One of his best books is *Man's Origin, Man's Destiny* (Harold Shaw, Publishers, Wheaton, Illinois.)

The Vastness of the Universe

It overwhelms a person to consider the distances and numbers of galaxies of stars in this amazing cosmos. One may be inclined to think this presents a difficulty for believing in God and creation, but the difficulty is more apparent than real.

If we can conceive of a Creator who could make the earth, and its myriads of marvels, including life, who are we to suppose He would be limited to making one solar system, or one galaxy? And, in a sense, a living cell is more an evidence of creative ability than a star!

There is considerable uncertainty just how big the cosmos is.[58] Dr. Jesse L. Greenstein, who at that time was head of the Astronomy Department at the California Institute of Technology, told the author that, although fifteen billion light years or so is used by many as the radius of the universe, it is more a matter of common acceptance than actual evidence.[59] He said we can discern spiral galaxies thought to be out as far as five billion light years.

Wernher von Braun remarked on this subject: "Astronomy and space exploration are teaching us that the good Lord is a much greater Lord, and master of a greater kingdom."[60]

---

[58] It might be noted that there is substantial uncertainty of measurements beyond a few hundred or a few thousand light years. These measurements could be completely off if current formulas are wrong. This would affect estimates of the age of the universe as well.

Astronomers measure distance of a star or galaxy partly by what is known as its "redshift" or tendency of the light waves to shift to the longer or red end of the visible spectrum. This is supposed to be caused by recession, as the sound of a train whistle lowers in pitch as the train passes and moves away from you.

There is disagreement, however, as to whether redshift actually indicates distance. Well-known British astronomer Fred Hoyle wrote (1973) concerning very high-flux radio sources: "The absence of a significant correlation between redshifts and fluxes can be interpreted in two ways: *the optical redshifts are not distance indicators*, or the 26 sources in question constitute a fluctuation. In the first case, issues striking at the root of *our most cherished cosmological beliefs would be involved.*" (Italics added.) He referred, of course, to the vast distances and long ages, and the theory that the universe began with a big bang. F. Hoyle, "Radio Source Counts in Cosmology," *Nature*, Vol. 242 (March 9, 1973), pp. 108, 109. His article brought immediate refutation from others who defend those "cherished cosmological beliefs." Many other scientists, however, are likewise casting doubt on the idea that redshifts indicate distance.

[59] Telephone conversation, November, 1971.

[60] Wernher von Braun interview, AP dispatch, *The Cleveland Plain Dealer*, (July 19, 1969), p. 5.

Where Are Heaven and Hell?

The question may have occurred to the reader, where is heaven and where is hell? Haven't astronomy and space exploration made these concepts rather unrealistic? On the contrary, discoveries in atomic physics may instead have made it easier to consider certain possible explanations that at first may seem bizarre, but which are less fantastic than many presently accepted scientific truths would have seemed a few years ago. Facts that are now commonplace knowledge, such as atomic power, television, the DNA code, were beyond the wildest speculations of reasonable people.

Later in this section, we will let our imaginations run unchecked over some possible locations of heaven and hell, since only speculation is possible in the absence of any clear indication in the Bible, and of any definite material clues of their whereabouts. Lest anyone think some of these ideas are too "far out," it may be noted that highly respected physicists come up with theories about the nature of this universe that seem extremely weird to us who are in other fields. If we are inclined to dismiss such ideas with a smile, it is worth remembering that the same general brand of physics is seriously considered by the physicists who got our astronauts safely to the moon and back.

One of the strangest articles along this line, in the layman's way of thinking, may be "Gravitational Collapse," by Dr. Kip S. Thorne, who teaches theoretical physics at the California Institute of Technology. He tells of *Penrose's theorem,* an idea which has been held in high esteem by some scientists. It was proposed by Roger Penrose of the University of London, and the theorem is described by Thorne as having been "proved" by Penrose (in 1964).

This theorem relates the things that might happen during the gravitational collapse of a large star or of a galaxy or possibly of the whole universe. It is seriously thought that stars may reach this stage in some cases. The gravity would be so unopposed in its effect that the star or other body would collapse rapidly inward, eventually (get this!) reaching "zero volume."

In describing this process, Professor Thorne explained Penrose's theorem as follows:

> In realistic nonspherical collapse, as in spherical collapse, a critical stage can be reached beyond which no communi-

> cation with the outside universe is possible. Once this stage has been passed ... *a universe with which we had no previous contact may suddenly be joined together with our universe* by the collapse event ... bringing in outside information that influences future events (italics added).

Elsewhere in the article, Dr. Thorne gave this exotic picture of what might happen to the matter in the star or other body when it reached zero volume: "The matter might then emerge [through a topological hole in the photon-3 surface], bubbling upward like a spring in the mountains, in some other region of our own universe or in some other universe."[61]

Some of the ideas that follow in this section are not meant as serious hypotheses but merely to point out that there are many possibilities within the realm of scientific conjecture regarding the location of heaven and hell, some of the possibilities being more likely than others. (After the foregoing description of Penrose's theorem, the wildest of speculations may seem tame.)

We now know that atoms are mostly empty space. If the space were removed from the atoms of the earth, the entire globe would be compacted into a volume less than a mile in diameter. This makes it conceivable that two things might occupy the same space, if their "solid" parts—protons, neutrons, electrons, etc.—were synchronized so that they did not interfere with each other. A Creator capable of designing atoms and DNA and galaxies would certainly be able even to engineer a way for electron orbitals and gravitational forces to mesh without conflict even between comparatively similar physical realms in such a way that the effect of one on the other was undetectable.

---

[61] Kip S. Thorne, "Gravitational Collapse," *Scientific American*, Vol. 217 (November, 1967), p. 97.

Along the same line, Professor T. Gold, of the Center for Radiophysics and Space Research, Cornell University, recently wrote that "unseen mass can exist in several forms that would have escaped present means of detection." He seriously discusses the far-out idea that our universe may possibly be part of a larger universe, and that if so, "we would have no access to any information about any larger scale than that of our closed space." Also, he says, universes smaller than our own may exist, undetected by us, within our own universe. "There would be a system of 'nesting universes' in which each is perhaps only slightly smaller than the one in which it nests." He thinks we may eventually figure out ways to tell, "and therefore it will be possible to answer the question whether there are other universes nesting within our observable space." (T. Gold, "Multiple Universes," *Nature*, Vol. 242 [March 2, 1973], pp. 24, 25.) Scientists at Cambridge University have even said that one difficult question in astronomy could be sidestepped "by proposing that there are an infinite number of universes with all possible combinations of initial conditions." (Reported in *Science News*, Vol. 103 [March 31, 1973], p. 213.)

A completely different type of realm might exist. There is no reason to doubt *this* possibility. By analogy, hundreds of radio and TV programs are all around us, but without a receiving set we might never know they existed. Heaven or hell could be *anywhere,* in such a case, and we would have no way to detect their existence while in *this* physical realm. Other possibilities:

Astronomers now think that there may actually be what are called "black holes," stars with gravity so strong that even light cannot escape (as in Penrose's theorem), making them very difficult to detect. Again, unknown celestial or elysian bodies might be concealed in distant parts of our own galaxy or elsewhere, behind the haze which is known to block vision in some areas such as is the case near the center of our own galaxy.[62] There is no scientific reason to rule out belief in the actual existence of heaven and hell. Science can neither prove nor disprove things that are beyond the realm of experiment or observation.

Ray Brubaker asked this provocative question: "Could it be that the powerful radio emissions being recorded on earth are coming from Heaven?" He told of the shock experienced by Dr. Frank Drake, astronomer, when the world's largest radio telescope, located in Puerto Rico, first revealed a *pulsar.* "When I saw it I got weak in the knees," Dr. Drake was quoted as saying. "It was so incredible . . . to have a distant cosmic object radiating intense impulses, precisely regular, with the pulses lasting only 1/100th of a second."[63]

In line with Brubaker's suggestions, if newspapers should ever report evidence of a distant super-civilization being detected by astronomers, the first logical question to ponder might be: "Have they discovered heaven?"

On the other hand, heaven and hell might be so distant that we could never detect them. It is conceivable that instant space travel by molecular reassembly might be possible. If atoms at the distant site were put in the exact arrangement that is a particular person's body, it would be indistinguishable from the original. A universe in which memory and human telemetry

---

[62] "Two giant nearby galaxies were not discovered until 1967 because of obscuring interstellar dust," reported Palomar Observatory astronomer Jesse L. Greenstein, in the *1972 Yearbook of Science and the Future* (Britannica), p. 188.

[63] *Radar News* (December, 1971), p. 6. (This is not primarily a scientific periodical.)

devices exist surely has a Creator capable of such reassembly (resurrection) and of correcting any physical shortcomings prior to the entry into heaven of those who are prepared.

Scientists now speculate on the future possibility of computer file systems listing the DNA sequence for each human being's entire body.[64] Coded memory of that person's experiences would be more difficult for science but not for the original Designer of the physical basis of memory.

As to a person's spirit (the real person or personality who resides in the body, as a driver in a car) and travel to a possible distant site of heaven or hell, we have little basis for knowledge whether there are space travel limitations for spiritual beings. Is there a finite spiritual speed limit? In the language of theologians, God is everywhere in agency, that is He can know and act anywhere in the universe (without implying the pantheistic notion that God is everything). Physical reassembly being scientifically conceivable, we may even surmise the Creator has ways to transport us in spirit at the same time.

Given the known truths of present-day nuclear physics and moon explorations, the science fiction of yesterday is tame compared to the scientific facts known today. This opens the way for far-out speculation which may not be so fantastic after all. There is the factor of relativity as it regards time and speed of travel. And microminiaturization or its opposite. . . . There is no dearth of possible explanations in this day of unbelievable scientific discoveries. (Some of the foregoing is merely meant to indicate that the range of potential answers is wide and intriguing.)

No Greater Entity Than a "Person"

Far greater than the best computer or the most sophisticated instrumentation of a lunar module are the men who make and pilot them. We find nothing on earth to surpass persons. The Bible indicates that the Almighty is an *infinite* Person, and that He is more wonderful than even nature reveals. The God of Creation is said to love sinners such as we are and to have made a way of release from our guilt. This is the wonder of all time!

---

[64] Biologist T. C. Hsu at the University of Texas has taken a step in this direction by assembling live cells of animals in danger of becoming extinct. He keeps these cells in test tubes imbedded in ice, in the hope that the animals may some day be reconstructed from these cells. ("Shape of Things to Come," *The Reader's Digest* [October, 1972], p. 61.)

The *1971 Britannica Yearbook of Science and the Future* gave more than one intimation that scientists sometimes have a feeling of rejection by the public. If this is true, it may be that the public has a vague resentment when evolutionary scientists cause people to feel as Mary Magdalene did when she sorrowfully complained at the tomb: "They have taken away my Lord, and I know not where they have placed him."

Many nonscientists have a sort of intuition that true science and faith in God go well together. They sense something wrong with that brand of "scientist" who disparages belief in *the most self-evident of natural truths—that logic requires a Creator back of the creature.*

13

Examples of Phenomena Unexplainable by Evolution

God created man for his own fellowship and to obey his will, and only through that obedience could the fellowship be maintained.[1]

—Encyclopaedia Britannica, "Genesis"

Powerhouse for the Cell

As you read these lines, a hundred thousand billion tiny chemical-electric motors are on duty in your body. They are the *mitochondria* which operate quietly and efficiently to provide energy in the cells. A mitochondrion is often called the "powerhouse of the cell."[2]

We live in a day of miniaturization. Engineers design smaller and smaller batteries, engines, and controls for use in spacecraft and elswhere. Consider, then, the mitochondrion. Within the space of one inch, you could line up more than 5,000 of these microscopic *organelles,* or specialized parts of cells.[3]

---

[1] *Encyclopaedia Britannica* (1967), s.v. "Genesis." The statement quoted gives God's purpose as understood from the book of Genesis.

[2] David E. Green, "The Mitochondrion," *Scientific American,* Vol. 210, (January, 1964), pp. 63-74.

[3] Evolutionary attempts to account for mitochondria have led to a widely accepted hypothesis that they were formerly separate organisms which eventually in some mysterious way took up symbiotic residence in the cells of *eucaryotes,* which are cells containing several specialized organelles. (Eucaryotic cells comprise almost all the more complex organisms. *Procaryotes* include bacteria and blue-green algae. [Alternate spelling: eukaryotes, prokaryotes.]) Mitochondria contain a circular DNA molecule and some "70-S" ribosomes. Using data by Watson, however, it can be calculated that this mitochondrial DNA is only about 1/10 of the amount required for the smallest theoretical living entity. Also,

Mitochondria are highly efficient. They use an exceedingly complex system to extract energy from food by an elaborate electron-transfer chain. They store energy in chemical "storage batteries," the molecules known as ATP (adenosine triphosphate). The use of ATP for energy "has proved to be an absolutely universal feature of living cells."[4]

Since it has become clear how limited chance is in ability to produce order, in this chapter attention will be called to *just a few* of the marvels of order existing abundantly in life about and within us. (Thousands more could be included if space allowed. An excellent book rich with such examples is Fred John Meldau's *Why We Believe in Creation, Not in Evolution,* Denver: Christian Victory Press, 1959. This book is timeless because its principles will continue to be applicable, though it may be difficult to find.)

A Bird That Found Its Way Home 3,200 Miles in Twelve and One-Half Days

A small ocean-going bird called the Manx shearwater nests in the sand on islands off the coast of Wales. Some shearwaters were banded, put in a crate inside an airplane, and flown to the United States. These birds have not been known to frequent the U.S. east coast.

Let's read the outcome:

> Manx shearwaters which were removed from their nesting burrows in Wales returned successfully from release points outside their normal range. . . . One of these birds, released at Boston, Massachusetts, returned to its nest 3,200 miles away in 12 days and 12.5 hours![5]

The account went on to say that the bird probably had to fly at right angles to its normal direction of migration, and that

---

as Watson and numerous others have pointed out, certain vital components of mitochondria apparently must be coded in the regular DNA of the cell's nucleus and then synthesized on the cytoplasmic 80-S ribosomes outside of the mitochondria. Mitochondria (and also chloroplasts) grow by lengthening and a fission process, but outside of cells they have not been made to grow and divide. (James Watson, *Molecular Biology of the Gene,* 2nd ed. [Menlo Park, Calif.: W. A. Benjamin, Inc., 1970], pp. 520, 521.)

The specialized complexity and interlocking dependency of mitochondria with other cell processes show the inadequacy of this theory of their origin, which was required only because of evolutionary overview. The same is true of chloroplasts, which similarly contain DNA and ribosomes. Centrioles, also, contain DNA.

[4] Philip Handler, ed., *Biology and the Future of Man* (New York: Oxford University Press, 1970), p. 93.

[5] *Encyclopaedia Britannica* (1967), s.v. "migration."

the 250 miles per day average speed suggested it took the shortest possible route!

Dr. G. V. T. Matthews of Cambridge University

> credits birds with . . . ability to estimate the sun's arc accurately. He claims for them the equivalent of a sextant and a chronometer running on "home time." With these they can learn their geographical location anywhere on earth.[6]

Anyone doubting that birds possess these instinctive skills "is left with the difficult task of proposing an alternative, simpler explanation" for the Manx shearwaters' demonstrated ability we have described, says the Audubon Nature Encyclopaedia.[7]

The wisest of men could never find his way, without charts and mechanical instruments and training, across 3,000 miles of open ocean, starting from a place thousands of miles from anywhere he had ever gone before, and in a short time locate an exact spot on a small specific island.

The reader may be aware that an extensive study of this phenomenon has been made by many other scientists. There is even strong evidence that some birds navigate by the moon, a more difficult feat, and some apparently use the north star and stellar constellations in navigating. Bats, on the other hand, can navigate blindfolded.

Feathers and Eggshells

There is no way chance mutations could have brought about the development of feathers. Each is a masterpiece of engineering. The center shaft has *barbs* projecting from each side. Then, smaller *barbules* protrude from both sides of the barbs. From these barbules, microscopic *barbicels* project, like tiny hooklets. In some species there are more than a million barbicels in one feather.

The hooks of the barbicels fasten neatly onto the neighboring barbules, and this makes a tightly woven *vane,* as the entire feather is called. If the barbs get pulled apart, the *bird can hook them back together merely by preening* or running its beak through the feathers! You can do this yourself.

---

[6] *Audubon Nature Encyclopaedia,* "Animal: Navigation," Vol. 1 (New York: Curtis Publishing Co., 1965), p. 89.

[7] Ibid. We recall the emotional experience of watching on film as scientists nightly checked the nesting burrow and the excitement as they recovered the weary traveler and verified the band number. The small bird looked quite normal.

Consider the chances of this developing naturally. A feather would be of no help for flying until completed. It would be in the way. When one understands the complex precision of a feather's design, it is amusing to consider evolutionary claims that feathers evolved from reptile scales!

To obtain a bird by chance mutations, one would have to overcome the odds against feathers, computed along with the improbability of occurrence of all the other marvelous abilities birds would need in order to operate successfully at all. The size of the resulting odds would be a figure that would more than fill the cosmos. (George Gamow estimated that a little over 10^{106} grains of sand would perhaps fill the universe.[8] On that basis, we could calculate that the number 10^{116} would be more than sufficient to fill all cosmic space if printed on thin paper. That is a figure with 116 zeroes.)

Evolution cannot explain the origin of the mysterious synchronized process whereby, deep inside a bird's body, the shell of the forming egg is made from calcium stored shortly beforehand inside the hollow bones.[9] The shell is painted with the specific identifying color and with dots, stripes, or shading. Many species can be recognized by these characteristic markings of their eggs.

The Amazing Mechanism for Wing-Lift in Birds

Natural selection cannot help one find an explanation for the way a wing is lifted for the upbeat in bird flight. The muscle that operates this lift is not situated on top, but far below the wing. It fastens to the "keel" bone (*sternum*) — low, center, aft. How does a muscle *below* the wing serve to *lift* the wing?

There is a tendon that leads upward from the muscle. It passes through a well-lubricated circular canal formed by the joining of three bones, one of which is the wishbone. The way the tendon traverses this opening reminds one of a pulley. At the top, the tendon attaches to the large humerus bone of the wing. The end of this bone is widened and rounded in such a way that the tendon obtains leverage and gives just the right twist to the entire wing for the uplift stroke.

With this enchanting engineering arrangement, birds fly, and hummingbirds beat their wings up to fifty times per second.

---

[8] George Gamow, *One, Two, Three . . . Infinity* (New York: Viking Press, 1961), p. 7.

[9] T. G. Taylor, "How an Eggshell Is Made," *Scientific American* (March 1970), pp. 89-94.

It is interesting to remember this wing-lift mechanism while watching a bird in the air.[10] It is fruitless to try to account for the origin of such adroit engineering without an extraordinarily ingenious Planner. (This tendon is the *supracoracoideus* tendon. The opening through which it passes is the *foramen triosseum.*)

The Brain, a Marvel Beyond Description

Consider the brain. Even a lizard's brain is "so complex it defies detailed analysis," says Dr. Robert Doty of the Center for Brain Research, University of Rochester, New York.[11] But let Professor Doty tell us about the human brain and its nerve cells or *neurons:*

> Each neuron can be in communication with millions of others within a few thousandths of a second.
>
> The wonder of this vast neural network is further increased by the fact that each neuron is itself an organization of extraordinary complexity. Each is packed with . . . some 6 billion molecules of protein, 10 billion of fat, 600 billion of ribonucleic acid (RNA), and many other molecular substances, most of which are still unidentified. . . . Two-thirds of the weight of a neuron is made up of about 1,500 mitochondria, those microminiature factories in a cell that shuttle sugar through a maze of chemical reactions to yield energy. Each neural mitochondrion utilizes ten million atoms of oxygen per second; if oxygen is withheld from them for only ten seconds, neural functioning is so impaired that consciousness is lost.[12]

The existence of rational thought, in our brains, defies all efforts to account for it without God. To believe that the human brain was not designed, but that it resulted from "irrational"—unplanned, random—causes is to take away any basis for trusting our reason at all.[13]

---

[10] The author has traced this tendon in several species, including the crow, Stellar's jay, and the turkey. It is standard equipment for most present-day birds. In the turkey, *two* tendons pass through this opening, apparently being needed because of the greater weight and width of the wing, and consequent widening of the end of the bone, providing the essential control of wing attitude.

There is no reasonable explanation of any evolutionary development of this and other flight equipment. Speaking of flight, William W. Ballard, Professor of Biology at Dartmouth College, wrote, "And the birds, having by quite unknown steps developed the ability to escape attack through the air, managed a parallel adaptation to many terrestrial niches." (Ballard, *Comparative Anatomy and Embryology,* [New York: The Ronald Press Co., 1964], p. 41.)

[11] Robert W. Doty, "The Brain," *1970 Britannica Yearbook of Science and the Future,* p. 36.

[12] Ibid., pp. 36, 37.

[13] C. S. Lewis, *Miracles, A Preliminary Study* (New York: Macmillan Co., 1947), p. 21.

Darwin's "Cold Shudders"

Consider the eye. Darwin said the intricacies of the human eye gave him cold shudders.[14] (They threatened his theory.) Even today, evolutionists prefer to bypass the eye. Whenever one does dare to tackle it, he usually brazens it out for a few sentences sounding much more confident than his actual logic would allow.

As we read, we are not conscious that innumerable pulses travel through the million nerve fibers from each eye. Professor Doty explains further:

> Nor is there any hint that our visual world is split precisely down the middle so that the right half of each eye projects exclusively to the left half of the brain, and the left to the right. Only after many relays and neural transformations are these two halves of the visual world finally put together.[15]

The corresponding halves of each eye, he explains, send impulses to sections of the lateral geniculate nuclei to which the optic nerves go. These sections of the brain then send their information to columns of the visual cortex, a computerlike area.

If you're still with it: "These columns," he says, "send their analysis to appropriately related columns in the visual association cortex of the other side of the brain."[16] So, at last, the two sides of the picture are put together again, after other relays and switchings which we have omitted. Thus, seeing depends upon this complex teamwork of the eye with the brain—a system developed by chance, no doubt.

Thus far, only some of the simpler facts of the eye-brain complex have been described herein. The system is absolutely incredible. It is now common knowledge among biologists that in the computer-like section of the brain's visual cortex, "cortical neurons need exquisitely defined stimuli if they are to fire."[17] One such *complex cell,* for example, might respond or "fire" only for a stimulus consisting of an object with a straight edge, of a certain length, in a vertical position, moving to the left across a precise part of the visual field, at a certain speed! The neuron would not fire at its maximum rate for anything else.

[14] Quoted by Loren C. Eisely, in *Mathematical Challenges to the Neo-Darwinian Interpretation of Evolution,* ed. Paul S. Moorhead and Martin M. Kaplan (Philadelphia: Wistar Institute Press, 1967), p. 3.

[15] Doty, "The Brain," pp. 38, 39.

[16] Ibid., p. 43.

[17] John D. Pettigrew, "The Neurophysiology of Binocular Vision," *Scientific American,* Vol. 227, No. 2 (August, 1972), p. 87.

If the same object is tilted at an angle or moving in the opposite direction, the nerve cell would not give its characteristic response, but the job would have to be handled by another which can respond to it.

It has also been found that certain such neurons are even more specific in that they distinguish *relative* motion.[18] Some complex cells will not respond, that is, unless the stimulus object is moving while the background remains stationary with relation to it.

The cells we've been describing are deep in the brain. Even before leaving the retina in the back of the eyeball, however, the electrical signal generated by light striking the rods and cones goes through sophisticated refinements as it passes through five layers of specialized retinal nerve cells which are common to all vertebrates. These are the *receptor, horizontal, bipolar, amacrine,* and *ganglion* cells. They perform a remarkably coordinated job which results, among other things, in making the eye exceedingly versatile under light intensities which may vary as much as a billionfold in brightness.

Dr. Frank S. Werblin, of the University of California at Berkeley, described the problem the eye faces by having to operate under widely different lighting conditions. Detailing two possible ways to handle this, he says, "The retina actually performs operations that incorporate the best features of both of the foregoing solutions. As a result it is capable of signaling with high contrast sensitivity over a broad range of field intensities without sacrificing acuity."[19]

Of the interactions of the five retinal nerve layers, he wrote, "One aim of the adjustments is to generate a high-contrast visual signal [regardless of what the light intensity happens to be]. . . ."[20]

In photography, Werblin notes, there is low-contrast film, which has the advantage of being usable under a wide range of light conditions but the disadvantage of low-contrast sensitivity. High-contrast film, on the other hand, gives a good, sharply contrasting image, but it is difficult to use and requires precise camera adjustments for each narrow range of light in-

[18] "Visual Receptive Fields Sensitive to Absolute and Relative Motion during Tracking," *Science,* Vol. 178 (December 8, 1972), pp. 1106 ff.

[19] Frank S. Werblin, "The Control of Sensitivity in the Retina," *Scientific American,* Vol. 228 (January, 1973), p. 71.

[20] Ibid., p. 76.

tensity. He then tells how the eye compares with modern cameras as a result of the modulation of the signal as it traverses the five layers of cells:

> Such a system outdoes any exposure-setting device on a camera. Imagine being able first to control for *general* illumination in the visual field (through the exposure setting function of the receptor cells) and then to fine-tune the exposure in *local* regions of the field as a specific function of the local intensity level! (italics added)[21]

The plan of the eye is so intriguingly interesting that the reader may perhaps wish to check into it more fully. The references given in footnotes of this section will lead to a wealth of additional information. This one system, when considered in the light of probability theory, leaves the thoughtful person with all the research data he needs for an intelligent decision on whether evolution is possible.

That we receive such distinct and varied sensations from different wavelengths of light, so that we see beautiful colors, is another wonder built in.

So also the amazing coordination of brain and ear makes available the discriminating intoxication of pleasure which a person may possess in the enjoyment of stereo orchestral beauty. His pleasure is enhanced if he acknowledges with gratitude the One who made it possible. Why are our brains coded to interpret it with such splendor?

Physical Properties of Elements and Compounds

What artful stratagem makes the chemical elements differ in properties just by adding a few more of the same identical building blocks—protons, neutrons, and electrons? Take the inert gas, neon. Merely add one more proton, one electron, and a couple of neutrons and behold, there is the metal, sodium, that is so unstable and excitable that it "catches fire" in water!

Combine this reactive element, sodium, with a yellowish green poisonous gas called chlorine, and the result: common table salt! Who can adequately explain these interesting physical qualities on the basis of mere chemistry and physics apart from intelligent design? It takes more than unplanned electron orbitals to account for the variety of crisp and exciting differences in properties which are so useful and enjoyable.

---

[21] Ibid., pp. 78, 79.

Picture a banana. Could chance, using chemistry and physics, engineer this homely but delightful fruit? Or, could chance produce from the same brown soil, red strawberries, pink peaches, blue eggplants, green-striped watermelons, orange-colored oranges, and purple elderberries? We can describe the chemical processes, of course, that produce some of these colors (e.g., changes in the acidity in the fruit, as with autumn leaves also). But is it not superficial to suppose so many things would turn out so perfectly without advance design, involving timing and chemicals, and even the planning of basic structure and orbitals of atomic particles which affect their "properties"?

More Wonders in Molecular Biology

The speed and accuracy of DNA replication are superior to that of a secretary who could type at the utterly fantastic speed of 6,000 words per minute *constantly* for a 40-hour week, averaging less than one incorrect stroke during the whole week![22]

Universal precision processes in the cell are described glowingly in *Biology and the Future of Man.* The authors, all eminent biologists, conclude that: "... The metabolic machinery of the cell is a finely tuned, tightly synchronized orchestra built to function, in the main, without a conductor"[23] unless one considers the hormone system as conductor.

Evolutionists agree that the existence of universal procedures in living things must mean that such processes originated near the postulated start of life on earth before the branching into different types began. Is it not more logical to consider that the same Engineer decided to use the same efficient processes in a variety of "inventions"?

R. G. LeTourneau, inventor of road-building machines, used the same kind of electric motors in individual wheels of his machines, from steering wheels to the giant wheels of jungle-clearing tree-crushers, because these electric motors suited the purpose well in any wheel. It is logical to assume the Creator would use similar standard parts in a variety of living organisms, with minor changes to fit the specific needs.

It is hard on evolution when we discover that the eye of a

---

[22] Calculated in part from data by James Watson, *Molecular Biology of the Gene,* 2nd ed. (Menlo Park, Calif.: W. A. Benjamin, Inc., 1970), speed: page 528; accuracy under optimal conditions: page 297.

[23] Handler, ed., *Biology and the Future of Man,* p. 119.

frog is more complex than ours,[24] though quite similar in many ways, and that the nerve cells of a lizard are about the same as those in man.[25]

Cell membranes of intricate structure are basically similar in practically all living creatures, and are so thin that over three million could be stacked in a single column one inch high. They have the unique trait of "selective permeability," allowing some things to pass through and not others.[26] This is still not completely understood, but it involves what is called "active transport," a process with active molecules in the membrane bringing in the proper substances, apparently by combining with them and then rotating in the membrane.

Photosynthesis and Magnesium Atoms

Consider the miracle of photosynthesis. Starting with the raw materials of mere water and carbon dioxide, plants build up molecules of sugar and starch. This occurs after light energy is absorbed in the chlorophyll molecule, which has a beautiful arrangement of over 130 atoms. In the very heart of it, surrounded by a quartet of nitrogen atoms, there dwells one lonesome magnesium atom.

How does a plant know how to obtain a magnesium atom from the soil and build it precisely into position by "chelation" at the center of each and every chlorophyll molecule?

At one point in the description of cell respiration and oxidative phosphorylation, the authors of *Biology and the Future of Man* state: "The strategy of what ensues is elegant in the extreme."[27]

In cell respiration, the sugar molecules formed by photosynthesis are used entirely for energy via the mitochondria. The cell ends up with products that are exactly the same as the raw materials with which the plant started when making the sugar molecule! The end products are just water and carbon dioxide (plus energy stored in ATP molecules). Could this strikingly efficient recycling system have arisen without planned engineering? It is estimated that the entire supply of carbon dioxide in the atmosphere (0.03 percent by volume) would be used up in twenty years at the present rate of photo-

---

[24] Charles R. Michael, "Retinal Processing of Visual Images," *Scientific American* (May, 1969), p. 114.
[25] Doty, "The Brain," p. 36.
[26] J. David Robertson, "The Membrane of the Living Cell," *The Living Cell*, ed. Donald Kennedy (San Francisco: W. H. Freeman and Co., 1965), pp. 45-52.
[27] Handler, ed., *Biology and the Future of Man*, p. 101.

synthetic activity.[28] The cycle by which it is returned for re-use depends in large measure on countless trillions of one-celled creatures in soil and water which decompose organic matter, reducing it to the simple molecules from which the building process began. Consider the delicate balance necessary for such an equilibrium, vital to life on earth.

The great difficulty in writing on this subject is choosing from the multitude of remarkable systems which exemplify a degree of intelligent design that is unmistakable to open-minded reason. These molecular processes invoke the highest of praise from a great many biologists: systems involving the simultaneous turning off of one type of enzyme and the turning on of another in the liver under the stimulus of the emotion of fear in the organism, or the principle of self-assembly of component parts by their prefabrication such that they automatically fasten together in intricate and stable precision, or long chains of reactions in the vital metabolic pathways of all living cells. It is now thought, for one other example, that individual matching nerve cells find their specific partners by means of a complex carbohydrate coating,[29] which may be unique for each such pair among the trillions in the organism. This would require vast numbers of such polymer molecules, each coating being different from all others except that of the nerve cell's one and only partner. How this is brought about is not yet fully understood. The words of a western song about natural wonders suggests a profound thought: "All this that we may see the mystery of His way."[30]

Age-Old Questions

What about the many difficult questions—disease, parasitism, aging—about which men have wondered through the centuries? There are no *complete* explanations in this present age.[31] Much of this may be explained by the curse that came upon the world because of sin, as described in Genesis 3, and by the flood, which also came as a consequence of man's corruption. If the

---

[28] Roger Y. Stanier, Michael Doudoroff, and Edward A. Adelberg, *The Microbial World,* 3rd ed. (Englewood Cliffs, N.J.: Prentice-Hall, Inc., 1970), p. 691. The ocean contains a larger supply of CO_2 in dissolved form, which serves to regulate the amount of CO_2 in the atmosphere, part of the balance of nature.

[29] Handler, ed., *Biology and the Future of Man,* p. 103.

[30] "The Mystery of His Way," by Bob Nolan.

[31] An excellent book which gives clear answers to some of these problems is: C. S. Lewis, *The Problem of Pain* (New York: Macmillan Co., 1940, sixteenth printing, 1965).

flood involved loss of a hypothetical canopy of water vapor in the stratosphere as mentioned earlier, this might have increased the incidence of ultraviolet rays reaching earth's surface. Consequently, an increase in mutations could be a partial cause of aging, which is thought by some scientists to involve cumulative "somatic" mutations (in body cells).

Scriptures that mention Satan also hint at an explanation. He is called in the Bible the prince of this world, and the prince of the power of the air. In anthropomorphic terms, we may surmise that before he rebelled against God, he may possibly have been given some kind of contract putting him in charge of the earth, and that God must honor the contract as given till the end of the present age. At any rate, at that time, the Bible says, Satan will be banished. There is potential indirect benefit even from our burdens, however, as they furnish opportunities for character education and spiritual growth.

Life's diseases are tempered with mercy. Consider the healing mechanisms of the body, including "*antibodies,*" which are proteins known as immunoglobulins. Each of these specialized chemicals produced by the body has a variable section coded to "recognize" and lock on to one specific foreign invader and to neutralize it. This involves an interesting synchronized teamwork between antibodies and eleven different proteins in the blood, which go by the unusual group name of *complement.*

We earlier referred to the repair system for damaged DNA. When one strand is injured, special enzymes snip out the injured part; then the loose ends remaining are neatly trimmed, and new nucleotides are put in by base pairing. Another enzyme thereupon connects these up and the double helix is as good as new![32]

Heaven will rid us of the deformities and losses which the human race has suffered through harmful mutations. Of course, we have to make it to heaven first through personal faith in the Son of God who suffered the direct insults of His creatures via the cross in order to make a way for us to get on good terms with a holy Creator against whom we have sinned.

The Bear and the Boeing 747

A Boeing 747 airliner flies over a forest where, far below, a

[32] Philip C. Hanawalt and Robert H. Haynes, "The Repair of DNA," *Scientific American,* Vol. 216 (February, 1967), pp. 36-43. Some of the details mentioned above are from other research since that article.

bear wanders through his native wilderness far from man. The bear has only dirt and rocks and plants and other animals for his use, along with air and water. The human beings in the plane miles above sit comfortably and listen to their choice of channels of news and music while they eat a variety of vari-colored foods. Even the pilot may relax somewhat, allowing the inertial guidance system to compute and direct the course of the plane inerrantly to its destination at a speed of hundreds of miles per hour.

Man developed that plane with its electronic marvels from the same raw materials existing in the bear's habitat below in the forest: dirt and rocks (with their metallic ores), wood from the trees, just the nondescript materials of the wilderness—*plus the human brain.*

Dare we consider this and withhold gratitude—gratitude for the mind of man and for raw materials from which we invent and construct our planes and skyscrapers and freeways and space ships, our television and automobiles?

Consider how handicapped we would be if the universe had no such capacity as electromagnetic waves by which we may transmit the signals on which radio, radar, and other communications ride. Suppose electrons would not flow along a metal conductor, and we therefore could not have electric current.

The human brain and the building blocks with which it is furnished both call forth appreciation for the thrill of existing and operating in a well-equipped universe where we are allowed to experiment and to "create" in cooperation with the Creator who told man to have dominion over the earth.

It would seem that whoever designed DNA and the ear and the eye has concealed countless wonders, like veins of gold ore, for man to search out. This provides on a giant scale for adults the adventure and fascinating search which an Easter egg hunt provides for children.

The engineering plan of the heart, the tongue, the semicircular canals for balance, all are so intricate and efficient that science has studied for centuries to fathom the wisdom built in so compactly. To study the arrangement of nerve fibers and muscles is to see evidence of wise planning. When one examines charts of lungs and blood vessels, it is like looking under the hood of a modern automobile, where careful planning for the wise use of available space is evident.

To say that the simultaneous, coordinated reactions which take place in every living thing are the results of unplanned development—even with natural selection—is to believe "a statistical monstrosity." The wisest of human engineers could not improve upon the control system in the tail of a California gray squirrel which involves some twenty tiny bones connected by universal joints and moved by synchronized multiple tendons to the very tip.[33]

When a mind becomes closed to truth by the blinding prejudice of atheistic unbelief, that mind will attempt to take away from the Creator all appreciation. "They have refused to honor him as God, or to render him thanks" (Romans 1:21 NEB). To whom do materialists give the credit which is withheld from God? To no one! Just to blind chance, which is nothing, and natural selection, which is also nothing but a mindless process.

"The Universe Is Friendly"

Freeman J. Dyson, of the Institute of Advanced Studies, wrote in 1971:

> Nature has been kinder to us than we had any right to expect. As we look out into the universe and identify the many accidents of physics and astronomy that have worked together to our benefit, it almost seems as if the universe must in some sense have known that we were coming.[34]

Professor Dyson goes on to assert:

> I believe the universe is friendly. I see no reason to suppose that the cosmic accidents that provided so abundantly for our welfare here on the earth will not do the same for us wherever in the universe we choose to go. . . . I hope that with this article I may have persuaded a few people . . . to look to the sky with hopeful eyes.[35]

As may have occurred to the reader, this is a wonderful thought. It stops just short of the most logical step of all, to look to the sky not with hope that the "cosmic accidents" will be friendly, but in gratitude, trust, and obedience to the Person who logically must be back of these events that have provided for our welfare.

---

[33] Examined by the author in 1971 and 1972.
[34] Freeman J. Dyson, "Energy in the Universe," *Scientific American,* Vol. 224, (September, 1971), p. 59.
[35] Ibid.

The Blasphemy of Ingratitude

When the Pharisees on Palm Sunday asked Jesus to stop the multitude from their spontaneous praise of the Son of God, He replied that, if they "keep silence, the stones will shout aloud" (Luke 19:40 NEB).

When we occasionally become aware of just how amazing is the wisdom built into this wonderful universe, we sense how awful a crime it is to withhold credit from such a Designer, even if He had not come to rescue us of the human race from our sins.

It is hard to imagine a greater insult than to say the song had no composer, the picture painted itself, the building came together without an architect or builder. A major sin of our time is ingratitude and we can only vaguely realize how heinous an evil it is.

Signboards That Point Upward

In the gospel of John, the apostle concluded by saying that the things he had written about Jesus were penned "that you may believe . . . and that believing you may have life through his name" (John 20:31 RSV).

Perhaps the same God who inspired the writing of the Bible has sent us a parallel or prior message in nature—that we might look up and see His great power and seek the Savior as planned from the beginning. Thus, nature would encourage us to go to the Bible to learn more than it can tell us about the Creator and His plan to redeem us.

His trademark may be discerned in the DNA of every living cell. The Artist's signature is on every sunset and is written in the constellations of the night sky. It is He that has made us and we properly are His by right of creation and redemption. We can be His in actual fact by choice to receive Him. This Creator has promised that "as many as received him, to them gave he power to become the sons of God" (John 1:12).

Rather than stifling freedom as the evolutionist fears, the Creator has provided through His plan a way that we human beings can get in on the most wonderfully rewarding living that can be imagined, in personal liberty under chosen obedience. This is possible on this earth now. Then there's the hope of heaven on beyond the dissolution and death that are presently the lot of earth's people. There we will perhaps have time to renew the research and discovery that make science on earth exciting.

He Made It for You

Concerning the reason for the wonders built into this amazing universe, perhaps that verse in the gospel of John might be paraphrased thus: "These are created that you may believe in the Creator, and that you may search out how to find Him, by going to the Scriptures."

Whatever other reasons God had for creation, there are so many things that are clearly adapted for our use and enjoyment that it is evident that He must have had His human creatures in mind in the planning, and gave them reasons to be aware of their Creator.

> The tiny wild rose that blooms on the mountain,
> Far from the haunts of civilized men,
> For you who will climb—its fragrance and beauty
> The Lord of Creation has fashioned for you!
>
> The deep-throated frog, the sharp splash of the beaver,
> The whippoorwill's loud trill, the cheery chickadee's high song,
> Big beartracks by the river where the rainbow trout is flashing—
> These all tell you God loves you, and to him you should belong!
>
> He made it for you, that life might be richer,
> That you might look up and share his great love,
> For he made your heart for himself, that you always
> Might never be lonely, and find heaven above.[36]

From the facts of science and from the Bible, it is reasonable to conclude that God has made us for himself, and, as St. Augustine explained, we will never find lasting contentment until we find our proper relationship with him. Such fulfillment for a human being is possible through personal saving trust in his Son, whom he sent to redeem us from our sins.

On that basis, an individual may arrive at an attitude of continuing gratitude for the privilege of knowing the Creator personally and living in his amazing creation. After a person has met the conditions of rightness with God and received forgiveness, it is possible to experience the fact that happiness is appreciating God.

---

[36] From a song which came to the author in Sequoia National Forest, 1959-60.

14

Increasing Your Certainty

Every age has its superstitions, and ours is the notion that science is an infallible and all-sufficient guide to truth.[1]
—Louis Cassels

ALTHOUGH MANY SCIENTISTS do not hold the exaggerated opinion quoted above, Cassels explains, it is nevertheless a commonly held view of educated laymen. We all know that almost every pronouncement by every scientist tends to be accorded the status of absolute and final verity. This is especially perilous when it is realized that a number of scientists, intentionally or not, are promoters of an overview that is materialistic.

"All of us," Cassels says, "have been conditioned by contemporary culture to reject uncritically the whole idea of a reality transcending the natural world of physical objects and forces."[2] That conditioning is not a result of what we hear from scientists only, but it comes at us from every direction, whether from a National Park Service display at the Grand Canyon, a wild animal program on television, or a novel such as *The Call of the Wild.* Evolution, the main vehicle of this materialistic promotion, is treated as fact. Darrell Huff reminds us, however, that "people can be wrong in the mass, just as they can individually."[3]

Darwin expressed on more than one occasion a feeling of

[1] Louis Cassels, *The Reality of God* (Garden City, N.Y.: Doubleday and Co., 1971), p. 6.
[2] Ibid., p. 2.
[3] Darrell Huff, *How to Take a Chance* (New York: W. W. Norton & Co., 1959), p. 122. (Huff was not discussing evolution.)

how much he did not yet know. He said in the Introduction to *Origin of Species* (later editions): "No one ought to feel surprise at much remaining as yet unexplained in regard to the origin of species and varieties, if he make due allowance for our profound ignorance in regard to the mutual relations of the many beings which live around us." He repeated this statement in chapter 4 of the same volume.

Although we too must be continually aware that there is much we have yet to learn, we are in a happier state than Darwin in that there can be an exhilarating certainty as to the overview that accords with the facts around us, through the principles of probability logic, as well as in more intuitive and spiritual ways. This assurance heightens the enjoyment of discovery and fills one with anticipation as he seeks to discern the plan so wisely built into nature. The fact that the Creator made things to run quite well without his having to step in constantly by direct intervention is more of an indication of design and infinite wisdom than if we could see Him physically at work in some visible form adjusting the machinery of nature. It gives a person the intriguing opportunity to try to figure out the amazing wisdom of the plan of operation of this organism and that galaxy, by using his own model of the Creator's masterpiece of design, the human brain.

In spite of the pressure from all this propaganda surrounding us all, the method we have been studying together in these pages can provide a reasoned and serene assurance of the truth that evolution is false. We have seen that the chain of reasoning on which it is based contains vital flaws which rob evolution of scientific validity.

Evolution Ruled Out by the Single Law of Chance

Evolution, as defined at the start of the book and as usually understood today, includes the origin of life from nonliving matter without intelligent planning. It was seen in chapter 5 that natural selection could not have helped at all before the existence of an accurate duplicating system. Chance alone would have had to produce the first complete set of genes and proteins for minimal life. This is the only alternative to intelligent creation.

Allowing many extreme concessions to make it easier for chance to succeed, we arrived at the figure of 10^{-236} as the probability of a usable random sequence gene or protein. That is: one chance in a figure with 236 zeroes, for just *one* gene or protein molecule. Before life could exist, many would be required.

The *law of chance,* as stated by Émile Borel, is that "events whose probability is extremely small never occur."[4] He defined "extremely small" as, on the cosmic scale, a probability of 10^{-50} or smaller. It can readily be seen that the probability of a gene or a protein, namely 10^{-236}, is drastically smaller. (A larger negative exponent means a smaller probability.)

In order to make this "single law of chance" more absolute in its certainty, Borel then did some interesting calculating, giving chance some inordinate concessions as we have done. The great French mathematician first considered matter as divided into the smallest possible atomic particles. To pack the universe, he said, would require no more than 10^{120} of these.

Next he divided time into the smallest intervals on the scale of atomic processes and said that 10^{40} would be the total of these smallest intervals of time that could happen in billions of centuries, aiming at a generous approximation of the life span of the universe, including our solar system.

Borel said that, if one considers collisions between these minuscule particles at the tremendous rapidity of such extremely short periods of time, then, by multiplying the two figures together,

> the total number of these infinitely small elementary phenomena does not exceed 10^{160} in the entire universe and during the longest period of time we can assign to the duration of our solar system. It is thus impossible to imagine that the simplest event could recur more than 10^{160} times, and it follows that a probability of 10^{-200} is very largely negligible from the cosmic perspective.[5]

This single law of chance, according to Borel, "carries with it a certainty of another nature than mathematical certainty . . . it is comparable even to the certainty which we attribute to the existence of the external world."[6]

Pierre de Laplace, mathematician and astronomer of earlier

---

[4] Émile Borel, *Elements of the Theory of Probability* (Englewood Cliffs, N.J.: Prentice-Hall, 1965), p. 57.

[5] Borel, *Theory of Probability,* p. 59.

[6] Borel, *Probabilities and Life* (New York: Dover Publications, 1962), p. 6.

years, believed that the utility of probability theory was to guide us in weighing assumptions.[7]

The world of living nature exists about us. Evolutionary doctrine assumes that it came about without the aid of intelligence from nonliving matter, which, as we have seen, is tantamount to saying it happened by chance. We have used "the science of probability" to weigh that assumption, and it has been found wanting. This began to be apparent from the moment we studied the multiplication rule and found that on the average it takes chance ten billion attempts in order to count to ten. Dr. John C. Whitcomb says: "Mathematics is deadly to evolution."[8]

The calculations we have studied together in these pages will not convince a *dedicated* evolutionist, of course. As we have seen, such a person's outlook is a chosen overview or faith and not a conclusion based merely on scientific evidence. We have written instead in the hope that calling attention to this evidence may be useful to openminded individuals in quest of the truth on this matter. A great many people among us are, to adapt a Cassels phrase, "reluctant evolutionists."[9] Evolution was accepted under the impression that it was proven science, but a lurking suspicion has persisted that all was not well on that subject.

If you are among the multitude of educated persons in that position, it may be noted that your certainty may not arrive in one lump sum. Instead, your assurance can grow as you continue to study and ponder these facts with courage. Those who earnestly seek will find. The half-hearted, of course, will not.

One's joy in finding God will be proportional to the urgency of the seeking. In athletic language, Cassels advises one to "hang in there and don't give up too easily."[10]

Applying the Principles We've Learned

The approach which has been introduced in this book can be applied by the reader in countless situations. We have related the laws of chance to only a few particular facets of the living world. Now that you realize the helplessness of chance when

---

[7] Huff, *How to Take a Chance,* p. 57.

[8] John C. Whitcomb, on a radio broadcast "And God Created," KBBI, Los Angeles.

[9] Cassels did not deal with evolution. He spoke of "reluctant atheists" and "wistful agnostics." (Cassels, *The Reality of God,* p. 1.)

[10] Cassels, *The Reality of God,* p. 4.

it comes to producing an ordered result, it will seem natural to apply that truth when you read of some new discovery in science, or when you personally happen upon some interesting fact in nature. Here is just one example of a case where this can be done (concerning the human stomach), reported by Dr. Horace W. Davenport, as a result of his work at Michigan Medical School:

> The gastric juice contains hydrochloric acid, one of the most corrosive acids known. At the concentration secreted by the stomach lining the acid is capable of dissolving zinc and is deadly to cells. Yet in the stomach the hydrochloric acid ordinarily acts only to perform the useful functions of killing bacteria in the ingested food and drink, softening fibrous foods and promoting formation of the digestive enzyme pepsin. The corrosive juice is prevented from attacking the stomach wall by a complex physical-chemical barrier that is not yet fully understood.[11]

Dr. Davenport continued with this engrossing information:

> The human stomach normally sheds about half a million cells per minute. Thus the surface lining of the stomach is completely renewed every three days. By virtue of this rapid renewal the stomach wall can repair even severe damage of the mucosal barrier in a matter of hours or days.[12]

It is patently absurd to try to find an adequate evolutionary explanation for such a system. Open-minded rational thought automatically suggests an intelligent Designer without whom such a plan would never originate. We might even consider that it could be dangerous attributing such a marvel as this to random mutations or any other nonrational source, since it would amount to a major insult to the Designer.

Your certainty will grow by continuing to apply probability thinking. Perhaps you, like many others, already realize that to get a clear grasp of some complex truths or computations, rereading and meditation are required.

Probability Calculations by Others

To date, I have found data on only three sound scientific calculations by others who applied probability reasoning to proteins, genes, or cells. The basic computations in this book were

---

[11] Horace W. Davenport, "Why the Stomach Does Not Digest Itself," *Scientific American*, Vol. 226, (January, 1972), p. 87.
[12] Ibid., p. 91.

done before these were discovered, except for the general conclusion of the first one listed below. We suspect that many evolutionists have avoided such investigations because they intuitively recognize that it will threaten evolutionary doctrine if they make such studies. In chronological order, here are the three mentioned above:[13]

Ulric Jelinek, who was chief metallurgist of the meter division of Westinghouse Manufacturing Company, wrote:

> Consider the very sensitive balance of this whole business. The earth is exactly the correct distance from the sun. It is rotated at the right speed. Its very size determines the proper density of its atmosphere, all to make life possible.
>
> In a protein molecule, there are two thousand atoms in definite arrangement. The mathematician has calculated in order for these to come in this particular arrangement by accident, he would have to vibrate them at the speed of light and then it would take you a time of 10 with 243 zeros[14] [meaning that many billions of years].

He referred to calculations made by Charles-Eugène Guye, the eminent Swiss physicist (who died in 1942). Professor Guye's computations were made long before the Watson-Crick DNA breakthrough, and were reported in detail in the book *Human Destiny* by Pierre Lecomte du Noüy to whom we have referred before.[15] His approach was from the fact of "dissymmetry" in a protein molecule in the sense that the atoms are not just evenly scattered like a quantity of thoroughly mixed black and white grains of sand. Using an oversimplification, Dr. Guye said that even if only two kinds of atoms were used in proteins, to arrive at a degree of dissymmetry of 0.9 would indicate a probability of 2.02×10^{-231}. This figure as applied in du Noüy's book results in the "10^{243} billions of years" required to obtain one

---

[13] There are doubtless others, in addition to numerous casual applications of the idea that chance cannot produce complex order. Henry Quastlar was writing a book on the subject at the time of his death in 1963. Friends completed it the best they could from his notes: *The Emergence of Biological Organization,* (New Haven: Yale University Press, 1964). The book is difficult to follow at times, perhaps because of its unfinished nature. We will discuss it more at length in Appendix 3, beginning on page 257. Though apparently biased strongly for evolution, Quastlar gave figures which produce the two outer limits of the probability of life occurring by accident—between 1 chance in 10^{255} and 1 in $10^{2,999,999,999,986}$. His other calculations are described in Appendix 3.

[14] Ulric Jelinek, in *Campus Challenge* (Campus Crusade for Christ, Arrowhead Springs, Calif., 1961, October), p. 6.

[15] Pierre Lecomte du Noüy, *Human Destiny* (New York: Longmans, Green and Co., 1947), pp. 33, 34.

protein molecule from a material volume the size of the earth, being shaken at the speed of light.[16]

A second type of study was reported in 1968 in the book *Energy Flow in Biology* by Harold J. Morowitz of Yale, whose important research has been mentioned throughout this book. Being a biophysicist, Dr. Morowitz considered the probability of chance fluctuations that would result in sufficient energy for bond formation to make the molecules needed for a living cell.

Assume an ocean with a concentration of all the small molecules that are needed to build proteins, genes, etc., for a cell. Under "equilibrium" conditions (the stable state reached after initial reactions have balanced), the probability of such a fluctuation during earth's history would be 10^{134} in $10^{340,000,000}$ for a minimal cell.[17] This would be 1 chance in $10^{339,999,866}$. Such a fluctuation, of course, has a probability "vanishingly small" beyond words to express.

It may be noted that if, instead of an equilibrium situation, we had energy flowing through the system sufficient to provide energy for the bonds, it would do no more than put us in the position from which our own studies began—with chance trying to arrange the units in a usable sequence, and failing miserably, as always.

The third probability study was one reported by Frank B. Salisbury, of the Plant Department of Utah State University. In an intriguing article in *Nature,* he began thus:

> Modern biology is faced with two ideas which seem to me to be quite incompatible with each other. One is the concept of evolution by natural selection of adaptive genes that are originally produced by random mutations. The other is the concept of the gene as part of a molecule of DNA, each gene being unique in the order of its nucleotides. If life really depends on each gene being as unique as it appears to be, then it is too unique to come into being by chance mutations. There will be nothing for natural selection to act on.[18]

Salisbury noted that in current evolutionary theory, during early stages there would come a time when a certain enzyme was required, and this was supposed to have been produced

---

[16] Ibid.

[17] Harold J. Morowitz, *Energy Flow in Biology* (New York: Academic Press, 1968), p. 99.

[18] Frank B. Salisbury, "Natural Selection and the Complexity of the Gene," *Nature,* Vol. 224 (October 25, 1969), p. 342.

by mutations from existing genes. He calculated that if 10^{20} planets had oceans of existing small DNA genes of 1,000 nucleotides in length, replicating a million times a second with one mutation each time, in 4 billion years only 10^{85} of a possible 10^{600} orders would occur. If by extreme concession it is allowed that 10^{100} different sequences would work, the probability would be 10^{-415} that the needed gene would occur in that time (one chance in 10^{415}, a figure with 415 zeroes).

Dr. Salisbury called on the biological community to resolve this dilemma "if our teachings are to remain internally consistent."[19]

In commenting on this article, L. M. Spetner of Johns Hopkins University's Applied Physics Laboratory wrote (*Nature,* 1970): "Salisbury's contention still seems to stand,"[20] namely, that there is indeed this apparent contradiction between these two concepts which are basic in current neo-Darwinian evolutionary theory.

Each of these three studies and the one developed in this book have approached the matter from very different sides. Guye dealt with dissymmetry in contrast to an even mixing of atoms. Morowitz calculated probability of correct bond energies for a minimal cell in an equilibrium grouping. Salisbury studied the chances of mutations producing a needed new enzyme. Our own calculations which we have studied together had to do with chance arranging just the sequence of amino acids for a protein or of nucleotides for a gene.

In each of these widely different studies of different facets of molecular biology, chance failed by such a preposterous margin as to erase all doubt.

Schrödinger the Physicist and "the Lord's Quantum Mechanics"

Erwin Schrödinger, the great Austrian physicist, made important contributions to our knowledge of the nature of matter, in quantum mechanics theory, especially with regard to the wave nature of atomic particles. In a famous series of lectures at Trinity College in Dublin in 1943, he stressed the fact that in physics at the atomic level, the only order known—except at absolute zero temperature—is the statistical type of order from averaging the motions of *large numbers* of atoms.

In "striking contrast," one finds that in living things "a single group of atoms existing only in one copy produces orderly

---

[19] Frank B. Salisbury, "Natural Selection," p. 343.

[20] L. M. Spetner, "Natural Selection versus Gene Uniqueness," *Nature,* Vol. 226 (June 6, 1970), pp. 948, 949.

events, marvellously tuned in with each other and with the environment."[21]

Continuing his glowing description of DNA, before its exact structure was fully known, Schrödinger said:

> Every cell harbours just one of them (or two, if we bear in mind diploidy). Since we know the power this tiny central office has in the isolated cell, do they not resemble stations of local government dispersed through the body, communicating with each other with great ease, thanks to the code that is common to all of them?
>
> Well, this is a fantastic description, perhaps less becoming a scientist than a poet. However, it needs no poetical imagination but only clear and sober scientific reflection to recognize that we are here obviously faced with events whose regular and lawful unfolding is guided by a "mechanism" entirely different from the "probability mechanism" of physics. ... It results in producing events which are a paragon of orderliness. ... The situation is unprecedented, it is unknown anywhere else except in living matter.[22]

When considered in view of the disruptive tendency resulting from thermal motion, Schrödinger said, "the gene structure ... displays a most regular and lawful activity—with a durability or permanence that borders on the miraculous."[23]

The single chromosome fiber, or DNA as we know it, said the noted physicist, "is not of coarse human make, but is the finest masterpiece ever achieved along the lines of the Lord's quantum mechanics."[24]

Perhaps one reason Schrödinger waxed eloquent about what he called "the hereditary treasure" is that, as a physicist, he was sharply aware of the usual tendency toward disorder which is expressed in the second law of thermodynamics—the inclination for things to run down or to become scattered.

Dr. Joseph L. Henson applies this law to the geological time scale and the probability of order occurring:

> If you have a tremendous period of time, does this make it more likely to happen? It is still statistically improbable and unlikely. ...
>
> Let's suppose this unlikely event happens, and we have

---

[21] Erwin Schrödinger, *What Is Life* (Garden City, N.Y.: Doubleday and Co., 1956), p. 76. (Given as a series of lectures in Dublin, 1943.)
[22] Ibid., p. 77.
[23] Ibid., p. 20.
[24] Ibid., p. 83.

> order created out of disorder. Now what is going to happen next? It is going to degenerate. This is the most statistically probable thing that would happen: not its becoming ordered again, but its going back to disorder.
>
> So you see that time is really not a solution. In fact, the longer time, the more statistically improbable.[25]

Small wonder that the order in living things seems amazing to physicists! The second law of thermodynamics is relied upon almost absolutely by scientists with almost no exceptions. In its technical form, it tells of the irrecoverable loss of heat to the environment. Its effect is the increase of disorder, which is called *entropy*. This "second law" stands in the path of evolution, blocking the way.

Sure Cure for Doubt Regarding Evolution

When you and I are bombarded by ceaseless propaganda to accept materialistic explanations of the universe and its living things, here are a few examples of effective ways we may keep our reasoning straight:

On a night when the moon is bright, go for a walk alone where orange or peach blossoms are fragrant while mocking birds sing, and ponder how it could have come to be. By mere natural selection?

Or, watch a kitten playing—a lively, furry ball of fun—and consider how it would strain chance for millions of aeons just to perfect the curve of one whisker. Chance would utterly balk at the task of bringing about through natural selection the kitten's built-in coded ability to scratch its ear rapidly or to land on all fours from any position.

Or, look into the eyes of a friend or loved one—in fact, consider any person whom you can admire. Who but an infinite Creator could have made possible such a being?

Or, consider a beehive with its exactly geometrically engineered honeycomb and its social organization; or a watermelon, or an elephant, or the tail of a peacock, or any tree! Even a cricket has DNA coding so exact that it gives the precise number of nerve impulses for his specific signalling sound.[26] Clifford Grobstein, biologist at the University of California at San Diego

---

[25] Joseph L. Henson, Bob Jones University, personal communication, December, 1971.

[26] David R. Bentley, "Genetic Control of an Insect Neuronal Network," *Science*, Vol. 174 (December 10, 1971), p. 1139.

has written of "molecular messages that underlie the entire fabric of life."[27]

The believer in naturalistic evolution must never have walked at 4 a.m. under a bright buttermilk sky—light white clouds patterned on blue background—and laughed with the absurd music of a rooster announcing, "Four o'clock and all's well," the message relayed like an African drum system across the countryside. The exotic call of a night bird winging his way through the darkness above the walnut trees adds to the crisp reality and glory of an unutterably exciting world.

The materialist must never have stood at dawn and watched the pink light begin to tinge the sky, spreading upward toward the brilliance of the morning star, as bright blue windows open up in the eastern clouds in anticipation of the sunrise.

A group of boys stood one night watching the huge yellow orb of the full moon as it came into view over the mountains in the east. It sounded sensible to them when a club leader commented, "If you can see a sight like that and not worship God, you don't deserve to be called a person!"

With Certainty, One Can Now Be More Aware, More Alive

Together we have looked at many interesting things in the realm of science, and have traversed, in this book, some of "that fascinating terrain where biology and philosophy meet,"[28] as did Schrödinger and many of the other scientists who have been quoted. This is a proper consideration for every scientist as an individual, since a person's overview will either help or hinder his research and its validity, as well as affect the meaning of his life and long-range destiny.

C. S. Lewis, after years of atheism, finally was forced by the evidence to admit the existence of God, alone in his room and quite reluctantly at first. He wrote a book about that. The title is *Surprised by Joy*.[29] Just discovering that there is a Creator was the beginning, which led on to joy in fuller measure through this Oxford professor's personal faith in Christ.

Knowing the basic laws of chance makes it possible for you to be more aware than ever before. This knowledge immedi-

---

[27] Clifford Grobstein, *The Strategy of Life* (San Francisco: W. H. Freeman & Co., 1965), p. 111.

[28] Harold F. Blum, *Time's Arrow and Evolution*, 3rd ed. (Princeton, N.J.: Princeton University Press, 1968), p. 7.

[29] C. S. Lewis, *Surprised by Joy* (New York: Harcourt, Brace and World, Inc., 1955).

ately points one to the only adequate explanation of the wonders above and around us. Life is continually filled with awe and mystery, as one discovers more of the wisdom built in at countless times and places. The natural response is to offer praise in one's heart to the Creator who designed the dew-jeweled rose and the song of the whippoorwill.

You'll laugh with the comic bray of the donkey, and you'll know the Designer must have been smiling when He planned the method of locomotion used by frogs—and crayfish and amebas—and when He formed the face of the walrus.

Eating will be more fun as the variety of colors, tastes, and shapes of fruits, vegetables, nuts, and spices tell us that God must have made this diversity and the attuned ability to see and taste because He wanted us to enjoy it. So we give thanks, marvelling at this evidence that He cares about us.

Many things apparently were planned for the benefit of human creatures, but God had something more important in mind. He seems to have made us for fellowship with Himself on a scale that is unbelievably exalted. In the words of Tresmontant, "We shall be, according to an epistle attributed to Peter, consortes divinae naturae, participators in the divine nature. The doctrine of divinization completes the doctrine of creation. It provides its key and meaning."[30]

A greater than Tresmontant stated that doctrine shortly before being nailed by Roman soldiers to a cross on a hill just outside Jerusalem. On the night of the Last Supper, Christ said it in these words, in his prayer to his Father: "That they also may be one in us" (John 17:21). He then voluntarily died to make this possible, in a cosmic plan we only partially comprehend.

Does this great privilege come about automatically or is there something we must do? Near the end of the Bible, this same Jesus, having risen from the dead on the first Easter morning, said to us all: "Behold, I stand at the door and knock; if any man hear my voice and open the door, I will come in . . ." (Revelation 3:20). He promised to enter the life of any person who as a humble penitent would make a definite life choice to welcome him, putting full confidence in him as Forgiver and Savior, Master and Friend.

Should anyone wonder about a treatise on science conclud-

---

[30] Claude Tresmontant, *Christian Metaphysics* (New York: Sheed & Ward, 1965), p. 105.

ing on a religious note, there is hardly any other logical way to conclude. Religion need have nothing to do with the process of seeking the answer to the question of the title, whether evolution is possible or impossible. For that purpose, all that is necessary is to examine the facts about us and the facts from valid research data in the light of probability reasoning. When one has arrived at the conclusion that what now exists cannot adequately be explained without a Creator, he or she comes to the point of unavoidable decision on a simple question: "So what?" So what should an intelligent individual do about his relationship to this amazing and infinite Creator and Owner of all things?

It would be tragic to stop with the mere negative knowledge that evolution cannot be true. With the certainty that chance could not account for our existence, we are in position to look up and find our true potential destiny.

Appendix 1

On the Origin of Left-Handed Components in Proteins

IN REVIEWING THE main attempts to explain why amino acids in proteins are exclusively left-handed, in connection with the study in chapter 3, we will follow primarily summaries by A. I. Oparin.[1] John Keosian has also listed succinctly a good number of such efforts.[2] A recent book entitled *Asymmetric Organic Reactions*[3] goes into great detail on one-handed molecules of other types, but has little on the subject of proteins. That book, when dealing with proteins, primarily refers the reader to studies by Oparin, Keosian, and others, and takes for granted that natural reasons for the left-handed phenomenon have been found, without giving any adequate basis whatever for such an assumption.

Here is a summary of efforts to account for this mystery:

1. *Photochemical Reactions.* Between 1904 and 1930, there were reports by German scientists on the use of circularly polarized light to bring about a photochemical reaction, in the attempt to obtain asymmetric results.[4]

Along this line, Werner Kuhn, in 1930, "using circularly polarized light of a wavelength chosen for its disruptive effect,

---

[1] A. I. Oparin, *Life, Its Nature, Origin and Development* (New York: Academic Press, 1961), p. 60. Also:
Oparin, *Genesis and Evolutionary Development of Life* (New York: Academic Press, 1968), pp. 80, 81.

[2] John Keosian, *The Origin of Life* (New York: Reinhold Publishing Co., 1964), p. 75.

[3] James D. Morrison and Harry S. Mosher, *Asymmetric Organic Reactions* (Englewood Cliffs, N.J.: Prentice-Hall, Inc., 1971).

[4] Ibid., p. 47.

preferentially broke up one of the members of a 50-50 molecular mixture of a certain ester."[5] This was not an experiment with amino acids. Moreover, the outcome was not an all-one-handed result, but merely a very slight excess, namely 0.7 percent of one enantiomer.[6]

Such experiments have always been inconclusive. Oparin is therefore quite vague in reporting these cases, although he hints that they might have had some success. This can be unintentionally misleading, because their "success" was actually far from convincing.

Light can be circularly polarized by reflection, and such polarized light may be present in moonlight.[7] Natural circular polarization of light "could at most be slight," and "the activities producible photochemically in the laboratory have always been extremely small."[8] (Consider the less-than-one percent result mentioned!)

2. *Formation on Quartz Crystals.* In 1950, crystallographer J. Bernal advanced the hypothesis that these amino acids may have been formed "on the surface of asymmetric crystals of quartz."[9] Two Russian scientists, Terent'ev and Klabunovskii, were mentioned by Oparin as attempting laboratory experiments of this type.[10] Again, Dr. Oparin vaguely implies success, but leaves the matter in serious doubt by his lack of explicitness.[11]

Quartz is composed of symmetrical molecules of silicon dioxide. It crystallizes, however, into dissymmetric crystals, "the two mirror image forms being formed with equal probability,"[12] in contrast to living things. Morrison and Mosher are skeptical how quartz could help in this dilemma.[13] Its molecules are not one-handed. Only the crystals are dissymmetric. Bias produced is low.

3. *Selection of Alpha Spirals in Proteins.* George Wald, in 1957, "expressed doubt, however, that any of these abiogenic factors could create conditions for the emergence of stable

---

5 Philip Morrison, Book Reviews, *Scientific American,* Vol. 225, July, 1971, p. 120.

6 Morrison and Mosher, *Asymmetric Organic Reactions,* p. 47.

7 Keosian, *The Origin of Life*, p. 75.

8 *Encyclopaedia Britannica* (1967), s.v. "stereochemistry."

9 Oparin, *Life, Its Nature, Origin and Development,* p. 60.

10 Ibid.

11 Dr. Oparin's vagueness here contrasts with his usual clarity and frankness.

12 J. M. Barry and E. M. Barry, *An Introduction to the Structure of Biological Molecules* (Englewood Cliffs, N.J.: Prentice-Hall, 1969), p. 52.

13 Morrison and Mosher, *Asymmetric Organic Reactions,* p. 47.

asymmetry."[14] Instead, he theorized, the selection of L-amino acids was made from both types at the time of the selection of alpha spirals in proteins.

An "alpha spiral" is a helical form of protein chain. Pauling and his colleagues discovered in 1950 that this was one of the most common types of protein secondary structure. (Left-handed amino acids form a right-handed helix, when such a spiral is produced.)

If, by chance, a helical chain had gotten started, using L-isomers fortuitously, there is no adequate reason to suppose that *only* L-amino acids would link up at the end of such a forming chain. (Appendix 2 discusses the matter of possible preference exerted for the same enantiomorph, but either L- or D- forms can and do join such a growing chain in the laboratory, and usually they seem to join with equal readiness.)

After both forms are used, the *spiral* conformation may be discontinued, but the chain can continue to grow, with units of either hand. Chapter 4 gives calculations on what the probability factor would be even if there were such a preference.

Actually, if the same isomer tended to join up next, this would result in about an equal number of each, in the long run. Sooner or later in any chain, by the laws of probability, the opposite hand would join up regardless of the degree of stereoselectivity. Then the preference would no longer favor the hand that had been predominant, and the other would take the lead. Blocks of each would occur in equal numbers. Even if the helical portion exerted a preference beyond the adjacent new monomer or unit just added, the eventual result by probability considerations would still be equal numbers of blocks.

The only way to obtain an all-left-handed chain would be to reach it by random polymerization, in spite of the almost infinite odds given in chapter 4 against such a result. This is unthinkable when viewed realistically.

As to the idea of alpha spirals being "selected," this would have been impossible, even if any such chains existed. Natural selection could not have operated at all before there was a complete duplicating system for all essential parts.[15] This logical precept is developed more in detail in chapter 5.

---

[14] Oparin, *Genesis*, pp. 80, 81.

[15] Theodosius Dobzhansky, *The Biology of Ultimate Concern* (New York: New American Library, 1967), p. 48.

We are left with a situation where, in the first place, there would have been no way to produce *any* all-left-handed chains, as is shown in chapter 4. In the second place, natural selection could not have been involved for lack of any reproductive arrangement for all the components.

4. *Asymmetric Polymerization.* A. Pasynskii supposed that this left-handed phenomenon came about when "high molecullar weight asymmetric catalysts were first formed as a result of stereospecific polymerization, and then, from this starting point, the optical asymmetry of low molecular weight components developed."[16] This assumed stereospecific linking is an idea concerning which I have found no evidence in the literature of its ever having been accomplished with amino acids to bring about the result described. If such a process is imagined to have happened in the time before life existed on the earth, it is strange that it is impossible to discover a similar procedure in present-day versatile laboratory settings. It is probable that this hypothesis is but another example of wishful thinking in the absence of anything better.

5. *Irradiation with "Chiral" Electrons.* "Chiral" is another term for one-handed, or asymmetric. A report, assertedly unconfirmed, tells of experiments in which irradiation with the chiral or handed electrons from the beta decay of strontium 90 destroys the D- form of one amino acid, tryptophan, at smaller dose than the L- form. Disappointingly for evolutionists, however, the D-L mixture "was not made measurably more left-handed during a few months of exposure."[17]

6. *Earth's Magnetic Field.* Another hypothesis, which has not gotten much attention, assumes "that the earth's magnetic field produced the necessary dissymmetric environment," but it also suffers from lack of laboratory or experimental confirmation.[18] Attempts by using the magnetic field of magnets failed also to produce the desired results,[19] because of the symmetry of the field perpendicular to the lines of force.

Morrison and Mosher, in 1971, made this telling admission with regard to all the attempts to achieve a solution: "Attempts to demonstrate true absolute asymmetric synthesis, as contrasted to this example of absolute asymmetric decomposition, have

16 Oparin, *Genesis*, p. 81.
17 Morrison, *Scientific American*, p. 120.
18 *Encyclopaedia Britannica* (1967), s.v. "stereochemistry."
19 Morrison and Mosher, *Asymmetric Organic Reactions*, p. 427.

been either negative, inconclusive, or controversial."[20] (Absolute asymmetric synthesis refers to synthesis without using already-existing asymmetric molecules such as enzymes from living things.) The decomposition to which this quotation refers produced merely a 0.7 percent excess of one enantiomer—less than 1 percent.

The simple fact is that no natural solution has been found which can even remotely be considered a satisfactory explanation for the exclusive use of L-amino acids in naturally occurring proteins. In spite of valiant efforts using every possible approach they could find, evolution adherents have found no answer to fill the gap left when they exclude intelligent planning by a Creator.

Even if such a solution were ever discovered, there are multitudes of other conditions, necessary for living things, which are far more improbable. Under the multiplication rule, these make the chance production of life completely unreasonable to consider as a rational hypothesis.

---

[20] Ibid., p. 48.

Appendix 2

The Question of Preference for the Same Hand

In this appendix, we will give more of the details on which the conclusions in chapter 3 were based, regarding the matter of preferential linking of amino acids of the same hand.

Left- and Right-Handed Amino Acids Can Link

Are the two forms of the amino acids shaped so that any of them could unite, whether they are L- or D- in type, as far as contour is concerned? The answer is yes, according to California Institute of Technology's veteran researcher, James Bonner. Whether left- or right-handed, any amino acid can be linked with any other of either hand.[1]

Sidney W. Fox, at the University of Miami, said he was inclined to agree with Bonner on this.[2] The resulting shape of the chain, whether it spirals and how it folds, will be entirely different, but numerous polymers or chains have been put together containing both L- and D-amino acids of a variety of types, including some with the largest side chains, such as the amino acids tyrosine and phenylalanine.[3]

Among others, Dr. Fox believes that an all-one-handed chain is "thermodynamically more stable" than one composed of both forms.[4] The stability is increased by hydrogen bonds between the turns of the spiral.

---

[1] James Bonner, telephone conversation, April, 1971.
Bonner is noted among other things for his discoveries in the biology of development, and the role of certain proteins (histones) in gene repression.

[2] Sidney W. Fox, telephone conversation, April, 1971.

[3] C. M. Venkatachalam and G. N. Ramachandran, "Conformation of Polypeptide Chains," *Annual Review of Biochemistry,* Vol. 38 (1969), pp. 627-690.

[4] Fox, personal communication, 1971.

The big problem, which has no natural solution in sight, is how to get such a chain even the first time. It is important to keep in mind that natural selection could not logically have been operative at that stage (as shown in chapter 5).

This question of whether there would be "steric hindrance," or difficulty of opposite hands fitting together due to shape, was put to Dr. Linus Pauling at Stanford University. He mentioned that there was that possibility,[5] but for details he referred me to a section in one of his books. There he had written, "We have no strong reason to believe that molecules resembling proteins could not be built up of equal numbers of right-handed and left-handed amino acid molecules."[6]

On the same matter, Dr. Arthur Elliott, of the Biophysics Department at King's College in London, said that he knew of none of the common amino acids that could not be connected to any other opposite isomeric form.[7] Dr. Harry Block, at the University of Liverpool's Chemistry Department, was of the same opinion—he knew of no exceptions.[8] In other words, it is possible for any of the twenty amino acids to connect with any other of the same or opposite hand.

Linkups Under Primitive Conditions

Would linkups under the assumed conditions of primitive synthesis include both isomers? The experiments by Dr. Sidney Fox seem to indicate that if amino acid chains had formed naturally under those assumed early conditions, they would have had both left- and right-handed amino acids in the chains, instead of all L-monomers as proteins now contain.[9]

Will Opposites Join With Equal Ease?

At the present stage of experimental knowledge in this field, there is nothing like complete certainty on whether in general there is equal preference for either hand, or, if not, what degree of selectivity exists. Study of reports on experiments to date seems to warrant this conclusion: There is either equal

---

[5] Linus Pauling, telephone conversation, April, 1971.

[6] Linus Pauling, *College Chemistry*, 3rd ed., (San Francisco: W. H. Freeman & Co., 1964), p. 731.

[7] Arthur Elliott, telephone conversation, April, 1971.

[8] Harry Block, telephone conversation, April, 1971.

[9] Sidney W. Fox, in *The Origins of Prebiological Systems and of Their Molecular Matrices* (New York: Academic Press, 1965), pp. 361-382.
Also: personal communication, 1971.

probability *on the average,* or else some limited degree of preference usually unnoticed.

In the literature, there are hundreds of write-ups of experiments where D- to L- linkups were made and vice versa. Almost never does one find any mention made of any more difficulty in joining opposite hands than in linking similar isomers. There have been some rare exceptions to this general picture which we will look at in more detail and which seem to indicate a degree of selectivity in some particular joinings.

An article in *Biopolymers* by E. Klein et al. is a good example of a description of matter-of-fact linking of opposites.[10] In this instance, the amino acid chains formed were "poly-D,L-leucine, co-D,L-methionine." Dr. Klein is a research scientist for Gulf South Research Institute at New Orleans. When I asked if he and his colleagues knew of any preference of L- for L- or D- for D- in their experiments, he said that if there was any selectivity, they had not detected it in their work which often involves the joining of preformed blocks of each isomer within the same chain.[11]

One of the best ways to get an understanding of this matter is to work with models of the amino acid residues. If ready-made atomic models are not available, it is possible to get by with styrofoam balls or other round objects. It is very important to make the models to scale. Attention must be given to comparative sizes of the different atoms, length of bonds, bond angles, and bonds which allow rotation.

A convenient source for most information one would need is Pauling's *The Chemical Bond,* perhaps available in your local library. Dr. Pauling gives tables of effective radii or size of the atoms (van der Waals radii), bond lengths, angles, and positions.[12]

In general, some rotation is allowed on the single bonds. In the backbone of an amino acid chain, these bonds which allow rotation are on either side of the alpha carbon atom.[13] There is also rotation permitted on single bonds in the side chains, especially in the case of "methyl" groups.

---

[10] E. Klein et al., "Permeability of Synthetic Polypeptide Membranes," *Biopolymers,* Vol. 10, No. 4 (April, 1971), pp. 647-655.

[11] E. Klein, telephone conversation, June, 1971.

[12] Linus Pauling, *The Chemical Bond* (Ithaca, N.Y.: Cornell University Press, 1967), pp. 136, 152, 229.

[13] Douglas Poland and A. Scherage, "Theory of Noncovalent Structure in Polyamino Acids," *Poly-Alpha-Amino Acids,* ed. Gerald Fasman (New York: Marcel-Dekker, Inc., 1967), p. 396.

Where two amino acids are joined, the four atoms involved (C'O-NH) are "co-planar" or in the same plane, and therefore are more or less fixed or rigid. For this reason, we have found it logical to make the models in two separate units. The peptide linkage group can be one item (the co-planar C'O-NH just mentioned). The other consists of the alpha carbon, with its hydrogen atom and R group.

You can get a reasonably complete understanding by selecting a few representative shapes of the twenty types and experimenting with those. Tryptophan, phenylalanine, and proline are good examples of the more complex ones. P. K. Ponnuswamy and V. Sasisekharan, of the University of Madras in India, give helpful information on positions of the atoms.[14] It is out of the question to try all conformations, for the number is virtually infinite. We might mention that electrostatic forces may in some cases restrict bond rotation to a degree, but this does not seem to be a barrier to more or less equal ease of fit.

If one experiments with molecular models, the impression grows that the probability is *approximately equal, on the average*, that opposites will fit as well as those of the same hand.

Some Indications of Preferential Linking

A few experimenters have reported cases where one isomer would join up easier than its opposite, as a chain is polymerizing.

Dr. Akiyoshi Wada, at the Department of Physics of Tokyo University, discussed the implications of certain experiments in the 1950's by Doty, Lundberg, Blout, and others.[15] These experiments seemed to show that a preformed chain consisting of L-residues begins reaction more rapidly with another L-unit than with the opposite isomer, in the case of polymers of gamma-benzyl-glutamate NCA, an amino acid altered for experimental purposes.[16]

Important work on the same question was done by C. H. Bamford and Harry Block, who are at the University of Liver-

---

14 "Studies on Conformation of Amino Acids," *Biopolymers*, Vol. 10, No. 3 (March, 1971), pp. 565-582.

15 R. D. Lundberg and Paul Doty, "A Study of the Kinetics of the Primary Amine-initiated Polymerization of N-Carboxy-anhydrides with Special Reference to Configurational and Stereochemical Effects," *American Chemical Society Journal*, Vol. 79 (1957), pp. 3961-3972. Also:

E. R. Blout and M. Idelson, in *American Chemical Society Journal*, Vol. 78 (1956), pp. 3857, 3858.

16 Akiyoshi Wada, "Chain Regularity and Dielectric Properties of Poly Alpha Amino Acids in Solution," *Polyamino Acids, Polypeptides, and Proteins*, ed. M. A. Stahmann (Madison, Wis.: University of Wisconsin Press, 1962), pp. 131-146.

pool.[17] Put in simplest terms, they found indications that an L-amino acid was five or six times more likely than a D-unit to connect at the end of a preformed L-chain, and vice versa, in certain circumstances.

The synthetic polymers used in much of this type of work are not made of simply the amino acid molecules. Instead, an attachment consisting of a carbon ring and several other atoms has been added to the usual side chain of glutamic acid, which is one of the twenty amino acids. It seems likely that this long and bulky extra portion of the side chain might cause more steric hindrance than a normal amino acid would have. (Glutamic acid and aspartic acid are amino acids which have an acidic group in their side chains, and this must be protected from reaction with other molecules in the solution. The protection of these and other reactive groups—including the ends of amino acids—is one of the main problems in peptide chemistry in the laboratory.)[18]

Dr. Elliott called my attention to other polymerizations that are done, e.g., poly-alanine, where extra attachments are not left on the amino acid residues in the chain.[19] I later asked Dr. Block if, in cases of the kind just mentioned, any selective bonding of L- to L- as compared to D- to L- had been observed. He indicated that experiments with the amino acids alanine and phenylalanine did seem to show a preference. He did not have data on the degree of preference, but said there must have been some selectivity, because there were, in the resulting chains, blocks of L- and blocks of D-residues.[20]

Applying probability theory to this matter of "blocks" would seem to lead to this result: as soon as—by chance—one isomer happened to get four (apparently that is the critical number) in a row, probability would favor that type, by a certain factor. On average, the opposite would eventually show up, and then there would be equal probability until one isomer or the other got four in series again. The final result would not favor either hand as to total residues, but each would have the same average number and length of blocks and single residues.

---

[17] C. H. Bamford and H. Block, "The Polymerization of Alpha Amino Acid N-Carbonic Anhydrides," *Polyamino Acids, Polypeptides, and Proteins,* ed. M. A. Stahmann, (Madison, Wis.: University of Wisconsin Press, 1962), pp. 65-78.

[18] T. Wieland and H. Determann, "The Chemistry of Peptides and Proteins," *Annual Review of Biochemistry,* vol. 35, pt. II (1966), pp. 656-658.

[19] Telephone conversation, 1971.

[20] Telephone conversation, 1971.

On the question of whether the length of the helix increased the preference, Professor Block said it did not. (Drs. Elliott and Block have authored reports on such subjects.[21])

A mysterious reaction was reported by Bamford and Block,[22] in which the addition of lithium perchlorate to a reaction mixture eliminated optical specificity, leaving both forms reacting at the same rate with a 15-mer[23] helix as would be expected with a short 3-mer chain.

This was part of experiments mentioned earlier which involved gamma-benzyl-glutamate N-carboxy-anhydride. In those experiments, the same handed amino acid was thought to be five or six times as fast as the opposite hand in joining the end of a preformed helix. The experimenters reasoned that the lithium perchlorate reduced hydrogen bonding of the "NCA" to the helix. The result seemed to show "that the specificity may, in part, be connected with adsorption." (Adsorption is the attaching of one atomic or molecular entity to another through electrostatic forces.)

As a result of certain of the experiments by Doty, Bamford, Block, and others, some came to believe that this stereoselectivity was a result of steric hindrance or other conflict with the preformed helix. Dr. Fred D. Williams, at Michigan Technological University, doubts, however, that this is the cause. He and his co-workers report polymerization of the same glutamic acid complex in experiments where results seemed to indicate a selectivity even before a helix was formed.[24]

This is another case where one may wonder if the bulky artificial side chain mentioned earlier may be affecting the outcome.

Dr. Williams told me of quite opposite results in their recent experiments with D,L-alanyl-isoleucine.[25] These two amino acids exhibited a *crosswise* selectivity (D- to L- instead of L- to L- preference)!

---

[21] Arthur Elliott, "X-ray Diffraction by Synthetic Polypeptides," *Poly-Alpha-Amino Acids,* ed. Gerald D. Fasman (New York: Marcel-Dekker, 1967), pp. 1-64. Also:
Bamford and Block, "Polymerization."

[22] Bamford and Block, "Polymerization."

[23] *Mer* meaning part or unit—in this case, amino acid residue. Thus, *monomer* means one unit, *polymer* means many units.

[24] Fred D. Williams, M. Eshaque, and Ronald D. Brown, "Stereoselective Polymerization of Gamma Benzyl Glutamate NCA," *Biopolymers,* Vol. 10, No. 4 (April, 1971), pp. 753-756.

[25] Telephone conversation, June, 1971.

Shröder and Lübke in West Berlin reported a similar reverse preference in "cyclo" polymers of glycine and D,L-leucine.[26]

As can be seen, the picture is far from final on the preference factor, at this writing. There are many variables which enter into the reaction potentials. The type of solvent used, temperature, pH reading, protecting attachments, all these can affect the joining. The activating intermediates which must be used to bring about the linking also may complicate the picture.

Some chemical reactions, moreover, bring about "racemization" as a side-effect—changing some amino acids themselves to the opposite isomers.[27]

Then there is the problem of trying to "read" the results. When we recall that biochemists are working with molecules far too small for the ordinary laboratory microscope, it indicates how hard it can be to tell exactly what happened in a reaction, and to what degree. The results must be discovered by roundabout means. Sometimes a bit of guesswork has to enter in. Later experiments may disprove the tentative conclusions of the experimenter.

Equal Probability of Opposites Joining on the Average

A fairly good case might be made for the idea that there is equal probability of opposite antipodes linking, as an average of all types. These are some of the indications which point in that direction:

1. Numerous reports of D,L-chains with no mention of any stereo-selective factor, and specific statements by experimenters such as Dr. E. Klein that they have not noted any such preference.

2. The reports of a reverse preference (L- for D-) in some experiments, which may tend to balance reports of L- for L-preference in others.

3. The evidence from experimenting with models of amino acid residues, which seems to favor equal ease of fit on the average.

4. Opinions of prominent researchers such as Bonner and Fox who, in conversation with the author, made no mention of selectivity when commenting on the ability of all to fit.

---

[26] Eberhard Shröder and Klaus Lübke, *The Peptides* (New York: Academic Press, 1965), pp. 274, 275, 319-326.

[27] Abraham White, Philip Handler, and Emil L. Smith, *Principles of Biochemistry,* 3rd ed. (New York: McGraw-Hill, 1964), p. 92.

5. It seems likely that in a presumed primitive environment prior to the existence of life, the numerous variables that affect reactions would by chance be as likely to favor one type of hookup as another. Apparently, no steric reasons would prevent average equal ease of fit. There is no reason to suppose that nature would by chance provide the same highly specific reactions and conditions that a biochemist might choose from his artificially prepared supply.

Since there have been more reports of L- for L- and D- for D-preference than of opposites, however, we will consider that type of preference as one of the possible conclusions on the way things are on the average.

We may conclude, then, that any amino acid can link with any other, as to fit, and that opposites are either (1) equally likely to unite, or (2) in some cases there may be a preference for the same enantiomer, up to 6/7 probability. In chapter 4 the laws of chance are applied to both of these possibilities.

In both cases, the outcome is conclusive. Chance cannot at all account for even the comparatively simple fact that only left-handed amino acids are used as the components of naturally occurring regular proteins.

Appendix 3

Notes on Quastlar's The Emergence of Biological Organization[1]

The above-named book is the only one written heretofore, to our knowledge, which is devoted largely to probability and the origin of life.

Henry Quastlar died in 1963, leaving his book unfinished. Described by Yale colleagues as a man of kind disposition and great intellect, he was a former medical doctor who taught himself mathematics and physics and became a recognized expert in radiation biology and information theory.

By his own admission, the book did not pretend to convey certainty of any kind, but to set forth ideas. It was, in that sense, a position paper. The overview is evolutionary: "Evolution is considered at all levels," he wrote in the preface, "since evolutionary history is a very important feature of living things" (p. ix).

As our study has shown, when a person has chosen a philosophy of science, he will likely seek explanations which support his chosen overview. Quastlar naturally does this, and conveys the impression that the odds against the emergence of life might be overcome by certain applications of information theory (of which he was greatly enamored). Hope for such a natural origin of life was derived by making a number of unwarranted assumptions with no apparent support but which tend to bring to pass the result sought.[2]

We hesitate to point out fallacies in this small book of Quast-

[1] Henry Quastlar, *The Emergence of Biological Organization* (New Haven: Yale University Press, 1964.) In this Appendix, page numbers in parentheses are from his book.

[2] Note the difference when one makes lenient assumptions *in favor of* his theory. This tends to invalidate such a theory to the degree those assumptions were unfounded. In contrast, the way assumptions were used herein in our studies in chapters 6 and 10 was just the opposite. Chance was shown to fail *in spite of* those extreme assumptions in its favor, rather than *because of* any assumptions in favor of our position.

lar's in view of his untimely decease, but we will not be questioning his integrity,. since we have high respect for him as a fine though fallible human being.

One serious error is the supposition that in proteins only the active site matters. It may be true that in short peptides of ten or so amino acids there can be considerable variation without complete loss of function. The same is not true of protein chains, which are much longer and involve a complex tertiary folding in precise manner. This is considered more fully herein in chapter 6, page 99 ff.

Quastlar intimated that about all the information needed for enzyme specificity would be contained in an active site of from two to seven amino acids with an upper limit in size of fifteen Angstroms diameter, requiring only ten to twenty bits of information. He conceded, however, "It must be emphasized that we do not understand what constitutes the functional organization of a protein and that our information on that problem is crude and largely descriptive" (p. 26). In spite of this admission, a rather complete understanding does seem to be tacitly assumed in his computations. A growing body of knowledge during the ten years since it was written makes the position taken in his book all the more untenable.

Although Quastlar recognized the *central dogma* (that information cannot go in the reverse direction from protein to nucleic acid—except in the matter of inhibition via repressor molecules), he seems to have considered that feedback via repressors was an indirect means of getting information from protein back to DNA so that the system could evolve by learning from its past performance. This is apparently groundless. The discussion in his book is very difficult to follow on this matter as to conclusions. This may be due partly to its not having been completed.

To derive DNA naturally, Quastlar assumed linkups of preformed activated nucleotides without enzymes. He estimated that the polymerization of just one single-stranded chain might have taken *five million years* (unless some inorganic catalysts happened to be of some help) (p. 8). On the same page, he says, "In general, polymerization of a single-stranded polynucleotide is slow, and its hydrolysis [decomposition] fast. . . ." The utter impossibility of any such chain lasting long enough to be completed is evident.

Sometime later (granting such a chain existed) complementary pairing from activated nucleotides in the surrounding liquid is supposed to have made the chain stable by making it double-stranded. The formation of the second strand would also have taken some time, but less time than the original single-stranded polymerization. Also assumed without basis is a bridging mechanism at the end of a double-stranded molecule so it could unfold into a double-length single-stranded chain. This does not seem to be a feasible supposition when one considers the binding factors. At one point, Quastlar confessed, "The argument given is sketchy . . ." (p. 14). This is quite true, though perhaps its incompleteness was one factor.

His model then calls for these double-stranded DNA's to dissociate readily into single-stranded complementary types. This, however, rarely happens in living things, since double-stranded nucleic acids tend to be stable, except when purposefully denatured by laboratory use of acid or heat.

A strange implication is made that the beginning nucleic acid chain might perform somewhat like a computer, with memory storage and evaluation of results, search procedure, learning from experience, and adjustment of strategy (pp. 14-23). This is a most fantastic assumption without basis in reality, in spite of efforts to make it seem plausible.

He admitted that the protein-nucleic acid system could not have emerged until after it was membrane-enclosed (p. 65), but he has no explanation of how the complex membranes which are now a part of all living cells came about. Concerning the origin of the ribosome system, admittedly a key part of the DNA-protein system, he says, "We have no theory concerning this event" (p. 43). In spite of these tremendous gaps, he gives the indefinite impression that it would be no big problem for life to come about naturally!

The most serious fallacy of all perhaps is the idea that chance nucleic acid sequences just happened to produce proteins (usable chains of amino acids). As seen in the studies herein in chapters 6 and 10, it is completely unthinkable that this could happen, in the light of a careful application of probability reasoning. There are many other invalid assumptions which space will not allow us to consider.

Summarizing, the book evidences high intelligence and complete technical knowledge but these are used with thoroughly unwarranted, extreme assumptions that make the conclusions fallacious. Quastlar may have partially sensed the lack of basis for thinking such a system might have evolved, for he began the book with these words:

> . . . Even the simplest living things show great complexity. In terms of ordered structure the distance between a bacterium and a man is much less than between a bacterium and, say, a giant electronic brain. In the general course of events order tends to give way to less order, and not the other way around; hence it is not easy to see how life could have arisen from nonliving precursors. Several explanations have been proposed, some of which are not subject to scientific inquiry. Of those that are, the most attractive is the proposition that nonliving components have assumed a configuration compatible with life through some lucky accident (p. 1).

His reference to some explanations "which are not subject to scientific inquiry" doubtless was meant to include the idea of creation. Dr. George F. Howe, plant physiologist and biology professor, says, however:

> The special creation view is scientific to the extent that predictions can be made, based on this theory, and such predictions can be tested in field and laboratory. Predictions based on the special creation view are quite valid and have good "fit" with evidences from many sciences including geochemistry, genetics, geology, and others. . . . The origin of life is inexplicable in the evolution view but understandable in creationist terms.[3]

As mentioned in chapter 14 herein, Quastlar figured the extreme upper and lower bounds of the probability that this "lucky accident" had taken place. He came out with a lower bound (which, even with the extreme and unacceptable assumptions, is infinitesimally small) of one chance in 10^{255}, which by the single law of chance would, of course, never occur. The *upper* bound, which he did not carry through in detail, comes to one chance in $10^{2,999,999,999,986}$ when calculated from his data, the upper bound of the probability of life occurring by chance. That is a number which would fill 6,000,000 books the size of this one, and would pack a good-sized school or public library building.

---

[3] From a statement to the California State Board of Education in Sacramento on November 9, 1972, by Dr. George F. Howe, who received his Ph.D. in plant physiology from Ohio State University and was formerly Charles F. Kettering fellow at said school. He did postdoctoral work at Cornell University in radiation biology.

Appendix 4

Problems in Molecular Evolution Hypotheses

The names of A. I. Oparin and Sidney W. Fox are perhaps the best known among the many who have devoted much time to research efforts to demonstrate the feasibility of the assumed evolution of life from nonliving chemicals. Oparin began to describe his idea in 1924, which involved formation of *coacervate* droplets which have been described earlier. Almost as well-known are Fox's *proteinoid microspheres.*

Both Oparin and Fox seem to be dedicated researchers of high intellect and sincerity, who have done the best anyone could for the evolutionary overview. Both have received much criticism of their hypotheses, and as scientists they seem to recognize that the "challenging" of ideas is a desirable process. In fact, they have each criticized the other's plan, while apparently remaining good friends. (Oparin, for example, wrote an introduction to Fox's recent book.)

Concerning the proteinoid theory, Oparin wrote, "Fox's microspheres, since they are obtained thermally, do not present very promising results from this point of view [i.e., evolving to include metabolic processes]. Their structure is static. This . . . creates many difficulties when it comes to converting them into dynamic systems which could be used for modeling the evolution of metabolism."[1]

On the other hand, Fox pointed out these difficulties about the Oparin coacervates: "The coacervate droplet lacks stability; it falls apart easily on standing. The crucial difference is that the coacervate droplet is made from one or more polymers

---

[1] A. I. Oparin, *Genesis and Evolutionary Development of Life* (New York: Academic Press, 1968), p. 105.

obtained from living systems. . . ."[2] (Fox has recognized that if such experiments are to indicate anything useful, they must simulate closely what may have been natural conditions at the time of the assumed origin of life.)

All of the efforts by researchers to date are detailed in a comprehensive study by Fox and co-author Klaus Dose.[3] Naturally, they present the best possible case for the proteinoid system.

Earlier we told how Fox and his colleagues obtained a dozen amino acids by use of extreme heat (900-1100° C) in the presence of silica sand or volcanic lava. These were protein-type except that they were racemic.

A separate experiment resulted in thermal linking of all 20 of the protein-type amino acids, when a prepared mixture of these was heated dry. Usually this involved heating from 6 to 10 hours at 170-200° C, or for a week at 120°. This results in chains of amino acids called thermal proteinoids.

When proteinoid chains are put in water, they tend to form *microspheres*. These are described by the experimenters as open systems which are supposed to grow and divide. They are hailed as probable precursors of living systems.

Among unique features claimed for proteinoid microspheres are the following: "Information" is said to have flowed from the geochemical matrix to the first naturally formed amino acids, and then to the proteinoid chains and microspheres. (This, of course, is an attempt to circumvent having to depend on blind randomness.)

Also, "self-assembly" is claimed for proteinoid microspheres, and much is made of their nonrandomness and catalytic activity, as if they were well on the way to becoming protein enzymes. (Nonrandomness seems to be mistakenly assumed.)

Among the many difficulties besetting this plan, some have perhaps already occurred to the reader. When others have pointed out to Fox that the extreme temperatures involved, which he theorizes might occur at volcanoes, must be followed immediately by cooling of the amino acids before they are destroyed by the very heat that formed them, he says that rain is not unknown at volcanoes and would serve the purpose. The

---

[2] Sidney W. Fox and Klaus Dose, *Molecular Evolution and the Origin of Life* (San Francisco: W. H. Freeman and Co., 1972), p. 221.
[3] Ibid.

amino acids formed, however, are racemic, rather than being all one-handed as is necessary for proteins.

Carefully regulated heat for a rather exact period of time is next needed with the amino acids in the dried state, to bring about linking, but a far different temperature from that used earlier. During this time, there is no protection from destruction by ultraviolet radiation from the sun (of "primitive" times).

A major item is that such experiments in thermal linking have usually involved a quite artificial ratio of the amino acids in the starting mixture. One common plan is to have 2/3 of the entire supply to consist of aspartic acid and glutamic acid. Sometimes, a high percentage of lysine is used instead.

Clearly, the use of exorbitant amounts of these highly reactive acids and bases is the explanation back of the supposed catalytic activity which is described. Any strongly reactive chemical will cause a commotion in many situations. By analogy, fire causes many chemical changes, but is unhelpful unless carefully regulated, as in the cylinder of an automobile. The supposed enzymic activity is doubtless no more than could be expected in any mixture or chain where these particular amino acids predominate. In fact, it has been pointed out that chains of lysine alone have better such ability than when mixed with other amino acids.[4]

There has never been found any way to get *all* the needed amino acids by supposed natural means. Especially difficult are the vital sulfur-containing ones, cysteine and methionine. There is no way, either to bring about the proper *concentration* of even the ones that are formed, or to get them in proper ratio, since they are formed in a far different ratio from that used in proteins.

In thermal polymerization experiments, there is a serious absence of three important amino acids—serine, threonine, and cysteine—which are destroyed by the heat involved unless carefully protected by adding phosphoric acid or using lower temperatures. Even when L-amino acids are used in the starting mixture, there is racemization, changing of some of the amino acids to the opposite hand by the heat.

The degree of "catalytic activity" has been small (sometimes

---

[4] D. L. Rohlfing, *Archives of Biochemistry and Biophysics*, Vol. 118 (1967), p. 470. Also: Duane T. Gish, *Speculations and Experiments Related to Theories on the Origin of Life* (San Diego: Institute of Creation Research, 1972), p. 30.

infinitesimal), and in all cases is in strong contrast to the precise, delicately regulated teamwork of multiple enzymes—each with a specific reaction to attend—such as is found in even the simplest living things, as well as in the simplest theoretical autonomous replicating system.

Experiments to account for a natural way that sugars and nucleotides might have formed have been quite discouraging. Fox and Dose therefore believe proteins began first and somehow later became involved with nucleic acids. There is no plausible way for this to have come about, however, including no adequate solution as to the source of these precursors of DNA. Regarding the origin of nucleic acids, they wrote, "The evidence is in an uncertain state."[5] No one will dispute that. There is, of course, nothing like any *adequate* plan to account for the origin of the protein synthesizing system (RNA, ribosomes, etc.), and the orchestra of metabolic chains. The attempts are brave but in vain.

The esteemed scientists who authored *Biology and the Future of Man* (almost 200 of the top biologists in America) included this statement by the panel on the origin of life: "It must be admitted that few of the laboratory experiments [including ones described herein] are completely convincing simulations of primitive processes,"[6] although they hoped for better success in the future. The fact is, starting with the uncertainty that there ever even existed such a primitive atmosphere all the way to the final assembly into a living cell, the efforts are scientifically hopeless.

The reason for failure is not in the scientists but rather in the erroneous philosophy that there is no intelligent Being back of the origin of life. There could be no true "information" of enough degree to help in this matter by supposedly tracing it back to the "geochemical matrix." Information must be put in before it can be transferred out—under any but the most meager definition.

For an analogy, suppose that scientists for some strange reason had become convinced of the absurd hypothesis that the moon once consisted of green cheese. They would be duty-bound to try to account for the changeover to the present

---

[5] Fox and Dose, *Molecular Evolution and the Origin of Life,* p. 254.

[6] Philip Handler, ed., *Biology and the Future of Man* (New York: Oxford University Press, 1970), p. 185.

condition. Their ingenuity would bring forth many ideas, some far-out, some less so. *Portions* of some schemes would seem plausible, but there would be gaps and difficulties to softpedal or skim over. This is the case with the valiant but futile attempts to account for complex life with a naturalistic overview. It cannot be done. It is like determined men trying to jump across the Atlantic ocean. Some might jump farther into the water than others, but none would succeed.

Index

Notes

Notes

Notes

Notes

NOTES

Notes

Notes

NOTES

Notes

Notes

Notes

Notes